The Ever-changing
WOODLANDS
THE LIVING COUNTRYSIDE

A Reader's Digest selection

THE EVER-CHANGING WOODLANDS

First Edition Copyright © 1984
The Reader's Digest Association Limited, 25 Berkeley Square
London W1X 6AB

Reprinted with amendments 1988

Copyright © 1984
Reader's Digest Association Far East Limited
Philippines Copyright 1984
Reader's Digest Association Far East Ltd

Front cover picture: A misty autumn morning under the
beeches of Ashridge Park in the Chilterns.

The Ever-changing
WOODLANDS

THE LIVING COUNTRYSIDE

PUBLISHED BY THE READER'S DIGEST ASSOCIATION LIMITED
LONDON NEW YORK MONTREAL SYDNEY CAPE TOWN

Originally published in partwork form
by Eaglemoss Publications Limited and Orbis Publishing Limited

Consultant

Euan Dunn

Contributors

Mary Briggs	Paul Freeman	Richard Prior
Aune Butt	Chris Humphries	Oliver Rackham
Josephine Camus	Charlie Jarvis	John Robinson
Norma Chapman	Terry Jennings	John Sankey
William Condry	Roger Lovegrove	Peter Schofield
David Corke	David Macdonald	Diana Shipp
Ben Darby	Nigel Matthews	Keith Snow
Gordon Dickson	Chris Mead	Alan Stubbs
Steve Downer	Ian Montgomery	David Sutton
Chris Feare	Ernest Neal	Stephen Sutton
John Feltwell	Roberta Peacock	John Waters
Jim Flegg	Jane Ponti	Gerald Wilkinson
Pamela Forey	Keith Porter	Geoffrey Young

Contents

The Ever-changing
WOODLANDS

Introduction

Broadleaved woodland represents the most diverse assemblage of plants and animals in any habitat outside the tropics and it is above all a habitat that expresses a blend of balance, inter-relatedness and dynamic change.

The tempo of the lives of all woodland plants and animals is rooted in the highly seasonal nature of the British climate. Our warm, moist summer months enable trees to break into leaf and bank the sun's energy through photosynthesis, and with the awakening of a multitude of woodland flowers and tree buds a host of herbivorous insects appear to capitalise on the bounty of leaf tissue, sap, pollen and nectar, sustaining also a long chain of predators from wolf spider to red fox.

In spring and early summer an enormous variety of different animals draw on the energy reserves of the wood: the tawny owl hunts by night on silent wings for rodent prey; a parasitic ichneumon wasp scrutinises foliage for a weevil larva in which to lay its own egg; and the agile squirrel whisks along branches questing for nuts.

With the onset of autumn, however, the outward momentum of the woodland is disrupted by a marked deterioration in the weather. As the temperature drops, the root systems of trees find it increasingly hard to absorb water from the frozen ground and, to avoid dehydration, shed their leaves, assisted by the blustery autumn winds. In the relative warmth of the litter bed a mass of fungal threads and a little known community of invertebrates quietly practise their arts of decay, returning the chemical energy of the leaf-fall to the woodland system to fuel new possibilities for adaptation and change.

Left: A mass of fallen beech leaves carpet the forest floor in autumn, forming a rich habitat for a host of small animals.

BRITAIN'S WOODLANDS

Woodland in Britain has been more important to our civilisation and wildlife than its decline over the centuries would suggest; on its future rests the survival of many of our native creatures.

Broadleaved woods, whose leafy glades epitomize for many people the gentle countryside of lowland Britain, are the environment of many of our more interesting plants and animals.

Among mammals, the easiest to see are the several kinds of deer, which live in woods and come out to feed in the surrounding fields.

Squirrels make their home high in the branches. Dormice, now rare, feed and live in underwood and shrubs. If you wait quietly you may glimpse the wood mouse and yellow-necked mouse, which sometimes forage for buds, nuts and insects high in the trees as well as on the ground. Other woodland mammals include common and pygmy shrews, bank vole, mole, hedgehog, weasel, stoat, fox and badger.

Woods are a rich habitat for birds. The common species, some of which also frequent gardens, are the robin, wren, blackbird, woodpigeon, chaffinch, chiffchaff, great and blue tits and willow warbler. Less often you may hear, or occasionally see, cuckoo, woodcock, nightingale, and three species of woodpecker.

Insects and other invertebrate animals are plentiful in many woods. The most colourful creatures are the butterflies, such as speckled wood, small tortoiseshell and silver-washed fritillary, which feed on sunny days on flowers in glades and at the woodland edge. Caterpillars, aphids and flies are the chief food of many of the birds. Dead leaves and rotten

As you walk through a peaceful copse or wood you probably have little idea of the intense activity going on all around you. Woods support a complex web of wildlife in which every plant and animal has its place, making as efficient use of the available resources as the best-designed factory. The fresh green leaves have just opened in this beechwood at Selborne Lythe in Hampshire, casting a dappled shade on the woodland floor.

wood are the home of beetles, woodlice, centipedes and millipedes.

Woods and human affairs After the last Ice Age, the British Isles was almost entirely covered by trees—the natural 'wildwood'—until Neolithic men arrived in about 4000BC. These earliest farmers began to get rid of the trees to make agricultural land. It is likely that by the late Roman period (AD400) farmland and moorland—both man-made habitats—dominated the English landscape. Quite large areas of woodland remained; some of these were cleared in Anglo-Saxon and medieval times, and others were turned into managed woodland and some still exist.

Britain has for many centuries been one of the least wooded countries in Europe; but woodland, despite its limited area, has been most important to our civilization as well as our wildlife. Woods are, to some extent, wild places, in that their trees and other plants grow naturally and have not been put there; but all our natural woods, except those which have been formed very recently, have been managed, often for many centuries, to yield successive crops of produce.

Well over a thousand years ago, our ancestors decided to set aside some areas of the remaining wildwood as 'woodland', producing crops of timber and underwood, and to use other areas as 'wood-pasture', combining trees with grass on which domestic animals grazed. They also had 'non-woodland' trees in hedges and fields. These three traditions of tree management have remained separate ever since; you can still see wood-pasture in Epping Forest and Richmond Park.

Much later (from the 17th century onwards) the custom grew up of growing trees in 'plantations'. This fourth tradition is the basis of modern forestry, which is quite separate from the management of woods. Woodmen use the trees that grow naturally; foresters 'plant' their trees—which nowadays are usually conifers—disregarding any native trees that may already be there.

Not all woods are ancient, nor have all woods that are not ancient been planted. Left alone, the natural tendency of almost any land in Britain is to become woodland. Open land is invaded by trees such as birch and oak which readily colonize new territory. 'Secondary' woodland, formed in this way on land which used to be farmland, moorland, industrial waste-heaps, railway verges etc., will not be the same as an ancient wood; it lacks species such as hornbeam and lime, which do not colonize easily, as well as many characteristic woodland plants.

Coppicing and pollarding When visiting a wood you should look for signs, particularly in the shape of the trees, that tell of the history of the wood and what it has been used for.

Trees with multiple stems are a sign of the commonest management practice, 'coppicing'. This uses the fact, well known to all gardeners, that most broadleaved trees are not killed by being felled: the stump sends up shoots and becomes a 'stool' from which an indefinite succession of crops of poles can be cut at intervals of years. Aspen, cherry and most elms do not coppice; instead they send up shoots called 'suckers' from the root system.

Woods traditionally yield two products, timber and wood. 'Timber' is the large material suitable for planks, beams and gate-posts; 'wood' is the smaller material suitable for light construction or firewood. A typical wood consists mainly of 'underwood' stools, felled every five to 25 years and allowed to grow again; among these stools is a scattering of 'standard' trees, grown to timber size. The standard trees are nearly always oak or ash, chosen for this purpose because of their value as timber. The underwood may also be oak or ash but is often of a wide range of other trees. A 'coppice' is a wood managed in this way; but the term is also applied by modern writers to the underwood itself, whether standing or felled.

A year or two after a coppice has been cut the ground vegetation flourishes and encourages a rich diversity of insects. Later on, the underwood forms a dense thicket which casts an intense shade and the vegetation declines; at this stage, however, the thicket provides cover for nesting birds such as the whitethroat and blackcap.

An alternative to coppicing is 'pollarding'. The trees are cut like coppice stools to produce successive crops of wood, but at a height of 2-4.5m (6-15ft) above ground so that grazing animals cannot reach the young shoots. Pollarding is practised on wood pasture and hedgerow trees rather than those in woods.

In theory a coppice of 100 acres might contain 50,000 underwood stools and 2000 standard trees. Every year, the underwood on 10 acres would be felled, together with 20 of the 200 timber trees on those 10 acres. To replace the timber trees, 50 self-sown saplings or coppice poles of oak or ash would be left standing, in the expectation that 20 would eventually survive to reach timber size. In

Dead wood harbours life
Old trees have a special importance in woods as they support a particular range of animals and plants. Some species of lichen, for example, only grow on trees more than 300 years old. Different fungi colonize the dead wood, gradually decomposing it. Solitary bees and wasps nest in the crevices, while other insects hibernate in them. These insects attract birds such as woodpeckers, which nest in holes in standing dead trees. Later the holes are often taken over by other birds, dormice or hibernating bats.
Certain beetles live only in dead wood. The larva of the largest British species, the stag beetle (above), depends on decaying wood for its survival. It lives and feeds on rotting wood for three years before emerging for its brief adult life. If dead trees are cleared away, as much as a fifth of all such woodland creatures could disappear.

Below: The hedgehog emerges at night for food. You can sometimes hear the crackling of leaves as the hedgehog roots in the litter for slugs and beetles.

Grey squirrels build their nests (dreys) high up in the tree tops; they are active during the day, leaping from branch to branch. This one has descended to the shrub layer to feed on hazel nuts.

this way the whole wood would be felled on a 'coppice cycle' of ten years and would continue to yield the same produce for ever. This is an illustration of what is rarely so simple or so regular in practice. Woods can vary in any proportion from all standard trees and no underwood to all underwood and no timber.

The character and continuity of a wood are maintained by the coppice stools, which (like pollards) live indefinitely. Timber trees come and go at the whims of owners, but the underwood remains.

In the past wood was usually more highly regarded than timber and it may yet be so again in the future; but over the last 150 years —a period of cheap fuel—such woodmanship as there has been tended towards timber rather than underwood production. Most woods, where they still exist, have been left standing for between 40 and 150 years, a much longer interval than would normally elapse between fellings.

Kinds of woodland It is traditional to describe woods in terms of the 'dominant' tree, the one or few species which, by their abundance or size determine the characteristics of that particular kind of woodland: for example ash woods, ash-hazel woods, ash-maple-hazel woods, lime woods. For this purpose the underwood is of more significance than the timber trees, which are a relatively arbitrary and impermanent feature. Although almost all woods contain a scattering of oak

trees, which are invariably treated as timber, this does not make every wood an oak wood.

Much of the variation in woods is natural and can be related to differences (which are often subtle) in soil or topography. Many woods are a complex patchwork or 'mosaic' of different kinds of woodland. In Suffolk and Essex, for instance, a wood of less than 10 acres may contain areas of ash-hazel, hornbeam, lime, cherry and elm.

Conservation Woodland is threatened chiefly by the extension of modern forestry, which turns wood into plantations, and agriculture, which destroys them altogether. In replanting a wood it is necessary to get rid of the indigenous trees and to prevent their regrowth from interfering with the planted trees. If successful—and the process is expensive and uncertain—the result destroys the character of a wood almost as completely as grubbing it out to make a field.

The destruction of secondary woodland can in theory be reversed, but once an ancient wood has been destroyed it is lost for ever. Between 1945 and 1975 at least a third of the ancient woodland area disappeared, a rate of destruction without precedent since the Norman Conquest. Since 1975 there has been less destruction, partly because there is less money to spend on it, but also because more people are coming to understand and appreciate woods and intend not merely to preserve them but restore them to their proper use.

Woodlands of the British Isles

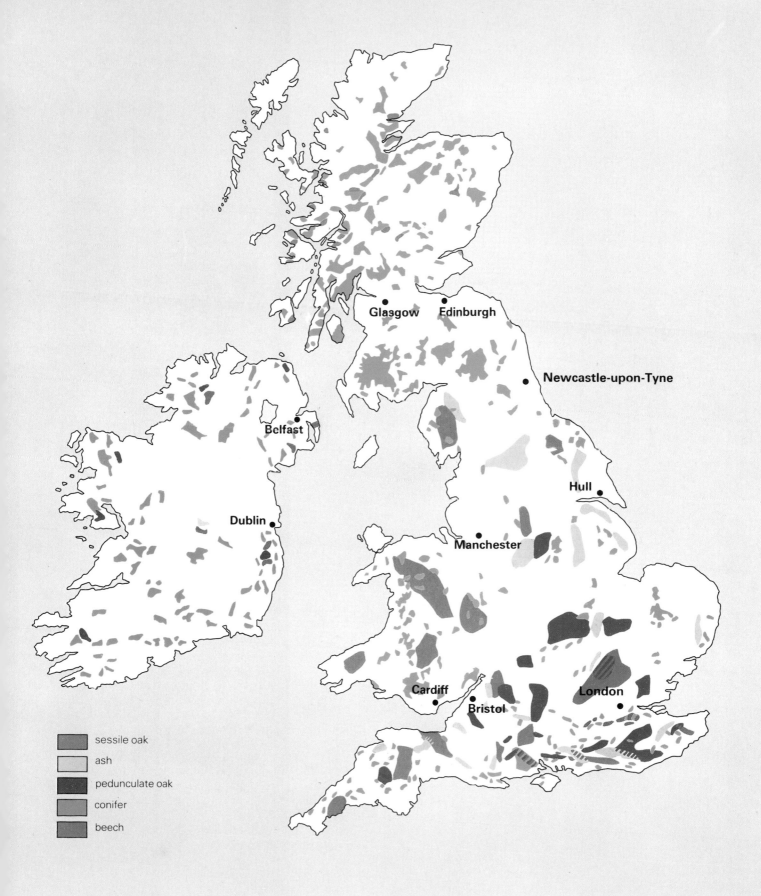

- sessile oak
- ash
- pedunculate oak
- conifer
- beech

Glasgow

Edinburgh

Newcastle-upon-Tyne

Belfast

Hull

Dublin

Manchester

Cardiff

Bristol

London

Above: The lack of a well established shrub layer in this Forest of Dean oak wood in Gloucestershire means that bracken can flourish in the field layer. Holes in the trunk of the holly tree offer birds nesting sites.

FOUR-TIER WOODLAND LAYERS

A wood can be rather like a four-storey house–with mosses at the bottom, two storeys of flowers, ferns and shrubs, and an attic made up by the canopy of foliage.

What chiefly distinguishes woodland from other habitats such as grassland or heather moor is that it has a dimension which they lack–that of height. This provides a series of habitats for many species of wildlife, ranged one above the other from ground level up to 20 or 30m (65 or 100ft). So a useful way of looking at a wood is to think of it as consisting of various layers of vegetation; and of these, four are usually recognised.

At the lowest level is the ground layer– the very small plants, chiefly mosses, which grow on the floor of the wood. Next comes the field layer (or herb layer)–the wild flowers and the ferns. Above them grows the shrub layer (or under-storey), of which hazel is a typical species. And high over the rest of the wood are the upper boughs and twigs of mature oaks, ashes, beeches and others which form the tree layer (canopy).

You don't need to look at many woods before you realise that there are great differences between them. Some may have all four layers well developed. Others, and they are more usual, may be lacking in one or more layers. Why are there these differences? Often there is no single answer. In ecology it is always necessary to be on the look-out for multiple causes, especially in so complex a site as a woodland. And because practically every British woodland exists to serve a human purpose, the presence or absence of any of the four layers is often due to man's interference rather than to natural causes.

Here and there, even in a quite natural woodland, you may find an absence or near absence of one or other layer. This often happens if the tree layer is particularly dense with summer leaves that suppress the layers below by cutting them off from the light they need. So the only type of wood which can have all four well-developed layers is one where plenty of light comes down through the tree layer even at the height of summer. In ashwoods, for instance, the divided, pinnate leaves of the ash allow much more light to filter through them than do the leaves of most other large trees. Pure ashwood, however, is not found in many areas. A more common type of wood is a mixture of ash and oak. In such a wood, provided the oaks are not too many or too close, especially if there are a few clearings and a variety of trees of different ages, you will probably find all four layers better developed than in most other woods.

Tree layer The upper branches and twigs of a tree are structured to expose the maximum number of leaves to the light. Since many of the young leaves, especially of oaks, are highly palatable and nutritious for insects, the canopy becomes the scene of immense activity in spring and early summer. Phenomenal numbers of caterpillars, mainly of mottled umber, winter and green tortrix moths, begin to eat the leaves as soon as the buds open. And the caterpillars in turn are taken in large

numbers by tits, warblers, finches, redstarts, pied flycatchers, starlings and many other birds which are feeding hungry broods of nestlings. In years of caterpillar plagues a wood's entire tree layer may be stripped of its leaves and the shrub layer may also be devastated. In such years an unusual amount of light gets down to the field layer. However, once the caterpillars have pupated, starved to death or been eaten, a replacement flush of leaves appears on the trees. Another group of insects active in the tree layer in spring produces oak apples, marble galls, artichoke galls and many others.

In winter the highest twigs are searched for tiny forms of animal life by sharp-eyed small birds such as the tits, nuthatch and lesser spotted woodpecker. But the most obvious birds of the tree layer are those large species which come in spring to build their nests there –the heron, rook, carrion crow, buzzard, sparrowhawk and several others. Many birds also use the tree tops for perching by day, and for roosting after dark.

Shrub layer This complex zone consists of shrubs, the lower branches of mature trees and saplings which, if they survive, will grow up to take their place in the tree layer. Some shrubs and young trees can tolerate quite a lot of shade; others survive only in clearings or where the big trees stand well apart. For hundreds of years, until the early 20th century, the shrub layer was very important in the life of rural Britain. This dense jungle of hazel, hawthorn, ash, hornbeam, sweet chestnut, willow and many other species was completely cut down (coppiced) at regular intervals to produce the sticks and poles that were in such demand in the farming countryside.

For two or three years after coppicing the ground was carpeted with wild flowers encouraged by the light suddenly let into the wood. There was also a great increase in butterflies, bees, beetles and other insects that revelled in the fragrance and the sunshine. But in another two years all this changed. New tall stems shot up from the cut stumps and the shrub layer again became impenetrable. The flowers began to die out, but there were more small birds; warblers, thrushes and, in the south of England, nightingales, all used the shrubs for nesting. But growth continued and in about three more years the coppiced shrubs grew into a dense mass of tall poles unsuitable for any of these birds. Then the shrubs were felled once more and the cycle began again.

Today most of the old coppices have been destroyed or are neglected. However, in many woodland nature reserves the old coppice system is being restored for the benefit of wild flowers, insects, birds and other creatures and the cut wood is used for fencing and wood-burning stoves and fires.

Field layer While the wild flowers of the field layer are at their best in clearings or in the dappled sunlight under ash trees, those beneath the closed canopy of beech woods are

The main layers
Although there are four main woodland layers it is unusual to find all four fully developed in the same wood. The illustration below shows what the various layers might look like in a lime-rich mixed beech and ash wood. Enough light filters down for a thin field layer to develop. Normally there is little or no field layer in pure beechwoods because the canopy is so dense. Each woodland layer offers different feeding, nesting and sheltering sites for wildlife.

Tree layer
The tree layer is also known as the canopy.
1 beech
2 ash

Shrub layer
3 hazel
4 bramble
5 ivy
6 holly

Field layer
7 hard shield-fern
8 wood-sorrel
9 wood anemone
10 sweet violet
11 green hellebore

Ground layer
12 mosses
13 elf cup fungus
14 common morel fungus

Opposite page: Mature oak
woodland with well
developed ground, field,
shrub and canopy layers.

Right: Small invertebrates
and insects are pecked out
from the cracks in the bark of
a tree by the agile tree
creeper. The eggs of the
mottled umber moth make
up part of this bird's winter
food supply. The tree
creeper's favourite nest site is
behind loose bark.

Right: The mottled umber
caterpillar is one of the main
defoliators of oak trees. As
the oak leaf buds open the
eggs of the mottled umber
moth hatch into caterpillars
which start to devour the
leaves.

Below: This wood of
coppiced hazel allows a
dense field layer of wood
sorrel to flower before the
hazel starts to leaf. The wood
sorrel is nourished by the
leaf mould of the ground
layer.

few. But even in these shady places there are
peculiar plants which, lacking chlorophyll,
manage to do without the process of photosynthesis by which nearly all other plants take
carbon dioxide from the air. Instead these
plants, called saprophytes, take their food
from dead organic matter as many fungi do.
The bird's-nest orchid is the best known of the
beechwood saprophytes. Also tolerant of
shade are the ferns which, in some woods, are
abundant.

The field layer is the world of the wood
mice, bank voles and shrews which dwell
among the thick cover. Here, too, live hedgehogs, rabbits, hares and their predators the
fox, stoat and (mainly in Wales) the polecat.
Among birds which hide their nests in the
field layer are woodcock, pheasant and, in
clearings, the nightjar. Among typical butterflies of the field layer are the speckled wood,
green-veined white and several of the fritillaries.

Ground layer This is the domain of the
shade-tolerant, earth-carpeting mosses, many
of which also cover fallen logs and the cut
stumps of trees. But mosses are not in every
wood. They need almost all-the-year-round
moisture and so are commonest in the west
and north of Britain, especially in upland
woods where rainfall is high and mists are
frequent. In drier lowland woods the ground
may only be covered by drifts of dead leaves
which shelter whole populations of small
creatures. Many fungi also inhabit the ground
layer. Their underground threads often grow
in close association with the root-tips of trees,
to the advantage of both fungus and tree.
They send up their fruiting bodies – toadstools
– mostly in autumn, bringing attractive
shapes and colours to the woodland floor.

While it is useful to think of a woodland
as built up in several layers, in nature these
layers never actually occur in such distinct
compartments as shown in diagrams. Also
many invertebrates and birds, and mammals
such as squirrels and bats, move freely from
one layer to another. Even a few plants – ivy,
traveller's-joy, honeysuckle and polypody
fern, for instance – belong to all layers. So do
tree trunks: different mosses, lichens and invertebrates are found on different sections of
the trunk from ground level up to the tree
crown.

The vitality of a woodland depends on a
powerful flow of life-giving substances cir-
culating through all the layers with every
plant and animal playing a part by its life and
death. For a healthy woodland, though made
up of various layers, is really one successful,
ever-changing community. For example, a
plant provides sustenance for an insect which,
in turn, is food for a bird that then falls victim
to a larger predator. Plants take nutritive
substances from the soil to the tree-tops and
return it again in falling leaves and twigs,
and the food-chains circulate organic material
through all the woodland layers.

READING THE SIGNS IN A WOOD

The local wood that you like to walk in of a weekend holds far more clues to its past than you may realise. Once you learn how to decipher these clues you can learn a great deal about the history of the wood and even estimate its age.

Above: A coppice of small-leaved lime with a layer of bluebells underneath. The regular cutting of the coppices–which in this wood last happened eight years ago–allows plenty of sunlight down to the woodland floor. This in turn encourages the bluebells to spread to a degree that would not be possible in an ordinary wood of standard trees (unless the soil was very sandy). The presence of such a carpet of bluebells in ordinary woodland indicates the trees were once coppiced.

Most people assume that our oakwoods, beechwoods and woods of our other native trees are all an old and natural part of the countryside, but this is a long way from the truth. Natural woods, completely untouched by man, no longer exist in Britain. Many of our woods are young, perhaps only a century or two old, and even our older woods were in almost all cases used or managed in past centuries. A great deal can be learned about the history of a wood by looking for signs of past management.

Clues to a coppice One very ancient tradition was to manage a wood as 'coppice with standards'. When shrubs and young trees are cut back to the ground they quickly sprout a

head of shoots which grow to about 2m (6ft) high in a year and then begin to thicken. The resulting plant is called a coppice. After about seven to fifteen years the shoots of the coppice used to be cut to yield a supply of poles, staves and brushwood. Scattered through the coppices were the standards–trees allowed to grow unhindered and then felled for their timber when they had reached an age of about 70 to 150 years. The standards were sometimes obtained by a process called singling, which involved cutting out all but one of a clump of coppice shoots. On other occasions the standards were simply planted, oaks often being favoured for this because their branches cork-screw slightly as they grow, thus supplying ready-shaped timbers for shipbuilding.

The most obvious sign of past coppicing is the presence of 'many-trunked' trees growing on the site of old coppice stumps. But there are more subtle indicators. First, it was important in past times to keep out livestock, otherwise they would destroy the young coppice shoots, and so the wood was often surrounded by a ditch with a large bank inside it, which was once fenced. The remains of the bank and ditch can still be seen today in many places.

Another important clue to woods that were once coppiced is the abundance of spring flowers. The regular cutting of the coppices allowed plenty of sunlight to reach the floor of the wood, and this encouraged the growth of plants. Some of these plants are normally slow to spread, or seed poorly, so their presence in large numbers on the woodland floor is an excellent indication that the wood is ancient and was once coppiced. Take, for example, bluebells. They spread only slowly on heavy clay soils, so a carpet of them under trees growing on such a clay soil could be the clue to an old wood, especially if wood anemones and early purple orchids are also present. (Bluebells spread quickly on light soils, however, so beware that the carpet is not picking out a patch of sand in the wood!) In such woods you may find rarities like herb paris, which prefers rather lime-rich soils. Even dog's mercury, which seems to be such a common woodland plant, is in fact rare in recent woodland–that is, woodland that has formed in the last hundred years.

Wild animals, as well as plants, were encouraged by coppicing. The coppice woods were usually divided into compartments, each being cut in rotation. The wildlife could easily move from one compartment to another to find the conditions they preferred. For example, fritillary butterflies, whose caterpillars feed on dog violets, are typical of such woods.

Looking for pollards Another tradition as old as coppicing was to allow livestock to graze the common land of the parish, which often included woodland. In time this wood pasture developed its own appearance: it had a bare grassy floor (for the animals destroyed the spring flowers and the undergrowth) and the trees were well spaced out because the animals also ate many of the new saplings. However, a supply of poles could still be obtained by cropping the branches of the trees at head height, out of reach of the animals, a system known as pollarding. Old pollarded trees can still be seen today, though the technique itself has all but died out, the last true echo being in the Langdale Valley, Cumbria, where the ash trees are still pollarded.

Guessing the age Many of the woods that were once coppiced or pollarded are extremely ancient; indeed they have existed since trees colonized Britain after the last Ice Age. First came the birch and Scots pine, and then, as the climate improved, these early colonizers

Above: Dog's mercury may seem a common woodland plant yet it is rarely found in recently planted woods and so is a good indicator of old woodland.

Right: Another indication of an old wood is a rich variety of flowers, particularly if bluebells, wood anemones and early purple orchids are present. Shown here are wood anemones with primroses.

Below: The Wyre Forest in Shropshire–an ancient oak woodland.

were shaded out by taller broad-leaved trees. The result was a tangled wildwood of oak, ash, elm, alder and lime, together with smaller trees and shrubs such as hazel, hawthorn and holly.

Later, as man arrived, he cleared much of this wildwood leaving only fragments behind which he used for coppicing or pollarding. Other woods used by man for the same purpose may have been 'secondary', growing on ground that had once been cleared but was later on abandoned. In time, however, the secondary wood would have assumed the character of a primary wood and be just as rich in its variety of species–and be just as likely to have been managed by man.

A clue to really ancient woodland is that it contains just native trees and shrubs, and some of them are excellent indicators of this type of wood. Look for Midland hawthorn, which has leaves with blunter lobes than does the common hawthorn and two or three pips in the haw rather than a single one. Small-leaved lime is another good indicator–its leaves are usually about 6cm (2½in) long with tufts of rust-coloured hairs underneath; other limes have larger leaves with white tufts or none at all present.

You will rarely see any of the many species of foreign tree introduced by man in an ancient wood. Even sycamore, which was introduced about four centuries ago and has become widely naturalised, is only found in recently established woods, or in woods that have been neglected this century (as many have).

Plantations and modern woods Even in an old wood the trees may not be as natural to the site as they look. Worries about the supply of timber for the Navy 400 years ago led to the birth of a new kind of wood management quite different to the old coppicing tradition. This was the close planting of trees to create tall trunks for timber. Oak was often chosen, and beech–the beechwoods north of Derby have this rather recent origin. Even the famous Burnham Beeches on the Chilterns grow on what was either open ground or coppice 200 years ago. Since then other plantations have been established: larch and Scots pine during the Victorian era, then foreign conifers during the present century.

The clues to a plantation, whether old or new, are the trees being of one age, of one kind and planted in rows (though in some of the older beech and oak plantations this consistency has been smudged by selective felling in the past).

Recent woods Just as the species, age and shapes of the trees, along with the variety of spring flowers, are clues to the wood's history and age, so there are similar clues to recent woods, the ones that are perhaps less than a century old. Ivy did not grow well under coppice management, and it did not survive in grazed woods, so it carpets the ground only of new woods.

Clues to a wood

When you go into a wood the first sign to look for is whether the trees are all of one kind, and about the same size and age, or are there many different kinds.

Trees of many different kinds, with oak probably dominant, indicates an old woodland. All the trees are native though sycamore may have invaded the wood.

Trees of one kind (such as oak or beech) growing close together with tall trunks, perhaps planted in rows, indicates high forest plantation more than 100 years old.

If the woodland is old it was once either coppiced or grazed.

If the wood was once grazed (ie, used as wood pasture) the trees would have been pollarded, not coppiced, for the livestock would have destroyed the young coppice shoots. Therefore look for old pollards and a lack of variety in ground plants as the clues to old wood pasture.

Other features of plantations include rides (often with ditches alongside) and narrow straight boundary banks. These features may, however, have been imposed on older coppiced woodland.

Cow parsley growing strongly beneath trees can indicate secondary woodland growing on what was recently open land.

The ground thickly covered with ivy also indicates secondary woodland. Ivy was cleared from older, coppiced woodlands.

Trees all of one kind and age, definitely planted in rows and usually foreign indicates a modern plantation. (Note the Forestry Commission was established in 1913.)

Midland hawthorn (which is not confined to the Midlands) indicates old coppiced woodland that has never been anything but woodland.

Look for signs of previous coppicing: perhaps there are 'many-trunked' trees growing from the site of the old coppice stools. The main point is that a wood that was being coppiced 100 years ago is likely to be an old wood.

Look to see if there is nothing but grass under the trees (see left). This suggests that grazing continues. Wood pasture is a dead tradition but some old northern coppice woods are now used for sheltering and grazing sheep.

Small-leaved lime is another good indicator of an old coppiced wood. Its leaves are noticeably smaller than the common lime.

Look for a great variety of flowers, such as bluebells, wood anemones, herb paris and others. Many different butterflies also suggest ancient coppiced woodland.

OAK WOODLANDS IN THE WINTER

Winter is sometimes called the dead season. But as you walk through the silent woods in January (below), do not be deceived into thinking that nothing is alive. Winter is a resting season, and life's chemical processes, although slowed down, still go on.

Think of the common woodland wild flowers. If such plants can be said to have a dead season, it is summer, rather than winter, when certain species show the least life. When lesser celandines and wood anemones have finished blooming in spring they quickly vanish – flowers, leaves and stems all rot away. And the carpets of bluebells, so colourful, lush and sappy in May, have quite disappeared by August. Yet these plants, and others, are all actively growing again, above or below ground, by the end of the year; and already in January, if the season is mild enough, celandines, anemones and primroses may be showing their first flowers.

Not all our winters are mild, and plants

and animals have to be able to take this fact into account. As they evolved over millions of years one of their continual and pressing requirements has been to develop a method of getting safely through the coldest winter. A common solution to this problem is to take refuge in the winter woods. To see why, you need only take a walk some bitter winter's day, when you have to struggle against an icy north-east gale along a frozen field path that leads you to a wood, especially one with plenty of undergrowth. Once well in among the trees you are in a different world – less cold, sheltered and altogether more habitable. A woodland has a climate of its own; and the bigger the wood the more sheltered are its depths where tender species can escape the worst frosts and drying winds.

Leaf mould To tell the complete story of oakwoods in winter it is necessary to begin in the autumn, when the leaves are falling, for they play a large part in the life of the wood at all seasons. They lie thick on the ground for a few weeks, but in the dampness of early winter they are attacked by moulds and fungi and gradually decay, adding their substance to the leafmould.

So the woodland soil is formed, not only of leaves but also of twigs, branches and fallen trunks, along with all the dead plants, dead animals and animal droppings that eventually fall to the ground. This soil and its leafmould cover become a deep and fertile layer, providing food and a habitat for countless forms of life, especially in winter.

As well as leaves there are acorns to help form the woodland soil. In some years they are produced in such multitudes that several hundred may lie in a single square yard below an oak. Then what happens? Few of them are left to lie. They are quickly found and either eaten or hidden by woodpigeons, jays, rooks, pheasants, deer, squirrels, mice, voles and insects. Most of the rest are attacked by fungi. The result is that only a very few of these millions of acorns ever germinate.

Evergreen plants Some midwinter wild flowers disappear in the summer time, but not all woodland plants are so ephemeral. There is wood-sorrel, for example, whose ground-covering carpets of clover-like leaves are green the whole year round and often climb decoratively over stumps and fallen trunks. Then there are mosses and liverworts. Because they flourish in cool dampness, winter is their best season; they can be enormously abundant, covering ground, tree trunks and high branches in an ever fresh, bright-green mantle. Hardy against frosts, many of them choose winter as the time to produce their fruits, which often stand up elegantly on slender stalks.

Many ferns, too, are evergreen and remain standing in the shelter of the winter woods; and those that die down, bracken for example, provide a thick warm shelter for numerous

Above: The brambling comes to the oakwoods in winter, joining the resident tits, nuthatches, tree creepers, woodpeckers, wood pigeons, crows, jays, robins and wrens. In contrast to the summer visitors, these birds know where to find the food that is available in winter, behind bark and among leaves.

Right: A wood cricket, one member of the large community of ground-dwelling invertebrates, ventures forth.

small animals. On tree trunks, branches and twigs many kinds of lichens occur, some bushy, some leafy and some formed into flat crusts. All are hardy and are not troubled in the least by winter's cold.

Hidden hordes Perhaps you have examined leaf mould in summer and found it crawling with invertebrates – all the myriads of mites, millipedes, centipedes, earthworms, beetles and other creatures. They are all there in January, too, some hibernating, some simply hiding, ready to creep out and seek food during mild spells.

Similar communities live up in the trees – woodlice, false scorpions, spiders and many others which exploit the warm damp micro-

Above: Hoar frost on a clutch of oak marble galls. Each one is the winter home of a larva which eventually emerges as a female gall wasp 3mm ($\frac{1}{8}$in) long – provided it has not been seized by a woodpecker or consumed by insect parasites. A smaller hole found in a marble gall may be where the wasp has already emerged; a larger one is more likely to be caused by the beak of some foraging bird.

climates to be found behind the sheets of loose bark or in decaying holes. There are also legions of beetle larvae burrowing away all winter into the wood of trees. Some moth larvae are found, too, like those of the clear-wings; or the big, red-brown caterpillars of the goat moth, which bore large holes into oaks and other trees.

Oakwood moths Go into the wood some mild winter night, preferably in the week or two before Christmas, and you'll find moths in plenty: these are winter moths and mottled umbers. They flutter round your torch, or you can see them crawling up the trunks of the oaks. The ones you see flying are all males which have just emerged from their pupae in the earth, and their one aim is to find a female with whom to mate. The female's story is just as simply told: she appears from the ground and crawls up an oak – lacking wings, she cannot fly. During her ascent she mates with one of the waiting males, then goes on climbing to some high twig, where she lays her eggs near the tightly closed leaf buds.

The scores of other oakwood moths, as well as the various butterflies, have each in their fashion evolved a way of coping with the cold and hunger of winter. Most have opted for dormancy, either as eggs or pupae. But in October or November the brimstone butterfly hides away among ivy or other green cover in adult form, and is ready to fly again before winter is over if a sufficiently warm day occurs. The footman moths, on the other hand, pass the winter as active cater-pillars, eating leafy lichens on the oaks during spells of milder weather.

Hibernators Only a few vertebrate animals have chosen hibernation as their means of survival. Toads, grass snakes and adders come into the woods in fair numbers to

A drey or nest (above) and its occupant, a grey squirrel (right). Some British mammals do not hibernate, although they are less active in winter than summer. In cold spells, grey and red squirrels pass a large part of the day in the nest, while badgers lie up for several days and nights in a row.

Opposite page: One bird that stays with us all winter is the robin – it can usually find enough food to survive severe weather.

Below: Bracket fungi are easiest to find in winter. They are leathery or even wood-like and are unaffected by the severest weather. This one, known as *Coriolus versicolor,* grows on fallen hardwood including oak.

get out of the cold, squeezing into holes in the ground. Hedgehogs make elaborate weatherproof nests of dry leaves, grasses, mosses and bracken in a sheltered spot and are snug the winter through. Dormice also sleep the cold weather away in mossy nests.

Travellers and residents Hibernation is an escape route the birds do not take. Instead, many of them migrate: warblers, redstarts and flycatchers depart south in the later weeks of summer. Soon afterwards come the first arrivals from cold northern Europe: woodcock, redwings, fieldfares and some of the finches from the Arctic.

Some of the woodland birds (residents or visitors) are solitary species – woodpigeon, jay and woodcock for example. Others move around the woods all day in parties of mixed species. Such a flock may afford a measure of safety in that a predator can be detected and warning given to the whole party, whereas a solitary bird must rely solely on its own watchfulness. As you follow a woodland path in winter the scene may seem silent and lifeless until you meet a bird party. Then you may see scores of tits, nuthatches, tree creepers and others fluttering about and calling frequently as they pass through the trees. They feed as they go, each species taking its chosen types of food and so not competing with the others. Then the whole flock moves on, leaving you again in the quiet of the woods.

TREE BARK: A PROTECTIVE SKIN

Bark–whether it be rough and fissured as on an oak, or smooth as on a beech–performs the same function in all trees: that of protecting the delicate living tissue in the trunk from the weather and from attack by animals and diseases.

Even the most casual visitor to a public garden will have noticed the immense variation in the barks of trees. The smooth, brilliant white bark of the Himalayan birch and the glossy, reddish-brown, peeling bark of the Tibetan cherry make these two of our most attractive ornamental trees. Among our more familiar species, the sweet chestnut has a

Below: The rich reddish-brown trunk of the sweet chestnut, combined with the spirally arranged ridges found on many older specimens, make this species one of the few common trees in Britain that can be identified by bark alone.

strikingly spiralled bark, while that of the Scots pine is a rich brown and falls away from the tree in flakes. To us, the bark of a tree is often a very useful aid to identification, particularly in winter when many trees have lost their leaves. For the tree, however, the bark performs a vital function in protecting it from extremes of weather and against the attacks of a variety of agents, from bacteria and fungi to rabbits and deer.

How bark functions Bark consists of a living inner layer of tissue (the phloem) and an outer dead layer. The phloem plays a vital role in transporting sugars down from the leaves, where they are manufactured by photosynthesis, to the roots and other parts. The outer layer of bark is waterproof and so protects the underlying tissues from drying out. In parts of the world where seasonal fires are a potential hazard some trees have extra-thick barks to insulate the living tissue from the heat. The best known of these is the cork oak from the Mediterranean region, the bark of which has thermal insulating properties rivalling those of glass fibre. Furthermore, the presence of air spaces makes the material light and compressible. Combine this with its waterproof qualities and you have the ideal material for sealing bottles–cork. The cork oak is not often seen in British parks, but its hybrid with the Turkey oak, called Lucombe's oak, appears much more frequently, especially in the West Country.

Bark is also a tree's first line of defence against attacks by bacteria, fungi, insects and larger animals such as deer and rabbits. In most cases it repels these attacks effectively, though large herbivores may destroy so much of a tree's bark in winter when other food sources are scarce that the trunk is completely encircled by the damage. When this happens the tree inevitably dies.

To provide extra protection against this possibility, trees with thin barks higher up often have much thicker barks near the base. This may be seen on both silver birch and Scots pine.

Bark formation Bark is formed by the activity of a special sort of cambium (the wet, green tissue lying just underneath the bark). Known as the bark cambium, this layer plus the corky cells it creates are together known as the periderm. In the young tree, the periderm first arises in the outer tissues of a shoot and can be seen as a colour change, usually from green to grey. The colour change is caused by the presence of waterproof waxes and other materials in the walls of the bark cells.

In some species, such as beech and hornbeam, the periderm thus created can last for many years, slowly increasing in size by cell division as the tree's girth expands. In the majority of trees, however, the first periderm is soon followed by others arising from progressively deeper layers of the stem. With the formation of each periderm, the tissue layers lying outside it are cut off from their

source of water and nutrients, and so die.

Different bark types As the branches and trunks increase in girth resulting from cell division in the cambium, the bark must also increase in size. Thus new layers of bark are continually created within the stem. The number of layers of cork cells produced by the periderm and the depths at which they occur in the stem vary considerably and determine the thickness of the bark. A thin bark, such as that of *Stewartia* species, is smooth while a thick bark, such as that of English oak or black walnut, is rough and fissured.

In some trees the older layers of bark readily peel away or break off. This can be seen in the paper-bark maple and various species of strawberry tree. If the layers remain firmly attached, as in wellingtonia and coast redwood, then a thick bark builds up, which is only gradually worn away. Persistent barks often become deeply fissured because the older, dead, layers on the outside are unable to grow to keep pace with the expanding trunk.

In some species the periderm can completely encircle the stem and, if the outer bark falls away, then whole cylinders of bark can be discarded. Traveller's joy, honeysuckle and paper birch all have such barks. In the case of paper birch, large sheets of its bark were used by certain North American Indians in the building of their canoes.

In other trees the periderm is much more localised, arising one beneath another like overlapping scales. The resulting bark is therefore shed as discrete, irregularly shaped pieces. In Britain, the most familiar examples of this type of bark are those of yew and London plane.

Lenticels for air In common with herbaceous plants, the stem of a young tree contains structures known as stomata through which the stems cells obtain carbon dioxide and lose oxygen. When the stem loses its original epidermis it also loses its stomato and their job is taken over by small lens-shaped pores in the bark called lenticels.

Most woody plants have lenticels on their stems, though they can vary from being microscopically small to 1cm ($\frac{1}{2}$in) or more in diameter. In some species, such as birches, the

Above: In some species the first layer of bark laid down by the young tree quickly grows to build up a thick layer of corky tissue. On a young Dutch elm (a hybrid between the smooth-leaved elm and the wych elm) this corky tissue splits as the tree grows, forming corky 'wings' around the young shoots. These can be seen on the branches in the picture shown here.

lenticels enlarge with age.

Other features Along with lenticels, some trees also have spines on their branches or trunks. Hawthorns have spines formed from small branches, though at up to 1.5cm ($\frac{5}{8}$in) long they are insignificant compared with the branched thorns of some honey locusts, which can grow to a length of 10cm (4 in). The more familiar locust tree, or false acacia, has spiny stipules on its younger branches. These were originally at the bases of the leaves.

Occasionally trees produce masses of shoots directly from the bark. These arise from buds that, for most of the time, lie dormant within the trunk. This is a particular feature of the common lime, which often has large tufts of leafy shoots sprouting from its bark. Dormant buds can be very important to the tree as a means of regeneration after a forest fire, damage by lightning or even heavy pruning. The Judas tree is unusual in that it frequently produces bunches of flowers directly from its bark.

Bark products While some trees are grown for their ornamental barks, other trees have barks that are of considerable commercial importance to us. One of the most familiar bark products is latex, which is secreted by specialised cells arising in the phloem. By making incisions in the bark of certain trees the latex can be extracted and converted into products such as rubber and the gum of chewing gum. Few trees growing in Britain

Three bark types

Thick barks, such as that of the black walnut (right), are often rough and deeply fissured into small plates.

The London plane (right) has a thin bark that falls away in plates, reflecting the arrangement of the periderm layers underneath.

Some trees, such as wellingtonia (right), develop a thick, fibrous bark that is only very gradually worn away.

yield latex, but one such is the fig.

Some trees are tapped for the sugary sap carried in their phloem. The sugar maple, for example, yields maple syrup while in southern Europe several species of pine are tapped for their resin. Certain wines are flavoured with resin from the Aleppo pine. Other resin products from pines include rosin and turpentine.

Another very important source of bark products are materials produced by the tree inside the bark cells themselves, mostly as a form of chemical defence against animals and other potential attackers. An example is tannin, high levels of which are found in the barks of oak trees, making them important in the tanning of hides for leather.

Finally, a few barks are used as a source of aromatic products. Perhaps the best known of these is the spice cinnamon, which is the inner bark of a tree from south-east Asia. The scent myrrh is also extracted from the bark of a tree, in this case by tapping the bark and extracting the myrrh from the resin.

Above: The paper-bark maple is now widely planted in parks and gardens for its beautiful reddish-brown bark which peels away in strips.

Above right: The deeply fissured lower part of a white poplar's trunk contrasts with the much smoother bark higher up. Notice the conspicuous rows of lenticels on the upper half of the tree.

Right: Père David's maple, one of a group of snake-bark maples with distinctive silvery-white lines running down their olive-green barks.

Below: A close-up view of the bark of a beech tree—note the smoothness and metallic grey colour.

Barks in Britain

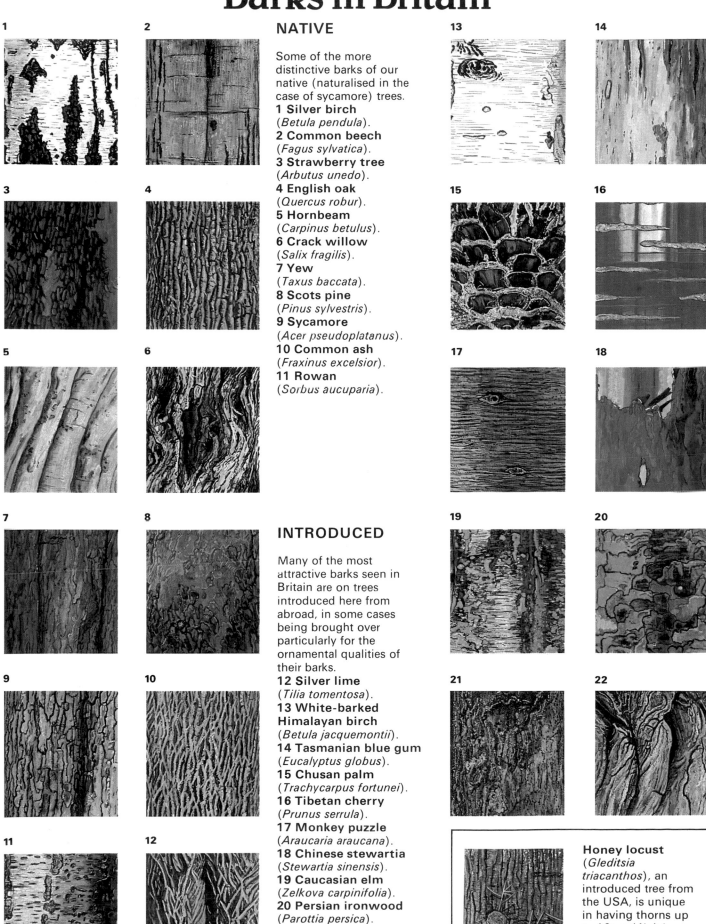

NATIVE

Some of the more distinctive barks of our native (naturalised in the case of sycamore) trees.

1 Silver birch (*Betula pendula*).
2 Common beech (*Fagus sylvatica*).
3 Strawberry tree (*Arbutus unedo*).
4 English oak (*Quercus robur*).
5 Hornbeam (*Carpinus betulus*).
6 Crack willow (*Salix fragilis*).
7 Yew (*Taxus baccata*).
8 Scots pine (*Pinus sylvestris*).
9 Sycamore (*Acer pseudoplatanus*).
10 Common ash (*Fraxinus excelsior*).
11 Rowan (*Sorbus aucuparia*).

INTRODUCED

Many of the most attractive barks seen in Britain are on trees introduced here from abroad, in some cases being brought over particularly for the ornamental qualities of their barks.

12 Silver lime (*Tilia tomentosa*).
13 White-barked Himalayan birch (*Betula jacquemontii*).
14 Tasmanian blue gum (*Eucalyptus globus*).
15 Chusan palm (*Trachycarpus fortunei*).
16 Tibetan cherry (*Prunus serrula*).
17 Monkey puzzle (*Araucaria araucana*).
18 Chinese stewartia (*Stewartia sinensis*).
19 Caucasian elm (*Zelkova carpinifolia*).
20 Persian ironwood (*Parottia persica*).
21 Tree of heaven (*Ailanthus altissima*).
22 False acacia (*Robinia pseudoacacia*).

Honey locust (*Gleditsia triacanthos*), an introduced tree from the USA, is unique in having thorns up to 10cm (4in) long sprouting from the trunk.

LIFE
IN DEAD
WOOD

Although an old log is itself lifeless, a close look may reveal within it a living community of invertebrates and fungi, all deriving sustenance from the wood.

Long before the arrival of man, forests covered most of lowland Britain. There were literally billions of trees. At any one time, huge numbers of them were reaching old age and dying, making dead wood one of the most abundant habitats in Britain at that time. Animals and fungi have thus had millions of years in which to evolve a large number of species adapted to feeding on, and living in, dead wood, promoting its decay in the process.

This is why there are in Britain as many as 1000 species of animals that have been recorded living in dead wood. Most are tiny, of course. Insects include many types of beetles and flies; among other invertebrates are slugs and snails, woodlice and centipedes. Many hundreds of species of fungi, too, are found on dead wood.

Today dead wood is relatively scarce because man has changed the character of the forests. Trees are often felled before they reach old age, and many pieces of woodland are kept so tidy that fallen logs are a rarity. It has been estimated that a tidy forest, free of dead wood, may be impoverished by up to a fifth of its fauna.

Recycling nutrients The animals and plants that depend on dead wood have an important role to play in the forest ecosystem. The living tree 'locks up' quantities of minerals and nutrients in its bark and wood. When a tree rots, its valuable chemical substances are returned to the soil where they can be recycled

Above: An old log, decked with moss and fungi, in a clearing in the New Forest. In some parts of the forest, a proportion of the dead wood is left to lie as part of a conservation policy.

Below: One of the many species of longhorn beetle that breed in dead wood. The adult beetles emerge from the wood and visit flowers, such as this wild rose, to gather nectar.

into the next generation of trees. A similar process, maintaining the fertility of the soil, occurs with leaf fall.

The decay of dead wood can be very slow unless it is speeded up by the growth of fungi and the activity of insects. This can best be appreciated if you look at the gaunt white trunks of elms, killed by Dutch elm disease, or the standing victims of a stroke of lightning. In exposed conditions, the dead wood is baked by the rays of the sun, which sterilise it and virtually stop all biological activity. The bark soon peels off, and the wood becomes too dry and, at times, too hot to support fungi and insects.

A log which lies in the shade and remains moist, on the other hand, is in an ideal condition for wildlife to thrive on it. It will retain its bark and support a varied range of fungi and many species of invertebrates, and soon the signs of decay are plentiful.

A sequence of decay It takes about 20 years for a large log to decay completely to the final stage in which all the nutrients have been used up and the wood disintegrates. The time varies with the type of tree, and also depends on whether decay had already started on the live tree.

The creatures that colonize the wood appear in a natural sequence: first are those that invade a dying tree, followed by those that specialise on recently dead timber, then others, through progressive stages of decay,

Above right: The lesser stag beetle breeds in wood that has begun to rot.

Right: Sulphur tuft fungus grows throughout the year on the stumps of dead trees. It is not restricted to just one species of tree.

to the species that predominate when the wood has reached a crumbly texture. The most specialised species (those most restricted to the habitat) are the early colonizers, while in later stages of decay many types of invertebrates that also live in leaf litter or soil become residents.

Spreading fungi A tree trunk consists of an inner layer of heartwood, and an outer layer of sap wood which is richer in nutrients. Some species of fungi develop in the heartwood, others in the sapwood. Their presence may not be easy to detect: for much of the time they consist of tiny transparent threads known as hyphae, which are normally invisible to the naked eye. Only when the hyphae produce fruiting bodies – toadstools or bracket fungi, for example – can the species be identified. The larger species tend to be seen in the earlier years of decay while the wood still contains the plentiful supply of nutrients they require.

The insect pioneers Bark beetles are often among the first colonists. The female bores a tunnel and lays her eggs along it; when these

The many agents of decay

A few examples are shown of the countless species that promote the decay of dead wood. Cap fungi (**1**) and bracket fungi (**2**) are host to a number of insects: fruit flies feed on the surface of some fungi, while residents within include devil's coach horse beetles and the larvae of fungus gnats (**3**). Stag beetles (**4**) breed in rotting wood, as do cardinal beetles (**5**) and some craneflies such as *Ctenophora atrata* (**6**). Many other invertebrates are likely to be present: besides woodlice, centipedes, millipedes and spiders, there may be molluscs such as the snail *Cochlodina laminata* (**7**).

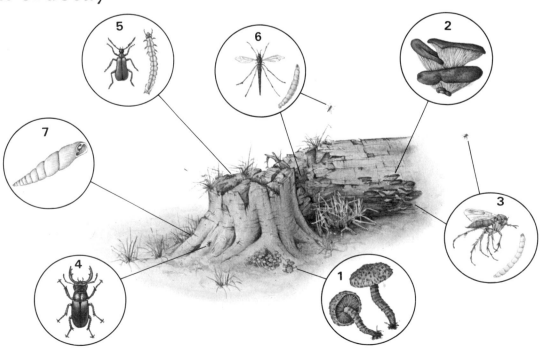

hatch, the larvae burrow outwards in a radiating pattern.

The bark beetles loosen the bark and enable other species to invade, such as the flattened larvae of cardinal beetles. Then woodlice, centipedes and other species are able to establish themselves, and these creatures dominate the community that lives in the area just below the bark.

Deeper under the surface, the wood is attacked first by the larvae of the larger beetles, for instance some of the longhorn beetles. The stag beetle has larvae which take several years to grow, preferring wood which has already started to rot. The more rotten wood is the home of various click beetle larvae and some uncommon cockchafer larvae.

Flies also breed in dead wood, for the most part under the bark or within partly decayed wood. The larger species of flies include a number of mimics, for instance hoverflies that look like bees and wasps, or craneflies that have a similar appearance to some of the large ichneumon wasps.

Also occupying the dead wood are the wood wasps; the largest species of these are found in conifers. One of our largest ichneumon wasps is a parasite of wood wasps, its long egg-laying tube or ovipositor being designed to penetrate deeply into wood containing wood wasp larvae. It is one of nature's mysteries that the wasp can locate the larvae

Above: The pied flycatcher prefers a small tree hole for its nest site.

Below: A hollow oak in Windsor Great Park. Dead branches are in effect 'aerial logs'—as they are not in contact with the leaf litter or the soil, they support a different range of wildlife from logs that lie on the ground.

so accurately.

Some habitats on old trees Whereas a log provides a habitat during a period of some years as it decays, an ageing tree is a longer-term habitat. There are even veteran trees that take a century or so to die. Hollow trees sometimes shelter bats and owls. The dead wood on the inside may be riddled with beetle burrows, the insects taking advantage of the fact that new dead wood is being added to their habitat as the live trunk grows outwards.

However, to many naturalists, old trees are of interest because of the birds which nest in natural hollows, or woodpeckers which chisel out their own nest holes. There are some 20 species that regularly nest in tree hollows: in large ones, birds such as the tawny owl are found, while the smaller ones are occupied by pied flycatchers or blue tits. Various insects specialise in living in the nests of these birds.

The forest web of life The dead wood fauna are an integral part of the forest wildlife community. They play a general role as a source of food for insect-eating creatures such as shrews, hedgehogs and some birds; and at the same time other roles are played in the life of the community. Hoverflies emerge from the wood and visit wild flowers, as do the longhorn beetles, to obtain energy from the nectar, providing the service of pollination in return. Another role is that of the predator—some species of solitary wasps, for example, catch flies and other insects, storing them up as a food reserve.

Taking care Dead or rotting wood is nowadays surprisingly vulnerable as a natural habitat—to see why, you only need look at the number of hollow trees wrecked by the bonfires of vandals. Even those interested in observing all the activity of the dead wood fauna should heed a warning: patience is required, and the dead wood should always be kept intact. Break it open, and you have already destroyed the habitat that you are investigating.

THE HIDDEN LIFE IN TREE HOLES

Tree holes–formed by the action of fungi, lightning or the excavations of animals–make ideal, securely hidden dwelling places for a host of different animals.

A walk through woodlands anywhere in Britain will reveal trees disfigured by long gaping fissures, deep callus-ringed holes and shallow depressions–all of them capable of harbouring a highly specialised community of animals that varies according to whether the hole is predominantly wet or dry.

Rot holes and pans When the bark of a tree is damaged, the underlying layer of sap wood, and eventually the inner heartwood, may be attacked by fungi. Various species of beetles can help to spread this fungi as they burrow into the timber. Between them the insects and the fungi cause the damaged area to enlarge and eventually a cavity is formed. This, called a rot hole, is one of the commonest types of tree hole.

The wound that begins the formation of a rot hole may be the result of natural damage by animals, high winds or lightning. It may also be caused by human activities; pollarding, coppicing and the pruning of trees can initiate rotting, as can accidental damage. Some rot holes occur in sheltered positions in trees and remain dry even in heavy rain. Others however, are exposed and rain water fills them, either directly or by running into them down branches. The water may drain away through the rotting wood or it may accumulate, especially when the tree hole is lined with rotted leaves.

Often the openings of rot holes become restricted, even though the cavity is con-

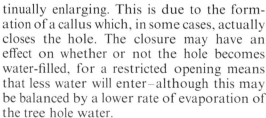

The holes in an old tree like this great beech in the New Forest (above) can harbour a wide range of animals— microscopic protozoans, creatures like woodlice and snails (below), and birds and mammals too.

tinually enlarging. This is due to the formation of a callus which, in some cases, actually closes the hole. The closure may have an effect on whether or not the hole becomes water-filled, for a restricted opening means that less water will enter–although this may be balanced by a lower rate of evaporation of the tree hole water.

A second variety of tree hole results from the growth pattern of certain trees. They are called pans and differ from rot holes in that they are shallow depressions, lined with unbroken bark, in the tree surface. They may occur when tree crowding leads to the distortion of trunks and branches and, in the case of trees like beech, may be found among the buttress roots. In most cases, pans are shallow and, although nearly always capable of holding water, may lose water rapidly by evaporation.

Both rot holes and pans are extremely common and can be found in a wide range of deciduous trees, including beech, oak, hornbeam and ash. They are less common in conifers but have been recorded in several species, including silver fir.

Wet holes When tree holes become filled with water they form a specialised aquatic habitat which is colonized by a wide variety of animal life. Numerous protozoans, including the cosmopolitan 'slipper animalcule' *Paramecium*, small crustaceans like *Cyclops*, and rotifers and springtails are found in almost all accumulations of water, and those in tree holes are no exception. Occasionally larvae of the drone-fly *Eristalis tenax* may be encountered; they are found in many stagnant waters breathing air through a telescopic tail which is held up to the surface. The rotting wood and leaves in these holes provide a rich source of food and can support large numbers of individuals.

Although water-filled tree holes cannot be classed as permanent habitats, they can persist for the entire life of a tree which, in the case of beech for example, may exceed one hundred years. Tree holes in the tropics dry out periodically and hence their fauna must either be capable of withstanding periods of dryness during their life-cycle, or else they must be capable of completing their life-cycles very quickly. In this country, however, most tree holes do not dry out completely, even in the summer (they are aided in some cases by water which rises within the tree itself). It has been found that nearly all the fauna can survive as long as the bottom layer

of decaying material remains moist.

Wet hole inhabitants Perhaps the most interesting and important group of animals are those specifically associated with the tree hole habitat in their immature stages and are seldom, if ever, found elsewhere. By becoming adapted for such a specialised habitat these animals have forsaken the variety of aquatic habitats elsewhere and therefore restricted their choice of breeding sites. But in return, they have escaped their natural enemies, for there are no predatory beetles and dragonfly larvae in tree holes.

In Britain three of our 33 species of mosquito breed exclusively in tree holes. In some areas all three may be found inhabiting the

Above: A willow tit bringing food to its chicks, securely hidden within the nesting hole. This type of hole may well have been made originally by a woodpecker. There are about 20 species of birds in Britain nesting in tree holes, among them the tawny and little owls, the nuthatch, the pied flycatcher and the blue and great tits.

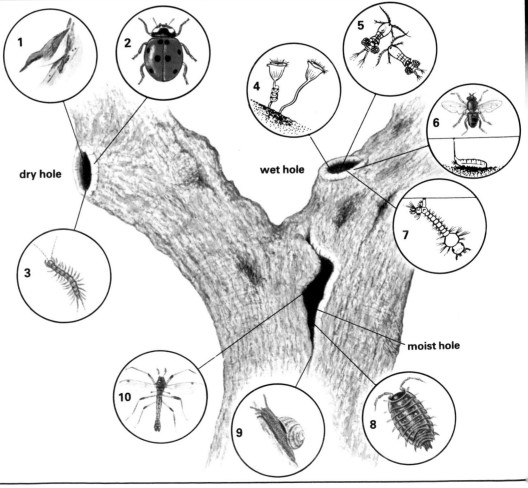

The teeming life in beech tree holes

One tree can often have several different types of hole.

Dry holes are usually produced by the removal of a branch (through natural means or by man). The hole develops a callus of scar tissue around it that may eventually close the hole. Since it is vertical it is likely to remain dry in all except driving rain. The dry hole is favoured as a nesting site by the nuthatch (**1**) in spring and summer, but a ladybird (**2**) uses it only for hibernating in winter. Centipedes (**3**) shelter in the dry hole by day.

Wet holes, often found in a horizontal position, receive water directly from the rain and also from stem flow. The wet hole is alive with tiny protozoans, such as vorticella (**4**). Other animals living in wet holes include crustaceans like cyclops (**5**), and the larvae of drone-flies (**6**) and several species of mosquito (**7**).

Moist holes Fissures running the length of the trunk or branch accumulate leaf litter and receive water from stem flow but dry out fairly fast. The dampness suits woodlice (**8**), snails (**9**) and cranefly larvae (**10**).

dry hole

wet hole

moist hole

Above: Fungus growing out of a callus in an old beech tree. Insects like beetles often assist in the spread of fungi as they bore into the tree. There is still much to be learnt about the life-cycles of tree-hole breeding insects and zoologists are using artificial 'tree holes' to find answers. Examination at regular intervals of glass jars and sections of tropical bamboo filled with water and placed at various levels in trees reveals valuable information on the egg-laying periods and duration of the immature stages of the insects. Another study method is to place traps over the openings of tree holes to monitor the emerging adults. Monthly sampling of tree holes and the counting of the number of individuals of each life stage also help to compile a picture of the insects' life histories and give information on the number of generations produced.

same tree hole, but often one species predominates. Little is known about the selection of individual holes by mosquitoes, but observations show that our rarest tree hole breeding species, *Orthopodomyia pulchripalpis*, selects holes containing water rich in tannin and therefore dark in colour. The more common *Aedes geniculatus* and *Anopheles plumbeus* are normally found in clearer water.

Female mosquitoes lay their eggs into the water of the tree holes in the summer months. The eggs may either hatch almost immediately or remain dormant until the following spring. The larvae feed on organic material suspended in the water and on bacteria and algae that they scrape from the walls of the cavity and from the surfaces of submerged leaves. The larvae are active swimmers and are often called 'wrigglers', which describes their way of moving. They are air breathers and so must spend time at the surface, taking in air through an opening at the end of their bodies. Mosquitoes pass through four larval stages and in spring or summer enter a pupal phase, which, unlike that of many insects, is active. Once again, their common name of 'tumblers' describes their movement. Like the larvae they rise to the surface to breathe, but they do not feed. In the summer the pupal skins split and the adult mosquitoes emerge

to mate, feed and repeat the life-cycle.

Apart from mosquitoes, a number of fly larvae occur in tree hole water. Among the most numerous are the larvae of the biting midge *Dasyhelea dufouri* and those of the non-biting midge *Metriocnemus martinii*. Both pass through four larval stages, like mosquitoes, and feed on debris in the tree hole.

The immature stages of the hover-fly *Myiatropa florea* are common inhabitants of tree holes, although they are generally found in low numbers. Once again, there is only one generation each year. Unlike the previously mentioned insects, the mature larvae leave the tree hole to pupate in crevices in the bark. The only beetle to breed in tree holes is *Prionocyphon serricornis*, whose larvae may live for up to two years in tree holes.

In addition to the fully aquatic fauna of tree holes, there is also a group of animals which is attracted to moist situations. They include woodlice such as *Oniscus*, snails like *Helix*, and larvae of the cranefly *Ctenophora* and of the moth-fly *Pericoma*.

Dry hole dwellers Dry tree holes offer a valuable and important habitat for a range of terrestrial arthropods, as well as for birds and bats. Some arthropods, such as centipedes and spiders, are found in holes throughout the year, while others, including ladybirds, are present only in the winter, using the protected environment of the tree holes as overwintering sites.

The most obvious inhabitants of our dry tree holes are birds, some 20 species of which nest in tree hollows. Tawny owls, little owls and stockdoves are among those occupying the larger holes, while starlings, blue tits, great tits, nuthatches and pied flycatchers reside in the smaller holes. Often these birds use holes which have been made in a previous season by woodpeckers. When other birds take over woodpecker holes, they may line the floor with nesting material – oak leaves and grass in the case of the pied flycatcher and flakes of bark in the nuthatch – or the nest hole may be used totally unlined as in little owls and stockdoves. Nuthatches are noted for the way in which they reduce the size of the entrance of the nest hole with mud in order to keep out larger intruders.

Like all tree holes, the excavations made by woodpeckers may be enlarged by rotting fungi, become filled with rain and so be transformed into aquatic habitats.

Mammals, too, make their homes in dry tree holes. Squirrels nest in holes in the higher branches, and bats may roost there. Wood mice inhabit holes lower down, while stoats and wildcats make use of holes set low in the boles of trees. In fact, most small wild mammals will make use of dry holes at some time in their lives – as refuge from enemies and shelter from rain and snow. Such rodents as field-mice may well gnaw the insides of the holes to enlarge them or to shape them more to their own liking for nesting.

MANAGING A WOODLAND

Good management of specially preserved areas of woodland (such as Wyre Forest), marsh and heath can provide valuable havens for many of Britain's wildlife species.

Places set aside specially for the study of wildlife are known as nature reserves and may take several forms. Some are looked after by County Councils and are known as local nature reserves, while others are in the care of the County Naturalists' Trusts and are bought with the help of members' subscriptions, as are the reserves run by the RSPB. The government agency responsible for conservation is the Nature Conservancy Council which, as well as managing its reserves, also commissions research into various aspects of conservation. While some reserves are acquired in order to protect plants or animals which are rare locally or nationally, others have a comprehensive range of species which typify a particular habitat.

Managing a forest The Wyre Forest National Nature Reserve in the West Midlands is a large area of oak woodland and coniferous plantations, among which are numerous old meadows and orchards. A trout stream runs through the valley into the River Severn nearby, and a disused railway

track also runs through the forest.

Most of the oak woodland is of an even-age structure. The coppice areas where charcoal burning and bark peeling once thrived are long since abandoned. To introduce a more mixed woodland age structure, the oak is thinned to let in more light and allow other species of trees, such as birch and wild service, to regenerate. This may be standard forestry thinning, or an experimental type where various techniques are tried in order to favour trees which will be growing on well when the final crop of larger or more mature trees is felled. These techniques require heavy tree handling and are carried out by skilled contractors. The felled trees are usually converted into fence stakes or planking timber, if large enough; this will often pay for the work and provide a financial return for the owner. It helps if, in certain areas, an extra tree or two is removed to create a glade, where regeneration of oak, birch and heather will be much quicker, because of the extra light admitted. If possible, a few trees are ring-barked, causing them to die and thus

Above: Deep inside Wyre Forest National Nature Reserve. Because there is a limited supply of funds for conservation, much of the reserve's management is done by volunteers who may be naturalists or simply people who enjoy the countryside. Some of the larger and more important reserves, such as this one, have wardens – part of their job being to co-ordinate this use of voluntary help. Much of the conservation work is done by parties of people from the Wyre Forest Society – a society which aims to preserve the beauty and conservation interest in the woodland of Wyre.

Opposite left: Columbines grace the forest in spring.

provide a valuable dead wood habitat. They may also be simply felled and left to die and rot where they fall.

Certain species of birds can be attracted if nest sites are provided. If there are few natural nest holes, interesting species such as the redstart and the pied flycatcher readily use the nest boxes erected in the woodlands and orchards.

In areas where oak coppice growth is favoured, the younger stems may be cut and sold locally for use as bean sticks or for making rustic furniture, leaving a stem or two on each stump as possible future trees. These older poles may be sold as firewood.

Many of the thicker and even-aged oak woods are relatively devoid of interest deep inside; they often have a ground flora consisting mainly of bracken. A much more diverse range of insects and plants occurs, however, on the edges – here such species as bramble, hawthorn and rose form thickets in a dense border. A wide ride cut through a wood will create two such new edges, and this can give a great boost to the variety of species within the forest, provided not too much timber is removed in the process. Butterflies especially welcome these sheltered flyways, and such plants as bugle thrive.

Woodland scrub The woodland edge is really a scrub habitat and scrub is also found in other parts of the reserve. It is important for different groups of plants and animals at varying stages of its development. For example, warblers may need small blackthorn bushes of five years old or so in which to breed, whereas hairstreak butterflies need much older bushes on which to lay their eggs, while silver-washed fritillary butterflies prefer to obtain nectar from bramble blossoms. Good management must therefore ensure

Sights to see in Wyre Forest National Nature Reserve – cowslips in the meadows (above), a redstart (left) and bark peelings ready to go to a tannery (below). The landscape of Britain as we know it today has nearly all been shaped by man. Even the wild hill country moorland is a man-made scene, created by sheep grazing and heather burning. It is, indeed, almost impossible to find any true primeval habitat, although some areas may come close to it, such as the pine forests of Scotland and certain parts of the coastline. Often, though, especially in areas of intensive agriculture, our wild areas of woodland, marsh and heath have become fragmented or widely detached from their nearest area of comparable habitat. They have become oases, in fact, with few connecting lines along which wildlife can spread or extend in range. Many of the wild species still existing in these isolated pockets are rare, some being found in just one spot in the country. We have only relatively recently started to understand some of the complex inter-relationships existing between plants and animals. To learn more in this field of ecology, it is necessary to set aside areas where species can be studied in conditions which are as natural as possible – areas like Wyre Forest, where good management ensures species survival.

that such areas remain – but only so long as other species needing an open habitat do not suffer in the process. In a large area such as Wyre Forest, however, it is possible to maintain some of each habitat.

The best example of a scrub habitat within the forest is that growing on the banks of the old railway track: being in linear form it is easy to split up into sections and manage on rotation. By cutting at different times, a complete range of age structures can be achieved, so that at any one time there is at least one area of each scrubland age group, up to a maximum of about 20 years old. Being of no commercial value, the work of cutting out the bushes must usually be done by volunteers.

Other scrub may be managed in a way that keeps the particular area in a static age class. This is done by removing all bushes except those in the age or size group required. Hedgerows in the reserve, which belong to the scrub

Above: An adder flattened out on an old tree stump. This snake is not dangerous unless it is disturbed. People use Wyre Forest extensively and generally do so with consideration for the peace and wildness – and wildlife – they come to find. Ramblers, riders, photographers and naturalists visit regularly. There is even a special 'horseshoe trail', provided by the Forestry Commission, where people can ride (for a fee) over many miles of special tracks.

Below: Mature scrub on the banks of Wyre Forest's old railway track.

group, are managed by being 'laid' in the traditional way; this too is done on a rotational basis. It is a skilled and time-consuming job but produces a worthwhile result. Areas of heather or gorse, if they need to be cut or removed, are treated with a tractor and rear mounted 'swipe'. This, a circular-motion mower using either blades or chains as the cutting edge, handles quite large stems.

Meadows It is difficult to imagine the small scattered meadows of Wyre Forest as part of the forest habitat, but after existing for hundreds of years they are an extremely valuable part of the woodland mosaic. Many species of butterfly need the woodland violet on which to lay their eggs, and the flowers which grow in the old meadows also provide a source of nectar for the adults. The large mounds or 'tumps' of the meadow ant, too, are a common feature of these small fields, and provide a valuable part of the diet of such birds as the green woodpecker. Combined with the meadows there are orchards, now becoming derelict, with old, gnarled or fallen trees, usually full of holes and crannies which are useful for wildlife. These fruit trees are usually the now rare old varieties of cider apple or perry pear, which are replaced wherever possible.

The meadows would soon form into scrub if they were not managed. Management is done in two of the oldest and most traditional ways known – grazing with cattle and cutting for hay. The cattle could be a problem because of the remoteness of some of the small fields, but fortunately there is a farmer quite near who is willing to drive his animals through the forest. They are removed in the spring when

This does not mean that long stretches of alder are removed; instead only a few odd trees are cut.

If too many trees were removed more light would fall on the water and could upset the ecology of the streams, especially the larger ones. As it bubbles over rocks and stones through its mainly sheltered tunnel of trees, the temperature is kept low, and much oxygen is thus dissolved. This provides just the right conditions for many aquatic species–mayflies and caddisflies and their larvae, and fishes such as trout, bullhead, loach and lamprey. Crayfish are common and provide food for a pest species which has moved into the area recently, the mink. This mammal is kept down to an acceptable level by trapping. This procedure is necessary since the mink's numbers could rise to pest proportions, to the detriment of other wildlife in the forest.

some of the meadow blooms appear–cowslips and green-winged orchids in particular. The adder's-tongue fern can also be found in spring, while the meadow saffron blooms in the autumn. After the hay has been cut in the summer, the cattle return. The hay cutting prevents the build-up of dead litter just above ground level and encourages the meadow flora, as does the fact that no chemical fertilisers are used.

Some of the more remote fields, however, are inaccessible and so cannot be treated in this way. They are cut with a mower and then raked. Horse grazing, when carried out sporadically, can provide an alternative to the better methods, but if too heavy or prolonged may cause damage. One or two areas in the forest display a wealth of blooms–betony, meadowsweet, knapweed, trefoils, marsh thistle and many others–as a result of light grazing by one or two horses.

The ponds One feature not met with often in the forest is ponds or areas of static water. A number of streams run through the steep-sided valleys, however, and most of the few ponds in Wyre Forest have been made by erecting a dam across such a valley. One pool created in this way holds a number of fishes, including roach, perch and carp.

The streams themselves require little looking after, but the trees that grow alongside are managed. One of the most common stream-side trees is the alder, which provides a home for such tree-boring insects as the rare alder wood wasp. This insect requires quite thin stems of alder in which to lay its eggs–coppicing of the trees provides a flush of new growth that meets this requirement.

Above: Oak tree felling in the forest. The larger trees will be converted into planks or stakes–an economical return for the labour of growing and felling. Thinning lets light into the forest and encourages a diverse ground layer of plants

Right: Meadow saffron or autumn crocus–a species that blooms in Wyre's meadows in autumn.

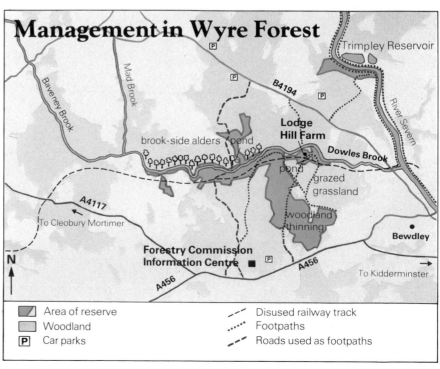

Management in Wyre Forest

Trimpley Reservoir

Mad Brook

Baveney Brook

B4194

River Severn

Lodge Hill Farm

brook-side alders / pond

Dowles Brook

pond

grazed grassland

A4117

To Cleobury Mortimer

woodland thinning

Bewdley

Forestry Commission Information Centre

A456

A456

To Kidderminster

N

	Area of reserve		Disused railway track
	Woodland		Footpaths
P	Car parks		Roads used as footpaths

TIMBER AND ITS PRODUCTS

Timber is the most valuable of all our natural resources. From fuel and building materials to tools, furniture and paper, we use timber for so many different purposes that it is almost impossible to imagine life without it.

A quick look at the wooden items found in a house soon shows that wood is not a uniform material but extremely variable, differing in pattern, colour and hardness. The most basic difference is between the wood of conifers, such as pines and cedars, which is called 'softwood', and that of the flowering trees (beech, oak and so forth), which is called 'hardwood'. However, these terms are confusing since they refer only in the most general way to the strength and durability of the two groups. For example, the softest, lightest wood is the 'hardwood' balsa, along with certain true 'softwoods', such as spruce.

Wood structure When looked at in cross-section, a tree trunk contains several different layers. On the outside is the protective bark; inside is the food-conducting phloem; inside that is a thin layer of cambium where the trunk forms new cells; then comes the water-conducting wood, the xylem, and in the centre is dead xylem, the heartwood.

For timber, the most important parts of a tree are the xylem and the heartwood. The xylem contains several types of cell, occurring

Below: Logs of beech after felling. Along with oak, beech is the most commonly used hardwood in Europe. Its combination of strength and lightness makes it ideal for furniture and a range of domestic products, such as handles and spoons.

Although all parts of a tree have their uses, commercially its most important part by far is its wood. Of all the timber felled in the world, about half is used for fuel in the form of logs or charcoal, much of it in the tropics and the Third World countries. The rest is used as timber or processed wood – plywood, chipboard and pulp.

Cutting a log

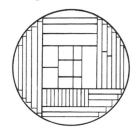

Above: There are many ways of sawing up a log. In this method, called 'round the log', each of the four sides is worked in turn to give a variety of planks, and the centre is then cut up for structural timber.

Left: A plantation of young poplar trees—note the close spacing and even rows typical of such plantations.

Below: A pile of cut logs overwintering in the broadleaved woodland where they were cut.

Structure and growth rings

The xylem of a hardwood contains vessels to conduct water and minerals, fibres to provide support and parenchyma to store food. In some species, such as oak, the vessels formed in the spring are larger, making the wood paler than at other times of the year—hence the appearance of annual growth rings. Other hardwoods, such as beech, show no such differences in their cells through the year. However, they do lay down different materials into the wood during the summer, so growth rings are still recognisable.

Softwoods also possess parenchyma, but the function of the vessels and fibres is combined in the tracheids, which perform a combined conducting and supporting role. Softwoods also show growth rings because the tracheids laid down in the summer have a smaller diameter and thicker walls than those produced in the spring.

hardwood (oak)

parenchyma
vessels
fibres
growth ring
thick-walled tracheids
resin canal
parenchyma
thin-walled tracheids

softwood (pine)

in varying amounts in different species of tree. The differences between hardwoods and softwoods are due to the fact that they contain different types of cells.

In hardwoods, the most important component is the vessels, which consist of tubular cells placed end to end to act as a passage for minerals and water. Surrounding these in most hardwoods are fibre cells—long, thin, tapered cells with extremely thick walls, which provide the vessels with a supporting matrix. The variation in hardness between the different hardwoods is due mainly to the properties of these two groups of cells. In balsa, for example, the fibre cells have thin walls and the vessels are large and closely spaced. On the other hand, ebony, which is one of the hardest and heaviest woods, has thick-walled fibre cells with small, widely spaced vessels, which are often made harder by extremely tough deposits of gum in the middle of the cells.

Most species of hardwood trees have a third component called wood parenchyma. These are thin-walled cells that store food materials. They are arranged in vertical stacks that radiate from the centre of the wood outwards in lines known as medullary rays. These are responsible for the characteristic grain patterns of certain polished woods.

Softwoods have a quite different structure. They lack separate vessels and fibres, instead having tracheid cells that perform a combined conducting and supporting role. They also have parenchyma. Both sets of cells have channels to allow resin to flow.

Heart of the matter The cells in the xylem have a limited life span. Over a period of years their walls become impregnated with a substance called lignin, which makes them become gradually harder and rigid. Eventually, the cells become blocked with lignin, die and become a part of the tree's heartwood. Since the cells retain the same shape in death as they had in life, the structure of the heartwood is the same as that of the xylem.

There are considerable differences in colour and hardiness between the heartwood and the xylem due to the presence, in varying degrees, of gums and resins produced in the cells. In the most prized timbers, such as ebony, the heartwood is almost black from the presence of hard resins and gums, which also make this wood extremely hardy.

Timber for building The different uses to which timber may be put are determined by its characteristics—its grain pattern, density, colour, hardiness and so on. For example, balsa is ideal for making model aeroplanes because of its lightness, whereas heavy woods —teak, ebony and box—are more suitable for furniture-making. Cedar wood is often used for the outside of houses because of its attractive appearance and resistance to rot. Elm is useful for lock gates and the bottoms of barges because it does not rot easily under water, while the lightness and toughness of beech

Commercial woods

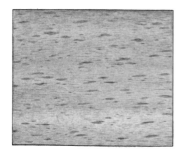

Beech is white or pale brown with a straight grain and characteristic flecks.

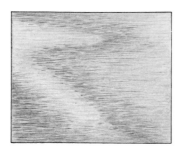

Ash is white and straight-grained with conspicuous growth rings.

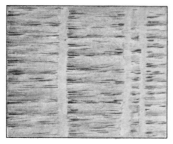

Oak is pale yellow-brown and straight-grained with a coarse texture.

Olive is pale to medium brown with dark markings and an irregular grain.

Cedar is a pale brown wood with a strong characteristic fragrance.

makes it a good choice for the roofing frames of houses.

However, before any wood can be used in building or furniture manufacture it has to be dried in controlled conditions. Fresh wood contains water (which is why logs crackle in a fire) and, as it dries, it shrinks, warps and cracks. Obviously, this cannot be allowed to happen to wood that has been incorporated into a building or a piece of furniture, so it is dried out before being used. This used to be done by leaving the logs or cut planks out in the open, but nowadays they are seasoned in humidity-controlled kilns to produce a large quantity of workable timber in the fastest possible time.

Processed wood The last 30 years or so have seen marked changes in the pattern of timber use. The value of timber has increased so much that the appearance of an end product is now often more important than the materials that go into its manufacture. A familiar example is chipboard which, when coated with a plastic laminate, is used for kitchen work surfaces and utility units in the home.

The advantage of chipboard is that it can be made from all sorts of wood, particularly trees too small to be cut into planks, and it can be made to any size and be manufactured by machines.

Plywood is a combination material of a different sort. Thin sheets of wood are glued together with the grain of each layer lying at right-angles to the grains of the layers immediately above and below. The 'ply number' – such as 3-ply or 6-ply – refers to the number of sheets. Plywood is much stronger than a plank of wood of the same thickness and the arrangement of its sheets makes it resistant to warping.

Timber for pulping Today, vast quantities of wood are pulped for paper. To give just one example, a top-selling national newspaper will consume up to 15,000 trees in a single edition.

Wood pulp is produced either mechanically or chemically. In the former process sections of logs are gradually pulped on a revolving grindstone and the fibres removed by water. In chemical pulping, the logs are chipped into pieces and then digested in either soda, calcium or magnesium sulphate or sodium sulphite. The resulting slurry is then beaten and chopped in a huge cylinder equipped with a rotating set of knives. China clay or starch is added to fill in pores in the wood fibres and give weight to the paper, and dyes and resins are added to reduce absorbency.

The mixture is then pumped into a paper-rolling machine, where it is passed through a series of rollers that squeeze the pulp into paper. Finally, after being dried, the paper is passed through chilled rollers to give it a finish. Fine-quality papers may be glazed with China clay or some other material to give them a glossy finish.

Products from pulp

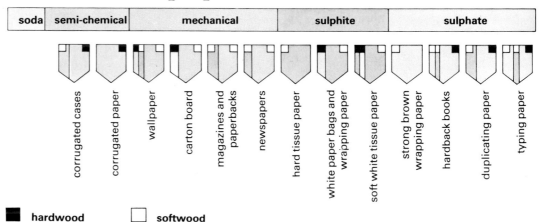

soda	semi-chemical	mechanical	sulphite	sulphate

Products (left to right): corrugated cases · corrugated paper · wallpaper · carton board · magazines and paperbacks · newspapers · hard tissue paper · white paper bags and wrapping paper · soft white tissue paper · strong brown wrapping paper · hardback books · duplicating paper · typing paper

■ **hardwood**   □ **softwood**

Above: The chart shows the different treatments given to pulped woods to achieve different products. For example, carton board is mainly produced mechanically out of softwood, although a proportion is manufactured from soda-treated hardwood.

Right: Beeches in spring leaf in Savernake Forest. Half the softwood timber cultivated in the northern hemisphere goes for pulping.

Left: Timber felling and burning in the New Forest.

Trees of deciduous woodlands

The characteristic structure of British deciduous woodland, with its mosaic of deep cover and sunny glades, derives much from the wide variety of shrub species and their success at coexisting with the trees around them. The distinction between trees and shrubs is fairly arbitrary, but trees generally exceed 5-6m (16ft-20ft) in height and grow from a single stem, whereas shrubs are smaller and often divide at ground level. There are borderline species such as hazel which achieve the stature of trees in optimal conditions, while some trees, for example rowan and hawthorn, are often held at shrub height by a closed canopy.

The vigour of the shrub layer is strongly determined by the sorts of trees distributed among it. A tightly knit canopy, casting deep shade, inhibits the development of any shrub layer. Beech is particularly effective at blotting out light and preventing shrub development. Associated with the struggle for light, some shrub species are notable for leafing early in the year–in mild winters elder and honeysuckle start opening in December or January.

In general, shrubs are competitive colonizers, quickly invading clearings made by fallen trees or created by man. In this respect the kind of patchy woodland we see today gives (if unchecked) unprecedented opportunity for luxuriant shrub growth. In prehistoric times lowland Britain was covered with a more or less continuous pelt of trees, but clearance began early with the Neolithic settlers and has accelerated ever since, so that now we have a mere scattering of trees representing about 10% of the original forest area. With rare exceptions this woodland cannot even claim to be primeval forest, for most was planted by man.

Man has not, however, been able to destroy completely the ancient pattern, and we still find many trees and shrubs distributed as nature intended–oak on rich clays, birch on lighter soils, ash on limestone and beech on southern chalk downland. Apart from soil and other environmental factors, the presence of local animals may also influence the composition of woodland. Elder, for example, is rife in many woods because its astringent bark protects it from being gnawed to destruction by deer and rabbits. Young spindle, on the other hand, is relished by rabbits.

CHECKLIST

This checklist is a guide to the trees you will find in broadleaved woodland. Although you will not see them all in the same woodland, you should be able to spot many of them as you walk through different woods during the changing seasons. The species listed in **bold print** *are described in detail in this book.*

Alder	**Hazel**
Alder buckthorn	**Hornbeam**
Ash	Horse chestnut
Aspen	Lime
Beech	**Oak**
Birch	Poplar
Bird cherry	Rowan
Blackthorn	Sallow
Common buckthorn	Spindle
Crab apple	**Sweet chestnut**
Dogwood	Sycamore
Elder	Wayfaring tree
Elm	Whitebeam
Field maple	Wild cherry (gean)
Guelder rose	Wild service
Hawthorn	Wych elm

Above: Leaves and acorns of English oak and sessile oak.

Left: Spring brings new life to the woodland—as yet the foliage is not dense and sunlight can reach the flowers.

43

THE MIGHTY OAKS OF BRITAIN

Oak trees live longer than all other native trees and support a greater variety of wildlife than any other species in our islands. Even when they die, they still give food and protection.

From the top of its spreading crown to the ends of its roots, which can extend as far below the ground as its branches reach into the sky, the oak tree provides shelter and food for hundreds of different organisms. Like a crowded highrise block, the oak is inhabited at every level: birds and squirrels build nests in the crown, insects such as wasps, moths, beetles and weevils devour the leaves; ivy, mistletoe, lichens, mosses, algae and fungi invade the branches and bark; birds, insects and mammals feed on the acorns. Even the roots of the young oak are sought out by such insects as weevils and, as the oak lets in quite a lot of light through its leaves, flowering plants grow underneath it.

Opposite page: A most attractive sight in early spring −oak and bluebell woods in the Walkham Valley, south-west Dartmoor. At this time of the year the tree canopy allows enough light through to enable wild flowers to grow on the woodland floor.

Below: Oak trees make up one tenth of all English woods. A fine specimen like this pedunculate oak may take up to 100 years to mature.

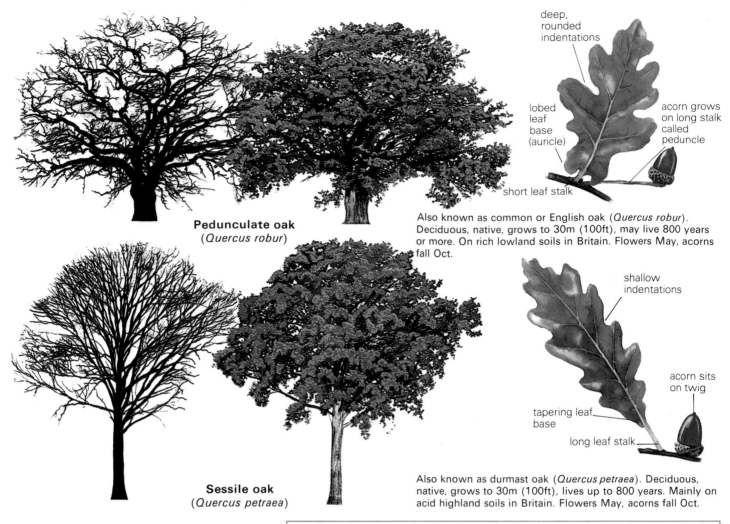

Pedunculate oak
(Quercus robur)

deep, rounded indentations

lobed leaf base (auricle)

acorn grows on long stalk called peduncle

short leaf stalk

Also known as common or English oak (*Quercus robur*). Deciduous, native, grows to 30m (100ft), may live 800 years or more. On rich lowland soils in Britain. Flowers May, acorns fall Oct.

Sessile oak
(Quercus petraea)

shallow indentations

tapering leaf base

acorn sits on twig

long leaf stalk

Also known as durmast oak (*Quercus petraea*). Deciduous, native, grows to 30m (100ft), lives up to 800 years. Mainly on acid highland soils in Britain. Flowers May, acorns fall Oct.

You may think that the oak must be quickly overpowered by this invasion of wildlife, but once a sapling becomes established the oak can live for up to 800 years, continuing to act as host to this multitude of creatures. In fact the oak has adapted itself so successfully in temperate regions that there are over 450 different species of oak in the world. Several of these oaks grow in Britain and Ireland, but only two, the pedunculate (also known as the common or English oak) and the sessile (durmast) oak are native to our islands. It is not always easy to tell the difference between them.

When it is growing in the open, the pedunculate oak is gnarled and tends to have lower, more horizontal and wider-spreading branches, so that the main trunk is hidden beneath a mass of boughs and leaves. The sessile oak has a straighter, less gnarled trunk, with branches growing from higher up.

You are likely to come across woods where both species of oak are growing, often among other trees. The huge forests of Epping and the New Forest are typical of such mixed woods. Here it is more difficult to distinguish the two species. For example, when the pedunculate oak competes for light with other trees it may lose some of its broad shape. To make it even more confusing, one species is frequently fertilized by the other and the result is a hybrid with characteristics of both species.

Close up If you get close to a true sessile or

Native or introduced?

Among the scores of different trees seen in Britain today only 35, including the sessile and pedunculate oaks, are native species (right), ie they spread into this country naturally, without the assistance of man. This was possible at the end of the last Ice Age—about 10,000 years ago—because at that time Britain still formed part of the European land mass.

To begin with only the hardiest plants, such as mosses and bilberry bushes could survive. But as the climate grew warmer trees like hazel, Scots pine, birch, elm and later oak established themselves.

Then about 7000 years ago Britain was separated from the rest of Europe. Melting glaciers caused the sea level to rise, flooding what is now the North Sea and English Channel. This watery barrier prevented further natural invasion by non-waterborne plants such as trees. So the trees that had managed to reach Britain by that time are our 35 native species.

The majority of different types now in Britain were introduced by man because they were useful or ornamental. When the Roman legionaries settled here they brought the edible sweet chestnut. Remains of walnut trees have also been found in Roman villas. The Norway spruce, the familiar Christmas tree, arrived in the 16th century and the handsome cedar of Lebanon and the horse chestnut in the 17th century.

COMMON NATIVE TREES
Aspen (*Populus tremula*)
Bay willow (*Salix pentandra*)
Bird cherry (*Prunus padus*)
Black poplar (*Populus nigra*)
Box (*Buxus sempervirens*)
Common alder (*Alnus glutinosa*)
Common ash (*Fraxinus excelsior*)
Common beech (*Fagus sylvatica*)
Common pear (*Pyrus communis*)
Common yew (*Taxus baccata*)
Crab apple (*Malus sylvestris*)
Crack willow (*Salix fragilis*)
Downy birch (*Betula pubescens*)
Field maple (*Acer campestre*)
Goat willow (*Salix caprea*)
Grey poplar (*Populus canescens*)
Grey willow (*Salix cinerea*)
Hawthorn (*Crataegus monogyna*)
Hazel (*Corylus avellana*)
Holly (*Ilex aquifolium*)
Hornbeam (*Carpinus betulus*)
Juniper (*Juniperus communis*)
Midland hawthorn (*Crataegus laevigata*)
Pedunculate oak (*Quercus robur*)
Rowan (*Sorbus aucuparia*)
Scots pine (*Pinus sylvestris*)
Sessile oak (*Quercus petraea*)
Silver birch (*Betula pendula*)
Small-leaved lime (*Tilia cordata*)
Strawberry tree (*Arbutus unedo*)
Whitebeam (*Sorbus aria*)
White willow (*Salix alba*)
Wild cherry (*Prunus avium*)
Wild service tree (*Sorbus torminalis*)
Wych elm (*Ulmus glabra*)

pedunculate oak, however, you should be able to tell them apart quite easily.

The leaves of the pedunculate oak are pale green and virtually hairless, with two obvious 'ear-lobes' (auricles) at the base. They have deep, rounded indentations all round. In autumn, acorns grow on long stalks called peduncles—hence its name.

The leaves of the sessile oak are dark green, have no auricles and the indentations are not so deep. Leaves grow on long stalks and have a few hairs on the midrib of the underside. Unlike the pedunculate, the sessile acorns sit on the twig.

Pedunculate oak woodlands are the most common, and are usually found on heavy clay soils throughout lowland Britain. The pedunculate oaks at Bagshot in Surrey and Hovingham, North Yorkshire, are well worth a visit. Sessile woodlands are found in the highland areas of Britain and usually occur on shallow acid soils. The Birkrigg and Keskadale oaks south west of Keswick in the Lake District are excellent examples of 'pure' sessile woodlands.

Acorn bonanza Trees are flowering plants but many of their flowers are not spectacular, large or colourful and the oaks are no exception. Inconspicuous female catkins (flowers) are pollinated by the wind-carried pollen grains from male catkins (so large petals needed to attract insects for pollination are unnecessary). The oak's acorn crop varies from year to year—in a bumper year each tree can produce as many as 50,000 acorns. But few of the hundreds of thousands that fall every year grow into full-sized trees. Acorns start to form in early summer (the warmer the summer the larger the acorns), and then during a few weeks of early autumn they fall to form a dense carpet. They do not stay long on the ground for they are seized by hordes of birds and animals, either to be eaten or stored away for the winter. Jays and squirrels in particular bury them (sometimes quite a distance from the wood) and then forget about them. This is one of the ways the oak is spread across the countryside.

Valuable tree Oak woods covered much of Britain in medieval times and our ancestors quickly discovered that oak made good fuel. The sessile oak was also valued for its acorns. From the Middle Ages until the 18th century people drove their pigs into the oak woods on common land to feed on the abundant acorns. Indeed, one way of assessing and comparing the size of each manor's forest was to count the number of grazing pigs that could be supported. Such grazing rights still exist today in the New Forest in Hampshire.

Oak wood was used extensively for shipbuilding and many parks, such as Regents Park and Greenwich Park in London, were planted especially to supply the Royal and Merchant navies. Oak wood was used extensively for supporting beams in country cottages and is still used by builders today.

Above: Woods often contain both pedunculate and sessile oak trees, in which case it is often difficult to distinguish between the trees by shape alone. Closer inspection is necessary for identification.

Left: In May you can see these tassels of male catkins dangling on the twigs. Female flowers are hidden at the end of the new leaf shoots.

Left: Acorns fall in autumn and germinate if kept moist, not producing leaves until the spring. Seedlings grow 15cm (6in) in six months.

BOLD AND BEAUTIFUL BEECH

The beech is one of our most handsome trees. Its massive, smooth silver-grey trunk, the purity of its spring foliage and its vivid autumn colours give it a stature few trees can match.

Early spring in the beech woods of Ashridge estate in Hertfordshire. The name beech comes from the old English word *bece*.

The beech is queen of the broadleaved trees. When it grows as an isolated tree its great limbs spread out to form a gigantic crown, but in a crowded beech wood the crowns are more compact. The trunks stand like the smooth, soaring columns of a cathedral, forced to grow tall in their constant struggle to reach the light. In these more cramped conditions most of the branches sprout from the very top of the trunk.

As summer progresses, layer upon layer of leaves cast such a deep shade that few plants can survive underneath the tree. The beech wood floor, therefore, tends to be rather bare, except for the carpet of dead beech leaves—always some of the slowest to rot and form

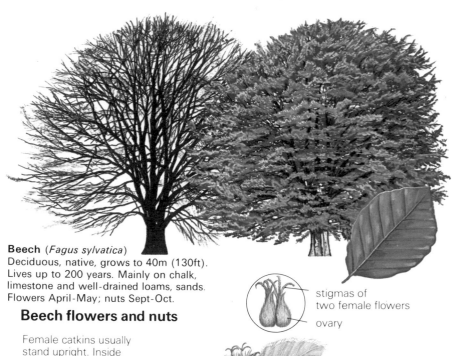

Beech (*Fagus sylvatica*)
Deciduous, native, grows to 40m (130ft).
Lives up to 200 years. Mainly on chalk,
limestone and well-drained loams, sands.
Flowers April-May; nuts Sept-Oct.

Beech flowers and nuts

Female catkins usually
stand upright. Inside
the hairy bracts are two
female flowers.

Male catkins always
hang down. Each one
is made from lots of
male flowers. The
catkins fall off when
the stamens have shed
their pollen.

stamens

bracts

stigmas of
two female flowers

ovary

cupule

two seeds

When the female
flowers have been
fertilized, the ovary
swells and the seeds
grow. The bracts now
develop into cupules.

leaf mould (humus)—and a scattering of young saplings ready to grow up into any gap created by the death or fall of the tree above.

A sprawling network of surface roots anchor the tree to the ground and, because they explore only the upper layers of the soil, the beech is easily toppled by strong gales. In the long drought of 1976 the beech was particularly affected because its roots could not reach down to water deep below the surface.

Native and cultivated The beech grows as a native tree only in southern England and south Wales. Ancient beech forests still survive on the Chiltern Hills in Buckinghamshire, in the Cotswolds and on southern chalk downs. Over the centuries and particularly in the last 200 years the tree has also been widely planted throughout Great Britain. Its value as an ornamental and landscape tree has been widely exploited in avenues, shelter-belts, hedges and hilltop clumps, serving to break up the bleak outline of rolling downland.

A superb beech avenue flanks the road alongside the Iron Age fort of Badbury Rings in Dorset. In summer the interlocking branches cast deep shade over the roadway and form a natural tunnel. There were reputed originally to have been 365 trees on one side of the road and 366 on the other: one for every day of the year. A few have been lost over the years. And at Meikleour near Perth in Scotland there is a massive beech hedge a third of a mile long and standing 28m (90ft)

Pollarding

Pollarding is the lopping of the main branches of a tree at a height of 2-3m (7-10ft) above ground level, out of the reach of browsing livestock. Removal of these growing points stimulates most broadleaved trees to send out a mass of small branches from buds hidden below the bark of the main trunk. The new branches are used in much the same way as coppiced wood but have the added advantage that grazing pasture can grow underneath.

Pollarding used to be common, but as coal replaced wood for fuel, the annual lopping ceased and shoots were allowed to grow into great branches. You can see overgrown pollards in many woodlands. The tree shown here is in Epping Forest.

branches
removed

new growth

high – a daunting prospect for all but the most seasoned hedge-cutter.

The winter twigs of the beech are very distinctive: they are slender, smooth, and tipped with a spear-shaped bud. Additional buds are arranged alternatively along the length of the twig. Each of the long, pointed buds is wrapped in a series of overlapping protective brown scales.

Spring leaves The beech breaks into leaf in April. The oval leaves, tapering to a short point, are borne on short stalks. After they unfold from the buds, the fresh limp leaves are fringed with soft silvery hairs. The young foliage has a bright shining, almost translucent, quality; but as the season advances the leaves become stiffer and turn darker green with a glossy surface sheen.

The flowers, which are usually half hidden among the emerging foliage, are wind-pollinated. The male flowers are grouped in clusters, hanging like tassels, and pollen is blown from their bright yellow anthers. The female flowers are in pairs, bound by a collar of prickly scales forming the cupule.

Nuts After fertilisation the cupule develops into a woody husk, clad in stiff bristles, enclosing a pair of three-sided, sharp-edged nuts. In October the ripe capsule splits and the four lobes peel back to allow the nuts, known as beech-mast, to fall out. The kernels are edible and delicious.

A really heavy crop of nuts is produced about every four or five years – known as mast years; this is an important time for forest wildlife. Mammals, such as badgers and squirrels, and birds, such as nuthatches and bramblings, are particularly fond of beech nuts and a good mast year can considerably increase their chances of survival through winter when other foods become scarce. In the past it was common to turn pigs out into woodland during autumn so that they could rummage about for nuts and acorns. This practice, called pannage, is still carried out on a small scale in the New Forest.

Autumn finery In autumn the beech has few rivals. The tree positively glows with colour, displaying a brilliant mosaic of flaming orange, russet and gold. Gradually the foliage darkens to a dull copper colour, reflecting the tree's gradual accumulation of waste products that form tannin. As the leaves fall, the ground beneath becomes smothered in a thick blanket of leaves. In the past mattresses used to be stuffed with dry beech leaves and they gave a comfortable, if noisy, night's sleep. In France they were called *lits de parliament* – talking beds – because of the noise they made.

Life under beech Pure beech woods are ideal places for walks on a hot summer's day. Occasionally you see holly, yew and wild cherry growing among the trees, but on the whole few plants can tolerate the deep shade. Two interesting species are the yellow birdsnest and birdsnest orchid, both of which feed

off rotting vegetation and therefore do not need sunlight to help make their food. All kinds of fungi flourish in the autumn, including the virulent death-cap, our most poisonous toadstool, and bracket fungi are common on tree trunks.

Mixed beech woods are generally far more hospitable to wildlife. The sudden shafts of light that beam down through gaps in the canopy of oak, sycamore or perhaps hornbeam encourage all kinds of wild flowers to grow – helleborine, wood anemone, arum lily, yellow archangel and bluebell, to mention just a few. Bramble, bracken, heather and mosses often carpet the ground, providing protection for numerous insects and birds.

Timber In common with most of our native trees, beech was used for firewood, even though it does not burn particularly well. Queen Victoria was supposed to have preferred to have wood from Burnham Beeches, near Slough, burned on the fires at Windsor Castle.

Beech trees used to be pollarded every 20 years or so. Use as building timber is limited because beech decays quickly. The wood is rather soft and springy but this has always been an advantage in furniture making.

The furniture industry has long been centred at High Wycombe in the heart of the Chilterns and, until quite recently, the surrounding beechwoods were the hub of a flourishing cottage industry.

Above: the edge of the mature beech woods of Ashridge estate in autumn, where many of the leaves have already fallen. Younger trees and beech hedges keep their leaves until the following spring.

Below: A young beech seedling with the remains of the seed case still attached to the young shoot and the cupule lying on the ground.

THE ASH: A STURDY LIME-LOVING TREE

Strong yet graceful, the common ash tree grows easily throughout the British Isles. It is particularly associated with limestone areas (below), where it flourishes in steep hillside woods, managing to take root in rocky, inhospitable crevices.

The ash is one of our commonest native trees. Although it does not achieve the grandeur of oak nor the majesty of beech, it is nevertheless a handsome species, noted for its graceful foliage and sturdy trunk clad with pale grey bark that becomes deeply furrowed with age.

The crown is rather loosely branched and the foliage relatively light so that the tree does not cast deep shade and a wide variety of plants grow beneath it. In winter, without the benefit of its leaves, the ash reveals its uneven branching and stout twigs which combine to produce a rather shapeless silhouette.

The ash is native to Britain and most of Europe. It is widespread throughout the country in oak woods, copses, in hedgerows

Ash (*Fraxinus excelsior*). Deciduous, native, grows to 25m (100ft), lives up to 200 years. Common throughout the British Isles in scrub, oak woods, hedgerows. Forms woods on chalk or limestone soils. Flowers May-June, fruits Oct-Nov.

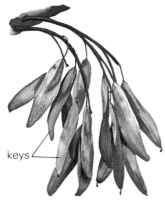

keys

Ash keys gradually change colour from green to brown in autumn when they ripen. Each key holds one seed at the base of the twisted wing.

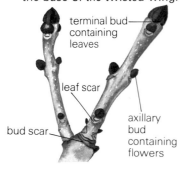

terminal bud containing leaves

leaf scar

bud scar

axillary bud containing flowers

In spring the silvery grey twigs are characterised by velvety black buds 5-10cm long containing leaves and flowers.

♂

♀

Male and female flowers emerge before the leaves and may be found on the same twig, on different twigs or often on different trees.

and along river banks. Woods dominated by ash tend to occur on steep limestone hillsides. Pure ash woods are often associated with outcrops of carboniferous limestone and fine examples occur in such widely dispersed parts of the country as the Mendip Hills, the Pennines and Cumbria.

Limestone pavements But by far the most interesting ash woods grow on limestone pavements, the largest areas of which are in the north of England around Morecambe Bay, Great Asby, Ingleborough and Malham. These pavements are platforms of rock which were carved and smoothed by the scouring action of glaciers during the last Ice Age over 10,000 years ago.

Huge flat blocks of limestone clints are separated from each other by crevices called grikes which are 2-4m (6-13ft) deep and up to 50cm (1½ft) wide. Ash is the dominant tree and forms open woods which allow a profusion of shrubs, such as hazel, blackthorn and bird cherry, and wild flowers, such as red campions, wood anemones and lilies of the valley, to mention just a few, to grow in the

light underneath. In addition, rather like a natural rock garden, a tremendous variety of ferns and mosses thrive in the damp shade of the grikes.

Recognising the ash is easy because the twigs in winter and the foliage in summer are so distinctive. The smooth pale grey twigs bear pairs of opposite buds along their length and are each tipped with a large, robust black bud. The buds owe their velvety texture and appearance to a coat of minute black hairs covering the bud scales.

The leaves are compound; 3-6 pairs of toothed lance-shaped leaflets are arranged along the leaf stalk which is itself tipped with a single terminal leaflet. The form of ash leaves is unlike any other British wild tree except for the totally unrelated mountain ash or rowan (*Sorbus aucuparia*). But because the species are different in every other respect, there is little danger of the two being confused.

Flowers Early in April the axillary buds break into flower, well before the emergence of the leaves. The purplish-green flowers that hang like tassels from the bare twigs are

Above: Ash growing out of a limestone pavement near Malham in the Yorkshire Dales. Ash is one of the last trees to leaf out and one of the first to shed its leaves in autumn, often while they are still green.

Left: Ash keys ripen in early autumn. The name dates from medieval times when door keys were fashioned in the shape of ash keys. Ash trees rarely bear fruit until they are over 40 years·old.

frost. Usually the leaflets fall before the leaf stalk. Occasionally the leaves turn pale yellow, but more often they fall while still green, making the tree one of the least spectacular in the autumn.

Keys Following fertilisation of the flowers, the fruits of the ash (samaras) hang in clusters popularly known as keys, which are green at first and ripen brown during autumn. Each key consists of a slightly twisted vane attached to a single seed. The twist helps to give the winged seed a spinning motion, keeping it airborne for as long as possible while it is transported. In autumn gales ash keys may be blown several hundred metres.

Bunches of ash keys last well into the winter and are thus important for birds as food becomes scarce. The amount of seed produced varies from year to year. A heavy ash seed crop may please orchard owners. It has recently been suggested that bullfinches, chief enemies of juicy 'young buds on fruit trees, are less of a pest when there are plenty of ash seeds available nearby.

Valuable timber Ash has always been a highly prized firewood because it burns 'green', that is when it has been freshly cut. This makes it an excellent fuel, as was celebrated by Walter de la Mare:

Of all the trees in England,
Her sweet three corners in,
Only the Ash, the bonnie Ash,
Burns fierce while it is green.

A great advantage of ash timber is that it is so tough and elastic that it can withstand stress, strain and sharp knocks. It is easily the best native timber for any sort of long handle which has to resist sudden shock. Axes, picks, mallets and various garden tools invariably have ash handles. Similarly it is used for sports equipment such as oars, hockey sticks and parallel bars.

Ash was widely planted in hedgerows because the wood was useful on farms, and in woodland ash trees used to be coppiced to provide poles. But ash wood is no good for fencing because it quickly rots in the ground. Ash poles are still specially grown in nurseries to make walking sticks. The young ash plants are cut back and replanted on a slant. Subsequent regrowth from the stump is vertical and so a stick with a bent handle is produced.

In the past ash was used for weapons, especially for the shafts of spears and lances. The Anglo-Saxon word for ash is *aesc*, which was also used to mean spear.

The ash played an important role in ancient Nordic mythology from Scandinavia where it was regarded as the 'tree of life'. From a huge ash tree, whose crown reached up to heaven and whose roots penetrated hell, the gods ruled the world. To watch over earthly affairs, they were helped by an eagle perching on the topmost branches. In turn the eagle was assisted by a squirrel, which spent its time scampering up and down the tree and reporting on what was happening below.

pollinated by the wind.

Generally ash flowers are bisexual, ie the male and female parts are produced together. The female organs are called pistils; the male organs are the pollen-producing stamens. However it is not unusual to find ash trees with flowers that are all male or all female. And what's more, the ash tree can undergo a sex change from year to year. A male tree last year may be female this year, and perhaps bisexual the next.

Short-lived leaves The ash is one of the latest trees to burst into leaf and is usually not fully covered until May. Generally the ash 'leafs out' later than the oak, but not always. The timing is the subject of a country rhyme which claims to forecast the weather we can expect in the coming months:

Oak before ash . . . we're in for a splash;
Ash before oak . . . we're in for a soak!

The ash loses its leaves quite early in autumn so it has a short cycle of summer growth. The leaves are highly sensitive to cold and are frequently shed at the first hint of

BIRCH: GRACEFUL LADY OF THE WOODS

Few trees match the style of the birch. The narrow trunk, silvery bark and slender branches ending in a mass of drooping twigs have the outline of a fountain that produces a cascade of delicate leaves. No wonder it has become known as the Lady of the Woods.

Birch woodland in early autumn with young oak and sycamore, and a ground-covering of bracken.

There are three native species of birch in the British Isles but only two, the silver birch and the downy birch, are common. They thrive particularly well on acid soils, but rarely grow on chalk. The silver birch grows best on dry sandy or gravelly soils such as those of the heathlands of southern England, but the downy birch prefers wetter soils and a cooler climate and so is most common in the uplands of Scotland, Wales and Ireland. However, their ranges overlap considerably and they are often found growing in the same areas, exploiting local variations in the wetness or drainage of the soil.

Differences in detail In general form the silver and downy birch are very similar and can be described together, although they differ in a number of details.

The silver birch, as its name suggests, has much whiter bark, whereas the bark of the downy birch is more variable, ranging from silver-grey to brownish in colour. The only way to distinguish the two species from a distance is by the colour of the bark. A characteristic of old silver birches is the patches of rough, knobbly black bark replacing the white bark at the base of the trunk. In downy birches the bark remains more or less smooth right down to the ground.

Secondly, unlike downy birches, silver birches typically have hanging or 'weeping' twigs—a feature that has been exaggerated by selective breeding to produce ornamental

varieties that grace many parks and gardens. And the twigs of the silver birch are smooth, whereas those of the downy birch are covered with short fine hairs.

Leaves, flowers and fruits The foliage appears towards the end of April, the leaves unfolding from small, pointed buds that are arranged alternately along the thin, purplish-brown twigs. The bright green leaves, about 3cm (1in) long, are usually triangular in outline but the shape may vary from diamond to oval. Their margins are rather unevenly toothed and they taper to a sharp point. They are borne on slender stalks which allow them to twist and flutter in the breeze. The leaves of young birches are often much larger than those on full grown trees because they grow much more vigorously. After a heavy shower in late spring the air in a dense stand of birch has a delicate fragrance from the aromatic resin washed from the unfurling leaves and from tiny warts on the twigs.

In autumn the leaves turn bright yellow, before falling in October to leave the trees bare, but still beautiful, their trunks gleaming white in the pale wintry sunlight.

Birch flowers are catkins and both sexes are borne on the same tree. The males develop during autumn and by April or May have turned into a dangling catkin about 5cm (2in) long, covered with reddish brown scales which separate to release their pollen. The female catkins appear with the unfolding leaves. They are held erect on the twigs, 2-3cm (1in) long, and are made up of overlapping green

Above: **Silver birch** (*Betula pendula*). Deciduous, native, grows to 25m (80ft) throughout the British Isles, on light soils, heathland, may form pure woods in the Scottish Highlands. Rare on chalk. Flowers April, fruits July.

Above right and below: **Downy birch** (*Betula pubescens*). Deciduous, native, grows to 20m (65ft) in similar areas to the silver birch though it prefers wetter, colder conditions.

scales, each shielding an ovary from which two purple stigmas protrude to catch pollen grains wafted on the wind.

After fertilisation the female catkins expand into club-shaped cone-like structures that slowly disintegrate in autumn to release the tiny winged fruits. These are so light they may be carried for considerable distances by strong winds.

Birch woods are a favourite haunt of redpolls and siskins (both our resident birds and winter visitors from Scandinavia). They feed on the seeds scattered on the ground.

Hardy pioneer The birch is an extremely hardy tree and has established itself in some northern-most forests at the frontier of the treeless tundra. The pollen record shows that birches and pines were the first trees to advance into the British Isles when the climate warmed after the last Ice Age. Both species formed vast forests but were confined to the better-drained uplands.

Today the birch is found in most woodlands on the poorer soils, from English oak woods to Scottish pine woods. It also forms pure birch woods – you can see good examples on the sandy heaths of southern England and the steep hillsides of Scotland.

The birch is an aggressive colonizer of forest clearings, ungrazed heaths, and areas which have suffered recent burning. Its tiny winged seeds spread in profusion and germinate quickly to invade new areas. The pioneer trees form dense thickets of fast growing saplings that develop into pure birch stands up to 25m (80ft) tall at maturity.

Fungi associates Birch trees have a remarkable relationship with the fly agaric fungus which sends up its striking red toadstools in autumn. The fungus is attached to the tree's roots and both benefit from this association: the fungus speeds the entry of soil nutrients into the root system of the tree in return for sugars manufactured by the tree.

You may also find the bracket fungus clamped on to the trunks of older trees. It is a parasite, feeding on the tree's sap but giving nothing in return. Indeed, this fungal

Right: Not birds' nests among the branches of a mature silver birch, but witches broom, a growth deformity.

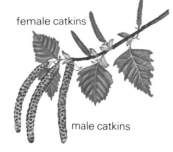

female catkins

male catkins

The ripe seeds in the fruiting catkins have large wings—2-3 times as wide as the seed in the silver birch (above) and 1-1½ times in the downy birch (below), allowing them to spread to great distances.

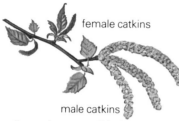

female catkins

male catkins

Opposite page: Birches growing among pines in Glen Affric in Scotland.

Below: A large gall growing on the trunk of a silver birch may damage the tree but is unlikely to kill it.

Below: right: The small bracket fungus (*Trametes versicolor*) thriving on a dead birch tree.

assault so weakens the tree that it soon perishes, and the fungus continues to feed on the dead wood. Although the birches' death is often hastened by fungal attack, birches do not live for a long time anyway – rarely exceeding 80 years. Dead or dying trees are favourite nesting sites for woodpeckers whose bills can easily tunnel holes into the wood softened by decay.

Witches broom Many birch trees appear to have large birds' nests among their branches. In fact these untidy tangles of twigs are galls, a growth deformity caused when the buds are attacked by either a fungus or a tiny mite. A dense mass of twigs sprouts at the point of attack to form the so-called witches broom. (Actually birch twigs are cut and bundled to make the sort of broom that witches are supposed to fly around on at night. They are also used for steeple-chase fences to fill out the jumps.)

Bark and timber The thin paper-like bark is shed in strips as the tree grows, and is replaced anew from underneath. Birch bark is remarkably resistant to decay – the bark on a fallen log remains for months after the wood inside has rotted to a soft pulp. It is also waterproof, and has been used in parts of Europe for roofing. Birch bark makes excellent kindling for camp fires and the wood itself burns very well. In parts of Scandinavia and Central Europe birch wood is still the main winter fuel.

Birch timber is a pale creamy brown colour and has been put to a wide variety of uses: for instance, the making of carts and packing cases, and smaller items such as floor tiles, cotton reels, spools and bobbins for the textile trade. But although it is a hard wood, it does not last long out of doors.

In spring there is a copious flow of sugary sap through the trunk and in some country districts this is collected by tapping the trees; the liquid is fermented into wine.

Dwarf birch There is a third species, the dwarf birch (*Betula nana*), an arctic-alpine shrub less than 1m (3ft) tall which grows at a few sites in the Scottish Highlands. It also has the distinction of being the only woody species to grow in the frozen wastes of Greenland – the world's northern limit for woody plants. Here it takes the form of a low wiry bush, spreading close to the ground, its growth stunted by the icy blasts of Arctic gales. Its leaves are smaller and rounder in shape than those of the other two species. A few specimens occur in Northumberland, but it is generally a rare species.

HANDSOME HORNBEAMS

The hornbeam grows as a native tree in the oak woodlands of southern England and is noted for its compact stature and its magnificent yellow and red-gold autumn colours.

As our climate became warmer after the last Ice Age ended 10,000 years ago, the British Isles were colonised by forest trees which spread across from the Continent. The pollen record shows that the hornbeam was a relative latecomer, arriving about 5000 years ago, whereas the oak was already widespread 2500 years earlier.

Since the hornbeam settled here, the climate has become wetter and cooler, pushing the hornbeam southwards until today it is common only in south-eastern England. From this area its natural range extends northwards and west to the Welsh border; elsewhere it has been introduced. It is a common forest tree in central Europe and the British distribution represents the western tip of its range.

Appearance The fluted trunk, covered in smooth pale grey bark, divides into a large number of limbs which sweep upwards to produce a densely branched symmetrical crown. The winter buds are 5-10cm (2-4in) long, pale brown and set alternately along the slender twigs. The buds are closely pressed against the twig–'like a crouching mouse', in one writer's apt description.

Flowers, fruits and leaves Flowering starts in April shortly before the leaves appear. Male and female catkins, borne on the same tree, appear towards the tips of the delicate twigs. The male catkins expand to form a

Above: A fine old hornbeam in Epping Forest. For centuries commoners held rights to firewood and until recently hornbeams were regularly pollarded, which explains their branching shapes.

Buds in winter

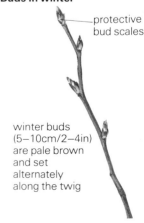

protective bud scales

winter buds (5–10cm/2–4in) are pale brown and set alternately along the twig

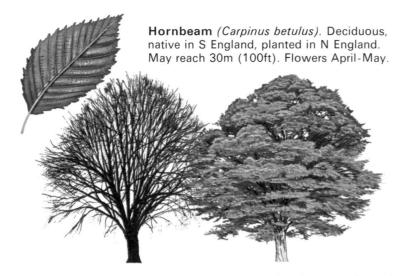

Hornbeam *(Carpinus betulus)*. Deciduous, native in S England, planted in N England. May reach 30m (100ft). Flowers April-May.

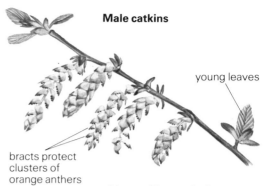

Male catkins

young leaves

bracts protect clusters of orange anthers

Above: The male flowers and bracts are clustered along a central stalk.

Female catkin

bud scales

toothed leaf margins

tips of bracts curl upwards

strongly ribbed young leaves

Above: Female flowers hang down from the top of the twig and resemble leafy buds.

hanging chain of overlapping yellow-green bracts. Pollen is shed from a cluster of orange anthers that are tucked under each bract.

The female catkins consist of a loose cluster of leafy green bracts with their tips curled upwards. Under each bract is a pair of smaller bracteoles which protect the red stigmas that catch the pollen grains drifting in the air.

Shortly after the catkins have fully expanded, the bright yellow-green young leaves push their way out of a sheath of pinkish bud scales and slowly unfurl like a fan. The unfolded leaves are oval in shape with a conspicuously toothed margin. The upper surface is slightly creased along the lines of the parallel veins.

After fertilisation a pair of nutlets are formed in shallow cups, and each bracteole expands to form a papery wing with three lobes, the middle one being the longest. Later in summer this wing acts as a sail, catching the wind and steering the seed some distance from the parent tree.

The autumn foliage undergoes a vivid colour change through various shades of yellow to a rich ruddy gold before falling. On young hornbeam trees and hedges the leaves become shrivelled and rusty brown but, as in the beech, they may stay on the tree throughout winter.

The small, ribbed nutlets, each enclosing a single seed, provide a bountiful supply of food for birds and mammals. The hawfinch in particular devours hornbeam seeds, and interestingly, they both share a similar range in this country. Squirrels too eat the seeds, either climbing the trees to get them or seeking them out on the forest floor. The seeds that escape being eaten lie dormant for 18 months or so before germinating.

Beech look-alike The hornbeam is frequently confused with the beech, and they are indeed similar in general appearance. But they can easily be distinguished at any time of the year. First, the winter buds of hornbeam are shorter and fatter than those of the beech. They also hug the twig closely whereas in the beech the buds are set at an angle and point away from the twig.

Secondly, the leaves, while similar in shape, can be seen to differ at close range. Those of hornbeam have sharply toothed edges whereas beech leaves have smooth margins. Hornbeam leaves feel rather rough to the touch, contrasting with the smooth, polished feel of beech foliage; and during summer beech foliage turns a darker shade of green.

Tough wood The name of the tree probably derives from the nature of the wood, which is hard like horn. Alternatively, some say it refers to the wooden yokes, often made of this wood, which join a team of ploughing oxen together, and are attached to the horns – hence hornbeam.

The hornbeam has the hardest wood of any tree in Europe. It is heavy, fine-grained, and creamy yellow in colour. Craftsmen have made little use of it for furniture or cabinet-making because it is too hard: their tools were blunted so quickly that much time was wasted in resharpening them. But it has been greatly used in musical instruments, particularly for the hammers of piano-keys, and for heavy-duty purposes, such as cogs and pulleys.

Although the wood is extremely tough it burns well. Before coal became the major source of energy hornbeams in woods near London, such as Epping Forest, were regularly coppiced and pollarded to provide fire wood and charcoal to fuel the city's furnaces.

Below: Hornbeam fruits appear in autumn. The bracts change into papery, green, three-pointed wings. The seeds are two tiny hard, green ridged nuts

THE TREMBLING ASPEN TREE

One of our less familiar native trees, the aspen is sometimes called the quaking aspen because its leaves tremble in the slightest breeze—a feature that has been the source of much folklore, all associating this pretty tree with evil and gossip.

Above: A stand of aspens by a lake. They are most often seen on hillsides and valleys, especially where the soil is fairly damp and light. They can be found in other habitats, however, and tolerate a wide range of soil types.

Although the aspen is not one of our well known native trees, it occurs throughout the British Isles, being more common in the north and west of the country than in the south. Valleys and hillsides are typical habitats for this tree, though it sometimes grows in hedgerows and copses, and it is quite often seen in open oakwoods.

Outside Britain the aspen is found as far north as Iceland, Norway and northern USSR, south to Sicily, Greece and North Africa, and east to Japan.

Trembling poplar The aspen is a species of poplar, its Latin name of *Populus tremula* reflecting the fact that its leaves quiver in the slightest breeze. Like other poplars, the aspen is a fast-growing tree, reaching a maximum height of about 20m (65ft). When young it has an open conical crown, which becomes broader with age.

The bole often leans to one side and suckers are freely produced around the base, so that single trees may eventually form dense thickets. The bark is grey-green and smooth, with darker oval depressions.

The shape and size of the leaves vary according to whether they come from the main part of the tree or from the suckers. Normal leaves have a blade about 3-7cm (1-3in) long and at least as broad as that, with shallow rounded teeth. The stalk is 4-6cm ($1\frac{1}{2}$-$2\frac{1}{2}$in) long and strongly flattened in such a way that the slightest breeze causes the leaf to flutter vigorously. Leaves borne on suckering shoots may be much larger—up to 15cm (6in) long—and are oval in shape, with more prominent teeth. Their stalks are also much shorter.

Both types of leaf are the same colour: copper-brown when they first emerge in the spring, gradually becoming grey-green or green on the upper surface and paler underneath. The leaf-stalks are much paler, being yellowish or almost white in colour. In late October, the leaves turn pure yellow and provide an attractive display in some years. However, aspens in other countries seem to have much better autumn colours than ours.

Spring catkins The aspen flowers in March, before the leaves appear, bearing separate male and female catkins on separate trees—as do other poplar trees. The male catkins are usually borne in great numbers and are quite thick, 4-8cm ($1\frac{1}{2}$-3in) long and greyish-brown, although they can appear yellowish when releasing pollen.

The catkins produce no scent or nectar and so are not visited by potential pollinating insects. Instead, pollination is carried out by the wind. After pollination the male catkins turn brown and soon drop off.

The female catkins are slimmer than the males and greenish with grey hairs and reddish bracts. They grow to about 4-6cm ($1\frac{1}{2}$-$2\frac{1}{2}$in) long and bear purple stigmas. After pollination they may lengthen and can be as long as 12cm (5in) by the time the seeds are fully ripe, which is in June. At this stage the female catkins appear whitish and release white woolly seeds. The seeds can often be seen carpeting the ground around female trees.

Versatile timber The timber of aspen, and indeed of other poplars, is not of particularly good quality, but it has been put to a number of different uses. The most important of these are the construction of various types of boxes

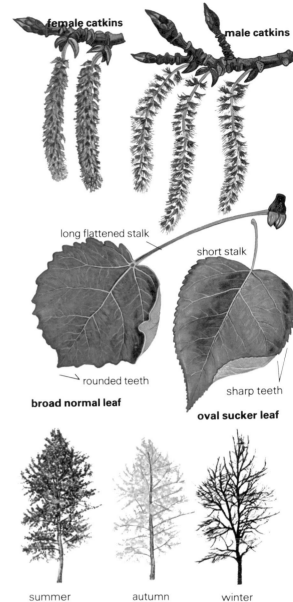

female catkins

male catkins

long flattened stalk

short stalk

rounded teeth

broad normal leaf

sharp teeth

oval sucker leaf

summer   autumn   winter

and the production of wood pulp. The wood is also used for making matches and, in the past, for arrows. Commercially, aspens and other poplars have the advantage over other trees of growing very rapidly in the right conditions.

Evil associations The aspen's almost constant leaf movement has been the source of much local folklore and legends throughout the range of the tree's distribution. Many have a biblical basis. In Wales it was said that the aspen was used to make the Cross and, for this reason, its leaves would never rest. In some areas of Scotland the aspen was regarded as evil because it was the only tree not to have bowed during Jesus' procession to the Crucifixion. As a result, people used to avoid using the wood. Indeed, feeling was so strong against the aspen in Scotland that some people used to throw stones at it.

There are similar legends elsewhere in Europe. In Germany, Jesus is said to have cursed the aspen because it would not acknowledge Him and, in parts of Russia, it was known as the tree of Judas.

The movement of the aspen's leaves seems to have led to associations with the sound of gossip and loose tongues, particularly (and rather chauvinistically) with the tongues of women. This association is found in parts of Scotland, where the tree is known as 'old wives' tongues'. In parts of Berkshire it was referred to as 'woman's tongue' and the Welsh name for the aspen, 'coed tafod merched', also refers to the same image, as does the Manx name of 'chengey ny mraane'.

Nowadays, it seems strange that such an attractive and pleasing tree should, in the past, have been the subject of so many evil associations and unpleasant stories. Without these, the aspen might perhaps have been more widely planted than it has been.

Above: Normal aspen leaves are short and broad with shallow rounded teeth, whereas sucker leaves are usually much larger and oval with sharper teeth. The difference can be seen clearly in a direct comparison (above right).

Aspen (*Populus tremula*). Native deciduous tree growing up to 20m (65ft) tall. More common in the north and west of Britain.

Below: Fruiting catkins dispersing their seeds.

The hazel tree in early spring: the male catkins—lambs' tails—dangle from leafless twigs and release clouds of dusty golden pollen.

Looking closely at a hazel catkin

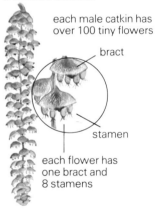

each male catkin has over 100 tiny flowers

bract

stamen

each flower has one bract and 8 stamens

The stamens will ripen when the temperature is over 0°C. The ripe stamens split open lengthways to release their yellow pollen.

THE VIGOROUS HAZEL

The hazel may be one of our smallest native trees, but it has had an important role to play in the history of woodland management. Apart from its value as wood, it also has—according to Celtic folklore—magical properties.

The hazel grows as a small native tree in the shade of woods and in hedgerows. In old neglected coppices it throws straggling limbs from old stools and is rarely able to form the single trunk to give it the status of a tree.

Yet it is an important tree. In the fossilized pollen records preserved in peat which are our guide to the earliest native plants after the Ice Age, hazel predominates over much of the British Isles—appearing at much the same time as the initial spread of other wind-pollinated trees such as alder, willow and birch. Remains of hazel nut shells have been found at the foot of peat deposits, suggesting that the early Stone Age hunters were probably at least partly dependent on the nuts for food, in the absence of any sort of cereal.

Since hazel is associated with man's earliest ancestors, it is perhaps not surprising that in Celtic folkore it was known as the tree of knowledge, and was supposed to have many magic properties. Irish aches and pains caused by the damp climate or elfin malevolence were thought to be warded off by a hazel nut carried in the pocket. A double hazel nut was said to cure toothache in Devon, and defend against witches in Scotland. Hazel is one of the magic trees of May Day, like hawthorn in England and rowan in Scotland: these are the three trees of white magic that oppose the forces of evil which many people thought were present in the woods.

In 1956 there were more than 16,000 acres of hazel coppice, little of which was used. Since then the coppiced areas have dwindled as foresters have gradually turned them over to conifer production. For truly wild hazel trees you must go to the Lake District, the Western Highlands or the Burren in County Clare, Ireland. You can see coppiced hazel in Hatfield Forest, the Sussex Weald and on the Wiltshire downs.

The hazel belongs to the same family as the hornbeam, which has more scaly catkins and winged nutlets. The hazel leaf is a dense, deep green colour which turns to brown then yellow-gold towards the end of the year. Hazel bark is shiny, brownish grey with horizontal pores (lenticels) which enable the tree to breathe.

Catkins and flowers The brownish-yellow male catkins begin to develop in autumn; early the following spring they open to a creamy yellow colour. The female catkins are small and brown with bright crimson styles and they generally ripen after the male catkins of the same tree, a mechanism which usually prevents self-pollination. Like all catkin-bearing trees, the hazel is wind-pollinated.

Nuts There are between one and four, and occasionally five, hard-shelled nuts on each talk. They are pale green in summer, but by autumn have turned to a warm, soft brown colour. Each nut is enclosed in a pair of downy husks or bracts with deep scallops. Many children's fairy stories show pixies wearing hats of a similar style.

Birds, especially pigeons and pheasants, and small mammals such as squirrels and mice, take the nuts for food and bury them. This is one way the trees become dispersed. You can grow the hazel in your garden either from a seed or from a sapling. For your own trees to produce nuts you will need at least two trees to ensure cross-pollination because the species is naturally self-sterile (ie the tree cannot fertilise itself). A hazel tree produces nuts in abundance from six years old. There are several varieties available, including *Pendula* which makes a standard tree with a trunk of at least 1.5m (5ft).

Selective breeding of the hazel in the 19th century produced the large Kentish cob nut which is redder and rounder than the wild nut. The more oval filbert nuts come from a different species, *Corylus maxima*. It is thought they originated in France and were named after Saint Philbert.

Today many English nuts in shops come from the Kentish nut plantations, although we import thousands of tons from the Mediterranean area for use in confectionery. Richard Mabey in *Food for Free* recommends using the nuts in salads, chopped or grated, in muesli, blended into a milk drink, or as nut cutlets. Weight for weight, he says, hazel nuts have half as much protein as eggs, seven times more oil and fat and five times more carbohydrate.

Management The management of hazel woods dates back to the late Stone Age. The tough straight poles produced by coppicing the tree are still used today in fencing and as bean and pea sticks and small stakes. The rod used by a diviner to detect the source of water is often made of hazel.

In the days of open field farming, split green hazel poles were woven into hurdles to fence in pigs, cattle and sheep to stop them eating the crops on adjoining land. The tree also produced the wattles for wattle-and-daub building as well as the spurs used in thatching. The brushwood was bundled into faggots that were used for the weekly firing of bread ovens.

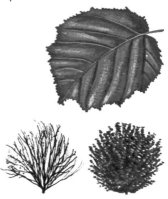

Hazel (*Corylus avellana*), deciduous, native, grows to 6m (20ft). May live hundreds of years if coppiced regularly. Common throughout the British Isles. Flowers Jan-April; cob-nuts Sept-Oct.

At least two hazel trees growing close together are needed for fertilisation and the production of nuts. This is because the female catkin usually ripens after the male flower of the same tree.

Hazel nuts are rich in oil and the oil from a single nut rubbed over the surface of a stout hazel walking stick will give it a good polish.

Coppicing

A copse is a small wood. A coppice, however, is a special sort of woodland, and coppicing the earliest known form of woodland management. It is a method of cutting broadleaved trees down to the ground at regular intervals—anything from five to 25 years, depending on the species. A cluster of new shoots sprout up from the stump (stool) and these eventually provide new, manageable straight poles.

The word coppice comes from the French *couper* to cut, but coppices were managed long before the French came to England. Trackways across the marshy areas of Somerset were built of poles which have been identified as coppiced alder, ash, holly and hazel dating from 2500BC.

By the 15th century large areas of southern England were coppiced. In the 16th century coppice-with-standards was common: standard trees—often oak or ash—were allowed to grow to maturity above the coppiced trees to increase the national timber reserves for the construction of buildings and ships.

Strict rotation in cutting and enclosure by a deep ditch or strong fence to prevent grazing animals from eating the tender shoots have always been essential in coppicing. A hurdle maker might spend a year working two acres, so a coppice of 14 acres would keep him and his billhook perpetually employed. Old coppices often retain the name of a man who worked there, perhaps for a life time, such as Emblems Coppice and Collins Coppice in Hatfield Forest.

Today coppiced wood is once again becoming valuable as firewood in rural areas; among the other values of these woods, willow is used for hurdles (see below), sweet chestnut for fencing, ash for tool handles and hazel for hop poles.

Many old coppices have become overgrown through neglect, but coppice-with-standards is still practised in a small way, and is encouraged by conservationists. Not only does coppiced woodland provide a number of different woods, but it is a haven for a huge variety of wildlife with its ever-changing layers: the ground of a freshly cut coppice is covered with wild flowers; the re-growing trees offer nesting places to numerous birds; and the mature coppice shelters yet more animals and carpets of bluebells.

Left: The base of a much coppiced hazel tree with dog's mercury and moss growing in the centre of the stool. Regular coppicing greatly prolongs the life of a tree.

Below: A hazel tree growing among standard oak trees. The hazel might be coppiced a dozen times before the mature oak is felled.

The sweet chestnut is often the last tree in the British Isles to produce flowers—they do not appear until July or even later.

SUPERB SWEET CHESTNUTS

The sweet chestnut is a large, handsome tree with fine leaves and flowers, and distinctive twisting bark. But its crowning glory is its masses of shiny dark brown autumn fruits.

We probably have the Romans to thank for introducing the sweet chestnut to the British Isles. It is a native of Asia Minor and eastern Mediterranean countries such as Greece and Yugoslavia. The Romans spread it throughout Europe because the nuts were an important source of food to them. The first evidence of the presence of sweet chestnut in Britain is as charcoal fragments excavated from sites of Roman forts and villas. It does not readily establish itself in the wild and most of the specimens you see have been planted.

The sweet chestnut is not related to the horse chestnut, and it would be difficult to confuse the two: in fact, it belongs to the same family as the oak and beech, and rivals them in grandeur. It grows up to become a massive tree reaching 30m (100ft) high, its huge trunk extending right up into the crown and sending out contorted limbs to form a broad leafy dome.

The sweet chestnut does best on deep, well-drained soils but tends to avoid chalk and limestone. It is most abundant in south-eastern England but it is. widely distributed elsewhere, although it is less common in northern England, Scotland and Ireland. It can be found in woods and plantations and has also been widely planted as an ornamental tree in parks and gardens.

The winter twigs are reddish-brown and bear plump buds, about 5mm ($\frac{1}{5}$in) long, set on little ledges spaced rather irregularly along the shaft of the twig. The tree breaks into leaf towards the end of April or early in May. The fully expanded leaves are 10-25cm (4-10in) long and a rich glossy green. A short leaf stalk supports the spear-shaped leaf blade, the edges of which are cut into long teeth where the prominent veins reach the leaf margin.

Flowers Both male and female flowers are set on dangling catkins up to 15cm (6in) long, which sprout from the base of the leaf stalks on the younger shoots. The yellow male flowers, consisting of a dense tuft of stamens, are much more numerous than the females which are confined to the upper part of the catkin near where it joins the shoot. The greenish

Above: **Sweet chestnut** (*Castanea sativa*). Deciduous, introduced, grows to 30m (100ft) throughout the British Isles, lives up to 500 years, sometimes longer. Flowers July, fruits Oct.

Below: The male flowers of the sweet chestnut are more conspicuous than the female flowers which grow on the upper part of the catkin.

female flowers are in groups of three set in a small prickly collar (cupule). Although wind pollination does take place, the pleasant scent from the catkins attracts insects which collect and feed on the pollen, some of which they unwittingly transfer to the female flowers.

Glossy fruits After fertilisation the cupule grows around the ovary in which the seeds develop and forms the familiar green 'hedgehog' case. During October, when the nuts are ripe, the spiny coat splits open, the four lobes peel back, revealing up to three glossy brown nuts packed snugly inside. The nuts are roughly triangular in shape, flattened on the side which lies next to another nut. A tuft of silvery hairs at the point indicates the remains of the stigmas.

The sweet chestnut, with its exceptionally large seeds, cannot be dispersed by the wind or by many animals. However, some animals – notably squirrels and jays – collect and bury them as an insurance against winter shortage of other fruits. Because most animal memories

Right: The most widely used chestnut timber comes from coppiced plantations; there are particularly productive areas in the Weald of Kent and Sussex. These are still cut regularly every 12-14 years to provide stacks of posts, piles and poles. Because sweet chestnut wood splits easily, the poles are cleft into sections which are wired together to make cheap, easily handled fences. In this plantation oak standards are growing in the distance. Pure coppiced sweet chestnut plantations are less hospitable to other forms of wildlife because the leaves cast a deep shade.

Left: The bole (trunk) of a sweet chestnut tree. When young the bark is smooth and brown, but with age it turns greyish and its surface cracks into deep longitudinal fissures which develop a spiral twist up the trunk. This gives the impression that the tree has been slowly twisting as it grows.

Above: Sweet chestnut seeds are well protected in spiny containers. Sadly, British sweet chestnuts rarely produce a generous crop of nuts because our climate is not warm enough. Even though they are small compared with those in the shops which are imported from Spain and Italy, they are still delicious to eat roasted.

Left: It is said that the leaves decompose to a compost unrivalled in its fertilising qualities.

are no match for their thriftiness, many caches are not relocated, and so for the sweet chestnut these creatures are important distributors and planters in the wild.

Crunchy golden leaves While the nuts are dropping from the trees the leaves acquire their autumn hues, paling first to yellow and then darkening to gold before dropping. The fallen leaves form a deep carpet beneath the tree and this rustles loudly underfoot because they remain stiff and dry – not soggy and shrivelled like those of so many other trees.

Durable wood Although mature sweet chestnuts yield a large volume of timber, the wood is not as useful as oak because cracks tend to appear during seasoning. This condition, known as 'shakes', severely limits the size of beams or length of planks that can be extracted from the bole. However, the timber is durable out of doors and even underground – it has been used for making coffins.

Long life The sweet chestnut is one of the few European trees that matches the oak for longevity. Its normal span is about 500 years but many specimens exceed this. In old age the tree becomes grotesquely misshapen with a gigantic gnarled trunk and huge twisted limbs so heavy they may touch the ground.

An enormous sweet chestnut grows in the grounds of Canford School, Dorset. The tree's bole is 13m (44ft) in circumference – the greatest girth of any living tree in Britain.

Flowers of deciduous woodlands

The pleasure we gain from a deciduous wood owes much to the myriads of smaller plants which gain a footing wherever they can. The flowering plants and ferns occupy the 'field' layer, below that mosses and fungi predominate, and the trunks and larger limbs of trees are colonized by mosses, lichens, liverworts and fungi.

To appreciate the whole range in this community, it is necessary to visit a given wood at different times of the year. The greatest diversity of flowers usually occurs in spring and early summer. In spring many flowering plants, such as primroses, wood sorrel and wood anemones, seize the twin advantages of rising temperatures (guaranteeing that there are insects abroad to pollinate them) and a still leafless tree canopy to admit ample sunlight. As the canopy develops overhead a dappled shadow engulfs the woodland floor and a second generation of more shade-resistant herbage flourishes, dominated in the southern lowland oakwoods by a green carpet of dog's mercury. Other more colourful inheritors of the shady floor are bugle, ground ivy and bluebell. The particular blend of flowering plants is conditioned partly by soil type (whether it is acid or alkali), the density of the canopy and the kind of trees and leaf litter around. Thus, in some damp northern ashwoods on limestone soils, the field layer is dominated in summer by ramsons, giant bellflower and yellow archangel.

Summer is also the high season for ferns which thrive well in the still, moist conditions found in the woodland interior. Best known is bracken, which flourishes in shade. In spring its uncurling downy fiddleheads are part of the magic of the quickening woodland.
Some species, notably polypody ferns, are epiphytic on the limbs of trees, often in association with mosses, lichens and liverworts. Unlike ferns, these latter plant groups have no tubular system for conducting water and so are dependent for survival on colonizing moist sites.

Fungi differ radically from the foregoing plants in having no chlorophyll for making food reserves, so they must either live off decaying wood or parasitise living tissue. Their fruiting bodies–the mushrooms, toadstools and bracket fungi–appear mostly in the autumn.

CHECKLIST

This checklist is a guide to the flowers and other plants you will find in broadleaved woodland. Although you will not see them all in the same woodland, you should be able to spot many of them as you walk through different woods during the changing seasons. The species listed in **bold print** *are described in detail.*

Bluebell
Bugle
Columbine
Common figwort
Common St John's wort
Dog's mercury
Early purple orchid
Foxglove
Helleborines
Herb bennet
Herb paris
Herb robert
Lily-of-the-valley
Meadowsweet
Monks-hood
Nightshades
Oxlip
Primrose
Purple crocus
Ramsons
Rosebay willowherb
Sanicle
Solomon's seal
Stitchworts
Sweet violet
Wild arum
Wild daffodil
Wood anemone
Wood crane's bill
Woodruff
Wood sorrel
Wood spurge
Yellow archangel
Yellow star-of-Bethlehem

FERNS
Buckler ferns
Hart's-tongue fern
Lady fern
Male fern
Shield ferns
FUNGI
Beech tuft
Bracket fungi
Death cap
Destroying angel
Fly agaric
Honey fungus
Inocybes
Oyster mushroom
Panther
Puffballs
Stag's-horn fungus
Sulphur tuft
LICHENS
Black-shields lichen
Parmelia
Tree lungwort
Yellow-scales lichen
MOSSES
Atrichum
Hylocomium
Hypnum
Leucobryum
Philonotis
Polytrichum
Rhacomitrium
Rhytidiadelphus
Thamnium

Above: The destroying angel fungus—it is poisonous.

Left: Bluebells and pink purslane grow in profusion on the woodland floor in Darroch Wood, Perthshire.

Bluebell (*Endymion non-scriptus*) flowers April-June in woods, hedgerows. Flowers occasionally pink or white. Ht 50cm (20in).

Ramsons (*Allium ursinum*) flowers April-June in damp shady places. Ht 20cm (8in).

A BRIGHT SPLASH OF WOODLAND COLOUR

Some of our best-loved wild flowers–among them the bluebell and wood anemone–bloom in woods in spring. Taking advantage of the lengthening hours of sunlight, they lend a splash of colour to a landscape recovering from winter and are a welcome reassurance that warmer days are with us.

Wood spurge (*Euphorbia amygdaloides*) flowers Mar-May in woods of England, Wales. Ht 20cm (8in). Fertilised female flower (inset).

Spring woodland flowers must seize the chance to blossom as the days lengthen but before the trees burst into leaf and block out the sun. As spring progresses, less light reaches the ground and woodland flowers that bloom later in the year are adapted to the shade.

Wood anemones flourish in coppiced woods and on the floors of mixed woodland. Each dainty white flower, borne on a separate stem, is tinged with pink, or more rarely reddish-purple, and very occasionally you see a blue form. The dark green leaves grow from a point half way up the stem and later in the year, when the flower has disappeared, two similar leaves rise from the base of the stem. Anemone means wind flower in Latin; one common English name is 'smell foxes', because of its sharp characteristic smell.

Spring lilies Two members of the lily family–bluebells and ramsons (wild garlic) –can tolerate the shade and appear in early summer. A bluebell wood in full bloom is a magnificent sight; the flowers grow close together and cover the woodland floor in a dense mass of dazzling colour stretching as far as the eye can see. We take this for granted, yet it is a purely British phenomenon; elsewhere in Europe bluebells only grow in small groups.

The bluebell's violet-blue or occasionally pink or white flowers are similar in structure to individual hyacinth blooms. The leaves

Dog's mercury (*Mercurialis perennis*) flowers Feb-April in woods and on shady mountain rocks. One of the few plants that can survive in dark beechwoods. It is easy to spot by its shiny green leaves. Wind-pollinated. Ht 30cm (12in).

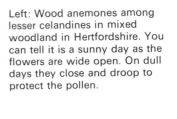

Left: Wood anemones among lesser celandines in mixed woodland in Hertfordshire. You can tell it is a sunny day as the flowers are wide open. On dull days they close and droop to protect the pollen.

Wild arum (*Arum maculatum*) flowers April-May, fruits July-Aug in woods and shady places. Ht 40cm (16in).

Oxlip (*Primula elatior*) flowers April May in Cambs, Essex, Herts, Bucks. Ht 30cm (12in).

Wood anemone (*Anemone nemorosa*) flowers Feb-April in most deciduous woods. Ht 30cm (12in).

emerge early in the year and the flowers follow in April. By the end of the summer the flowers and leaves have died back completely and all that remains is the bulb.

Under dark hedgerows and beside streams you may see – or smell – the garlicky ramsons. Their delicate spiky white flowers are star-like with six-pointed petals and long stamens and the glossy leaves twist through 180 degrees, like those of lilies-of-the-valley. The leaves can be used to flavour stews and fish.

Oxlips, once widespread in old woods, are now confined to the boulder clay area where Essex, Cambridgeshire and Hertfordshire meet, and further south in a few woods on the Hertfordshire-Buckinghamshire border. In these ideal conditions they flower abundantly. Do not confuse oxlips with the more common false oxlips – hybrids of the cowslip and primrose. True oxlips have nodding heads which droop like those of cowslips, but their flowers grow all to one side.

Wood spurge is common in the damper areas of southern England and Wales. Like all spurges, it has separate male and female blooms; each single female flower is surrounded by several male ones. Wood spurge is hard to miss, even on a crowded woodland floor. Its brilliant yellow-green flowers contrast with its darker green leaves which taper where they leave the stem; there is sometimes a ring of them at the base of the top cluster of flowers.

Solomon's seal *(Polygonatum multiflorum)* flowers May–June in woods of England and Wales. Ht. 60cm (24in).

WOODLAND FLOWERS WITH A SECRET

Many woodland flowers are difficult to find, even in their natural habitats. When you do come across them, you can easily be misled by their sweet scent. Some contain deadly poisons which belie their attractive appearance.

Yellow star-of-Bethlehem *(Gagea lutea)* flowers March–May in damp woods. Ht. 20cm (8in).

Lily-of-the-valley *(Convallaria majalis)* flowers May in England, Scotland, Wales in dry woods. Ht. 20cm (8in).

Columbine *(Aquilegia vulgaris)* flowers May–July in woods. Ht. 60cm (24in).

In spring most deciduous woods are full of flowers. That so many plants should blossom at this time is no coincidence: plants need sunlight for growth, and many woodland species flower before the increasingly dense foliage of the trees cuts out the sunlight. Even if these woodland plants do not flower now, they must at least store enough food reserves in their roots to enable them to bloom later.

Besides the well-known flowers such as primroses and bluebells, woods contain a number of attractive but less familiar flowers. Some of these have been cultivated in gardens; many were evidently once much more widespread than they are today since old records show they were widely used as medicines; others are fairly inconspicuous and easily overlooked.

Lily-of-the-valley used to be common in woodland throughout Britain and is now a popular cultivated plant. Its white pendulous flowers, borne on long spikes, appear in May. When in flower it is easy to track down by its fragrance alone. But its red berries, formed in summer, may be less familiar. If there are no flowers on the plant, you may need to smell the pair of long, spear-shaped, shiny green leaves to make sure that they do not belong to the similar looking ramsons which smell of garlic.

Individual lily-of-the-valley flowers are relatively small; but because they are grouped

Creeping buttercup *(Ranunculus repens)* flowers May–Aug in woods, disturbed ground. Ht. 46cm (18in).

Monk's-hood *(Aconitum anglicum)* flowers May–June in shady places in SW England, Wales. Ht. 122cm (48in).

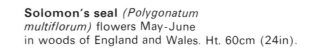

into clusters, they are conspicuous to many insects which are also attracted by the strong sweet odour. Insects visit the flowers to collect nectar and carry away and eat the pollen, some of which is transferred to other flowers. Like a number of other plants, lily-of-the-valley can spread vegetatively as well as produce berries. It sends up new shoots from its creeping underground stems, and these form new plants. All parts of this plant contain poison that can be fatal.

Solomon's seal is a relative of the lily-of-the-valley that occurs in woodland. It derives its name from the belief that its white, tangled underground stems represent the Star of David, the two interlinked triangles that were King Solomon's magic symbol for putting evil spirits to flight.

Solomon's seal grows in woods throughout Britain but is common only in the south. Elsewhere it is often a garden escape. The small white bell-shaped flowers, tipped with green, droop in small clusters from the gracefully curved stem. The flowers are replaced by blue-black berries that hang either separately or in clusters of up to three from the base of the pairs of broad, stalkless leaves on the upper part of the stem. The lower stem is bare.

The yellow star-of-Bethlehem has dainty pale yellow-green flowers that are somewhat similar to those of the more abundant lesser celandine. The leaves are quite different, however, being narrow, rather like those of the bluebell. It is rare to see large numbers of these plants growing wild as birds such as pheasants eat them if they get the chance.

Monk's-hood is a member of the prolific buttercup family that can be seen in spring. It bears helmeted purple flowers on fairly long spikes and its deeply indented leaves arise alternately from the stem.

The columbine is a particularly beautiful member of the buttercup family which grows in lime-rich soils in damp woods and fens. It gets its name from the Latin word *columba*, meaning a dove, referring to the structure of the flower. Each drooping dark violet or blue bloom has five spurred petals arranged like doves around a bowl of food, while the sepals resemble wings.

Above: Lily-of-the-valley and creeping buttercup (below left) are both poisonous if eaten in their fresh state. But a little poison, professionally administered, can be beneficial to patients; extracts from lily-of-the-valley have been used to relieve some types of heart disease.

Right: Monk's-hood is another deadly plant. The extract from its roots was in medieval times put on the tip of arrows used when hunting wild animals. Its leaves are easily mistaken for parsley, with disastrous consequences.

73

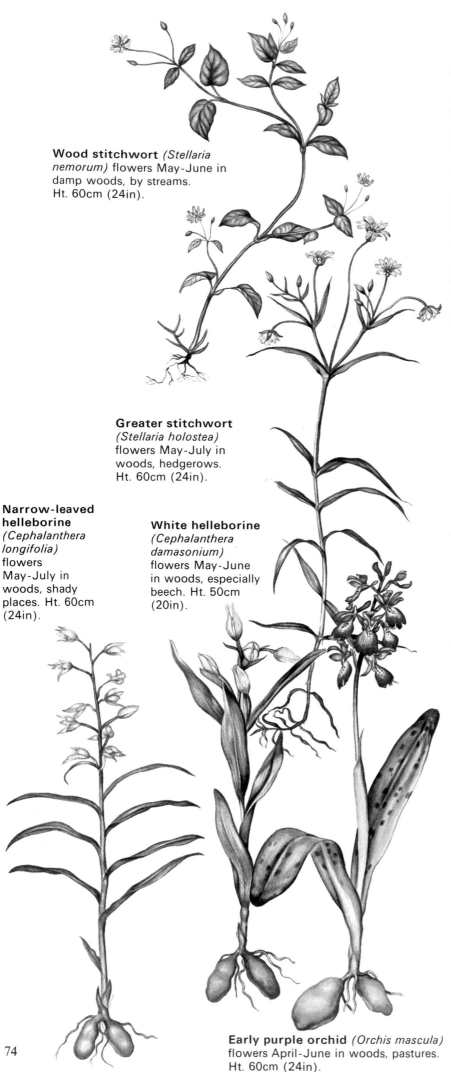

Wood stitchwort *(Stellaria nemorum)* flowers May-June in damp woods, by streams. Ht. 60cm (24in).

Greater stitchwort *(Stellaria holostea)* flowers May-July in woods, hedgerows. Ht. 60cm (24in).

Narrow-leaved helleborine *(Cephalanthera longifolia)* flowers May-July in woods, shady places. Ht. 60cm (24in).

White helleborine *(Cephalanthera damasonium)* flowers May-June in woods, especially beech. Ht. 50cm (20in).

Early purple orchid *(Orchis mascula)* flowers April-June in woods, pastures. Ht. 60cm (24in).

The nectaries of the columbine are hidden at the base of the long petals and can be reached only by long-tongued insects, chiefly bumble bees. As the bees drink the nectar, they support themselves by clinging to the sepals and stamens, and so receive pollen on the underside.

The stigmas ripen and grow longer until they project beyond the stamens, so that they are touched first by any visiting insect with a pollen-dusted body. However, not all insects reach the nectar by the proper route. Some bumble bees bite a hole in the base of the flower to reach the nectar. This hole then allows shorter-tongued honeybees and flies to join the feast. The flower can then be pollinated accidentally.

Occasionally pink or white columbine flowers are found. They are almost always a result of the escape from gardens of the familiar cultivated columbine, usually known by its Latin name *Aquilegia*. All columbines are poisonous.

The greater stitchwort is much more common than any of the flowers described so far. Its white star-shaped flowers form beautiful splashes in woodland and hedgerows in April. The blooms are borne on weak stems that lean for support against other vegetation. In some areas the plant is still referred to as 'dead man's bones' or 'old nick's ribs', folk titles that reflect the brittle nature of the stem.

Stitchwort, as its name suggests, was once thought to cure a stitch—a pain in the side—when it was mixed with powdered acorns and dissolved in wine. Cynics might be forgiven for speculating whether the cure came from the stitchwort or the wine.

The early purple orchid is one of the earliest and most abundant woodland orchids—and like most orchids, it thrives on soils containing chalk or limestone. The pinkish-purple flowers, borne on spikes, spring from between long leaves which are blotched with purple and black markings. After fertilisation, the orchid's scent changes from vanilla to an odour rather like that of cat's urine. This is thought to dissuade insects from visiting the flowers after pollination.

The early purple orchid is sometimes called 'dead man's fingers' because of the two finger-like tuberous roots where it stores its food. One root is filling up for next year's growth while the other, older one is emptying to supply present needs.

Helleborines are another group of orchids you will find in woods, especially beech woods. Few other plants can grow here, partly because of the deep shade produced by the canopy of foliage above; but helleborines thrive in these conditions. The white helleborine, which has white scentless flowers, is sometimes known as the poached egg plant because of its small orange-yellow pigmentation within each flower. The narrow-leaved helleborine has pure white flowers and shiny green leaves. It is the rarer of the two plants

Right and below: **Rosebay willowherb** (*Epilobium angustifolium*) was rare in this country 100 years ago and found only on scattered rocky outcrops. Today it is common on waste ground and in woodland rides, and grows to 120cm (48in).

CORRIDORS OF COLOUR

A well-managed woodland ride is a delight to the woodland visitor in summer, providing a corridor of showy blooms and humming insects – a striking contrast in an otherwise green world.

A ride is a break in a forest or wood where no trees grow that provides a suitable track for horse riders. It is thought that our ancient woodland rides were originally cut to aid deer hunting. In today's conifer plantations rides are important to allow foresters access to the heart of the forest and to act as breaks against forest fires. They provide an easy walk through woodland and a good place from which to observe wildlife. They are often rich in wild flowers and insects, especially butterflies, because they receive more sun than the forest floor.

In the recent past many rides were sprayed with herbicides, instead of being managed by mowing. This resulted in a limited number of flowers or insects. But in the last few years more enlightened, traditional management has encouraged some of our most colourful plants to thrive again.

Purple carpets Rosebay willowherb, often known as fireweed because it is one of the first species to appear after forest fires, is a striking and elegant species with leaves arranged in spirals up the stem. Many wild flowers have slowly disappeared or are far less common than they used to be, but rosebay willowherb has spread at a phenomenal rate. After pollination by a range of insects, the seed pod develops from the ovaries. When ripe, the pods burst and release the numerous cottony seeds, each with a tuft of delicate hairs. The slightest breeze lifts these tiny parachutes and carries them off to form young plants, often in new uncolonized habitats.

Foxgloves are magnificent flowers, with softly downy leaves and spikes of purple-spotted pinky-purple flowers at the top of the stem. Each flower is tubular and shaped like the finger of a glove. Indeed, their likeness to thimbles gives the species its Latin name, *Digitalis*, meaning thimble. The foxglove has

given medicine one of its most useful drugs, digitalin, which is used in the treatment of heart disease.

Nightshades Deadly nightshade is a powerful and sinister-sounding name for another poisonous species. It is a bushy, unpleasant-smelling plant, with lurid, greenish or purplish flowers drooping from curved stalks. The berries, flowers, and even the leaves can be extremely dangerous to man, though, surprisingly, it belongs to the same family (Solanaceae) as the tomato and the potato. Deadly nightshade dilates the pupils of the

Below: **Foxglove** (*Digitalis purpurea*) flowers June-Sept in woodlands, scrub, heaths and open places. Poisonous. Ht 100cm (40in).

Above and right: **Deadly nightshade** (*Atropa bella-donna*) grows on chalk or limestone. Its shiny black berries which appear in early autumn are extremely poisonous—one or two can kill a child. Ht 100cm (40in).

Right: **Enchanter's nightshade** (*Circaea lutetiana*) flowers June-Sept in woods and shady places. Ht 50cm (20in).

Left: **Common St John's wort** (*Hypericum perforatum*) flowers June-Sept in open grassy places. Ht 40cm (16in).

eyes, and was once used by Italian ladies to make their eyes more alluring. Today the drug atropine is extracted from the species and used to diagnose eye diseases.

Enchanter's nightshade, a member of the willowherb family, is a slender plant with oval, pointed leaves and small pink or white flowers in well-spaced spikes. Most willowherbs are wind dispersed, but this plant produces small seeds with stiff, hooked bristles that cling to the fur of animals or the feathers of birds.

Sweet and sour Meadowsweet grows in damp rides and meadows, its individual small creamy white flowers clustered together in beautiful feathery masses. They have a heavy fragrance, but the flowers do not produce nectar.

Common figwort, on the other hand, has an unpleasant smell to man, but attracts flies and wasps to its rather insignificant loose leafy clusters of flowers. This species is also known as knotted figwort because of its swollen rootstock which appears knotted.

Small balsam was introduced to the British Isles from Siberia but is now naturalised along our woodland rides. It has pale yellow flowers with a short spur at their base and, like other balsams, it produces seed pods that open to the slightest touch when they are ripe in autumn.

The golden yellow flowers of common St John's wort brighten many woodland rides in summer. Each flower has five shiny petals and numerous stamens surrounding a distinctive, pear-shaped ovary. This flower is also known as perforate St John's wort, since its leaves are covered with tiny glands that look like holes when the leaf is held to the light.

Meadowsweet (*Filipendula ulmaria*) flowers June-Sept in damp meadows and woods, marshes, fens and swampy areas. Very fragrant. Ht 90cm (35in).

Left: **Common figwort** (*Scrophularia nodosa*) flowers June-Sept in woods and shady places, especially hedgerows. Ht 60cm (24in).

Below: **Small balsam** (*Impatiens parviflora*) flowers June-Sept in woods and shady waste places, especially in southern England. Ht 40cm (16in).

Photosynthesis

Green plants make their food by a process known as photosynthesis. The plant is like a factory: the raw materials are carbon dioxide and water, the 'fuel' is the sunlight, and the machine is the chloroplast which contains the green pigment, chlorophyll. The factory makes sugar and oxygen from carbon dioxide and water. The sugar is converted into starch to be stored, or into proteins for the growth of the plants.

All green parts of the plant contain chlorophyll and can therefore photosynthesise, but the leaves do most of the work. Leaves usually have a large surface area that catches the maximum light. Many plants cannot grow in shady places because there is insufficient light for photosynthesis. However, some woodland plants are adapted to shady habitats, while spring plants grow, flower and set their seed early in the year before the leaves on the trees unfurl and cut out much of the light.

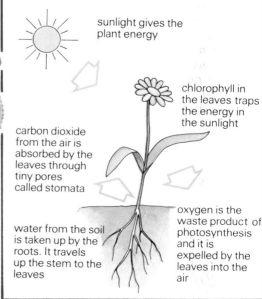

sunlight gives the plant energy

chlorophyll in the leaves traps the energy in the sunlight

carbon dioxide from the air is absorbed by the leaves through tiny pores called stomata

water from the soil is taken up by the roots. It travels up the stem to the leaves

oxygen is the waste product of photosynthesis and it is expelled by the leaves into the air

FLOWERING PLANTS OF WOODLAND SHADE

Plants that grow under woodland trees must be able to tolerate a certain lack of light, although not many flowering species grow in the deepest shade. In early spring, before the new foliage cuts out too much light, those species that prefer damp, shady conditions appear in profusion.

Shade-loving plants find that woodland provides the damp, sheltered conditions they need for growth. In deciduous woodland, the characteristic ground flora consists of plants that flower in early spring while the trees are still bare and the sunlight reaches down to the woodland floor. The most familiar plants in this type of woodland are primroses, violets and wood anemones, which often flower before the leaves open on the trees above them.

The density of shade depends upon the type of woodland; beech trees have leaves that are thick in texture and arranged in a close pattern that allows little light through, while in other mixed broadleaved woodland the shade may be more diffuse. In conifer woods and plantations the shade can be very dense, especially when the trees are mature. Here only ferns, mosses and a few helleborines and orchids can tolerate the lack of light.

Sweet-scented flowers Woodruff is a woodland species that grows on damp, calcareous soils throughout Britain. In some areas it grows in profusion and is welcomed for its

fresh growth in early spring. The small flowers, measuring only 5mm in diameter, have dense white petals and form umbellate heads. These are set off by the fresh green leaves which are arranged up the stem of the plant in symmetrical, rather rigid, whorls of six.

Sometimes known as sweet woodruff, this little plant, which is hay-scented when dried, contains the aromatic substance coumarin. In the past, it was gathered and used for strewing on floors in the home, for laying between clean linen and was also added to the stuffing in mattresses. The dried plant was also powdered and dissolved in wine to make a tonic drink known as 'Waldmeister Tea'; and in dried form it is still used today as a pleasant herbal tea.

White woodland carpet Although wood-sorrel–another white-flowered species–grows on shady rocks on mountains in the north and in sheltered hedgerows further south, it is mainly a woodland species. Less than 15cm (6in) high, this early flowering species may carpet the ground in beech woods. It is also found in oakwoods and mixed wood-

Above: **Woody nightshade** (*Solanum dulcamara*). Flowers June-September in woods, hedgerows. Ht 120cm (48in).

Right: In May, the delicate white flowers and clear green leaves of wood sorrel (*Oxalis acetosella*) often carpet the woods.

land, often in the leaf mould at the base of trees or in clefts of tree trunks above the ground. Here pockets of soil may first be colonised by lichens and mosses in which seedlings of small flowering plants can eventually germinate and grow.

The first flowers have distinctive white petals delicately traced with lilac-coloured veins, but they set few seeds, however. Later in the summer there is a second flowering when the flowers are smaller, short-stalked and without petals. These inconspicuous flowers are self-pollinated and set seed in quantity, although wood-sorrel also spreads by means of its creeping underground rhizomes.

The spring flowers nod forward at night or in the rain to keep the pollen dry, and the three leaflets fold back at night. They also stay folded in strong sunlight so that the delicate leaf surfaces do not receive the direct rays of the sun.

Country children often nibble the leaves of the plant; these contain tiny amounts of oxalic acid, which give them a pleasant, sharp taste. In small quantities this does no harm. In fact, in centuries gone by, when winter diets seemed very dull by the end of the season, wood-sorrel leaves were welcomed for their sharpness in spring salads. They were also used to make a green-coloured sauce for which the plant was valued and sometimes cultivated.

Bristly fruits Herb bennet or wood avens, which grows in shady areas, is found throughout Britain as a wayside flower in hedgebanks as well as in woods. The flowers are rather small and few and the soft yellow petals are sometimes partly covered by the green sepals. As the flowers wither, the seeds ripen in a round brown cluster of hairy fruits. Each fruit has a long hooked bristle which catches in fur, feathers or clothing and ensures the dispersal of the seed.

Herb bennet has been known since the Middle Ages, when it was thought to be a blessed herb, its name being taken from the Latin *herba benedicta*. It was once gathered by country people to boil in broth or 'potage' and was grown in gardens for this purpose. The roots have a fragrant, clover-like scent; like the woodruff herb, this 'clove-root' was used to scent linen closets.

Woodland colour The colourful wood crane's-bill also grows in a number of different habitats: on mountains, in meadows and on rock ledges, as well as in hedgerows and woodland. Its Latin name *Geranium sylvaticum*, however, means 'geranium of the woods' and was given to the species by Carl Linnaeus in his classification system of 1730.

In Linnaeus' native Sweden, wood crane's-bill is a common plant of deciduous woodland, while further south in its range it grows away from woods. In the Alps, the deep blue-violet of the paired flowers may often be the dominant colour of the hay pastures.

In the British Isles, the wood crane's-bill has an unusual distribution pattern, generally widespread and common in Scotland and northern England, but with less than five localities in Wales and Ireland. It has been introduced in a few places in southern

Above: Woodruff (*Galium odoratum*), seen growing here on a woodland floor dappled with sunlight, can be found in flower as early as April.

Below: **Green hound's tongue** (*Cynoglossum germanicum*). Flowers June-Aug in woods. Ht 61 cm (24in).

Right: **Herb bennet** (*Geum urbanum*). Flowers June-Aug in shade. Ht 45cm (18in).

England, but does not occur there as a native wild flower.

Rare species Green hound's tongue is now very scarce in Britain. A plant of woods and hedgerows, it was once widespread throughout central and southern England, but is known now in less than ten localities. The causes for this decline are not fully understood. The species is near the limit of its range here and possibly variations in climate through the years, or changes in woodland management, could have altered the conditions necessary for its growth.

In recent years, trees were felled in woodland where only two or three specimens of green hound's tongue were known and in the following year several hundred of these plants came up in the cleared area. This great abundance of plants shows that the seeds were lying dormant in the soil, waiting for favourable conditions before germinating.

Another, more familiar, species of hound's tongue grows in Britain. This is the common hound's tongue, which has grey leaves felted with hairs. It is found on chalk grassland and dry sandy soils, often near the sea—very different conditions to the damp shade required by the green hound's tongue of the woodland.

Symmetrical structure Herb Paris is another woodland plant that is rare in the British Isles. It has an unusual structure, with the four leaves near the top of the stem arranged in a single whorl, just below the single green star-shaped flower. This flower has four sepals and four narrow petals, with eight thin, pointed yellow stamens. The flower is followed by a single, poisonous black berry, often ringed by the still persistent stamens, petals and sepals.

Found in damp woods on calcareous soils, Herb Paris grows in the south on chalky soil

Above: Some of our most attractive flowers belong to the crane's-bill family, like the wood crane's-bill shown here. Its distinctive divided leaves and flowers vary from pink to violet in colour. The name crane's-bill is derived from the pointed fruit which is supposed to resemble the long beak of the crane. Wood crane's-bill is in bloom from May to July.

Opposite: The pink-purple flowers of foxglove can be found in woodlands from June to September. The flowering spikes can be up to 1.5m (5ft) tall.

Right: Herb Paris (*Paris quadrifolia*) used to be known as the herb of equality or equal parts because it had four petals, four sepals, four leaves and eight stamens. It was believed to be a magical plant, and although the berries are poisonous, they were eaten to guard against witchcraft or the plague. Ritual decreed that they should be taken in odd numbers. However, this theory was counterbalanced by the discovery of 'unequal' specimens of the plant—such as this one—with anything from three to eight leaves.

under beech trees, often with Solomon's seal and dog's mercury. In northern woodland on limestone soils it can be found under ash or wych elm trees and it also grows in the crevices of bare limestone pavement. These deep, narrow clefts or grikes produce similar conditions to those of woodland–shade, moisture and shelter; the grikes are therefore colonised by several species of woodland plants.

Colourful climber Woody nightshade or bittersweet is a plant of many different habitats, including shingle beaches and waste ground as well as woods and hedges. Although it grows well in damp, shady woodland conditions, it is not dependent on them and is also found at the edges of woods.

It is a straggling climber, with stems too weak to support the rather heavy heads of flowers and berries. So for support it grows between the stems of shrubs, or in hedges. The flowers are an unusual shape, with a ring of blue petals which fold back as the flower ages, and the yellow stamens are fused together in a forward-pointing cone. The berries are very glossy and green when they first appear, eventually turning yellow and finally red. In early autumn it is occasionally possible to find a spray of berries with all three colours appearing on a plant together in one cluster.

The name bittersweet is derived from the taste of the berries. Due to the presence of a toxic chemical in the plants, they taste bitter at first, and then sweet; and will make you sick if eaten. The plant is sometimes confused with the very poisonous deadly nightshade, which has cherry-sized shining berries, borne singly. When ripe, these are black rather than red and should never be eaten or touched under any circumstances.

NATURE'S WILD WOODLAND GARDEN

Primroses and wild daffodils, two of our most cherished spring flowers, grow in hedgerows and meadows, open clearings of woods, and also in weedy areas of gardens. Once established in the right soil conditions, they bloom in profusion and multiply, making rich, golden carpets of blooms.

Wild daffodils are particularly common around Newent in Gloucestershire. In the 1930s special trains took Londoners to see the spectacular drifts of yellow flowers.

Although wild daffodils–Lent lilies–are less widespread than they were, they are still prolific in the west and south of England and Wales, and some colonies persist in eastern England in old woods and churchyards. Their numbers have been much reduced not only by indiscriminate picking but also by drainage of land–daffodils do better in damp ground–and by their deliberate removal from pastures because their bulbs are slightly poisonous to grazing animals. However, where they are left undisturbed they continue to flourish, sometimes in the most unlikely places such as the banks of the M5 motorway.

The Lent lily is the only truly native type of daffodil in Britain, although some foreign species and hybrids have escaped from gardens and are now widely naturalised. It has solitary, drooping flowers with delicate pale yellow petals and a darker yellow trumpet. Possibly the Tenby daffodil, the symbolic flower of Wales, is also native; if it is a garden escape, it certainly escaped a long time ago. It differs from the Lent lily in that it has deeper yellow petals and is slightly taller.

The primrose was given the name *prima rosa*–first rose of the year–by medieval scholars. It is nowadays often difficult to find around towns; away from over-enthusiastic collectors, however, primroses still flourish in old grassland and hedgerows or in woods.

Like many other common and easily recognised plants, the primrose has been put to numerous uses. Its flowers and those of its cousin, the cowslip, were recommended as a flavouring in a 17th century recipe for minnows fried with egg yolks, and vast quantities of primrose and cowslip blossoms went into country wines and vinegar. Primrose leaves were boiled with lard by medieval New Forest woodmen to make an ointment for cuts.

Primrose flowers are usually pale yellow with a darker yellow eye in the centre. They have lines or honeyguides on the petals reflecting ultra violet light which, although invisible to us, is seen by insects and directs them to the nectar in the base of the flower tube.

Some primroses in the woods of south Wales have pinkish flowers, and in some plants the flowers grow on a common stalk instead of all springing separately from the base of the plant. With such variability existing naturally in wild primroses, it is not surprising that gardeners have seized on the opportunity to single out oddities–the long stalked, or large flowered, or brightly coloured mutants which, by hybridisation with cowslips and oxlips, have given birth to the enormous range of polyanthus varieties we see in gardens today.

Escapes While primroses and daffodils have been hybridised in gardens in seemingly endless permutations, other plants have escaped from gardens to the countryside. The spring crocus is a familiar spring flower of gardens that is occasionally found growing wild in meadows and woods. You can see it naturalised in a field at Inkpen in Berkshire.

The sand crocus, a relative of the spring crocus, is however a native plant which grows by the coast in south west England. It is uncommon probably because it is not hardy enough to withstand our winter frosts; it is much more widespread farther south in Europe. The sand crocus does not look much like its garden counterpart: its leaves are remarkable for being thin and twisted like a corkscrew, and the flowers are purple on one side and pale green on the back.

Wild daffodil (*Narcissus pseudonarcissus*) flowers March-April in damp woods, meadows and by riversides. Locally abundant. Ht. 23cm (9in).

Tenby daffodil (*Narcissus obvallaris*) flowers April in Tenby, Pembrokeshire. Ht. 30cm (12in).

Primrose (*Primula vulgaris*) flowers Feb-May in woods and shady places. Ht. 15cm (6in).

Looking at primrose flowers
Many plants have special mechanisms to ensure cross-pollination (the exchange of pollen for fertilization). Primroses have two types of flowers—pin-eye and thrum-eye— which grow on different plants. Seeds are only produced when one type of flower has been pollinated by pollen from the other type of flower.

The pollen grains of thrum-eye flowers are large and only fit onto the surface of a pin-eye stigma. Similarly, the smaller pollen grains of the pin-eye flower only fit the surface of the thrum-eye stigma. The structure of the two flowers is neatly arranged so that visiting insects transfer the right pollen to the right stigma.

Purple crocus (*Crocus purpureus*) flowers March-April in meadows. Ht. 5cm (2in).

Pin-eye flower
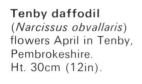

bee fly

stigma on a long style

stamen

ovary

nectar

pollen rubs on to the insect's proboscis

Thrum-eye flower

pollen rubs on to the insect here

stamen

stigma

ovary

pollen from the pin-eye flower rubs off here

As a long-tongued insect reaches for nectar in a pin-eye flower pollen rubs on to the middle of its proboscis. If the insect then flies to a thrum-eye flower, this pollen is at just the right level to rub off onto the short thrum-eye stigma.

At the same time the insect's head and base of its proboscis are covered with more pollen from the thrum-eye stamens. If the insect now moves to a pin-eye flower, this pollen is in the right position to rub on to the tall pin-eye stigma.

Sand crocus (*Romulea columnae*) flowers April on sandy grassland in S Devonshire. Ht. 15cm (6in).

WOODLAND FUNGI

The fruiting bodies of fungi are the visible evidence of the vast and intricate breakdown process which is happening all the time in our woodlands.

Fungi not only appear on living trees as parasites, they are also active on dead and decaying matter as saprophytes, most of them playing an important part in the breakdown of organic matter.

Whereas green plants build up complex food substances from simple ones, using energy from the sun, fungi do the opposite. They have to take their sustenance from living and dead plants, since they lack the chlorophyll necessary to manufacture their own food. Therefore, they break down complex substances into simple ones on which they can feed and grow.

There are several hundred wood-inhabiting fungi in Britain and most of them are remarkably selective in the conditions they demand for survival. Some need wet or even soggy conditions while some prefer the relative dryness of standing trees. Generally, they need damp conditions in order to produce their fruit bodies and wet woodlands provide the ideal setting. Most are host specific, that is they infect only one species or group of species.

Infecting trees Infection of wood by fungi can take place in two ways. Standing trees

Above: The beech tuft *(Oudemansiella mucida)* is a white fungus with a rather translucent appearance due to its coating of slimy fluid. Such an appearance gives rise to the other names by which it is known—the porcelain fungus or poached egg fungus. On standing beech trees, it generally appears fairly high up the trunks and on the branches.

Opposite: Prolific honey fungus growing on a tree stump in the New Forest. The fungus shown here is infesting dead wood, but it can also attack living trees.

are infected by spores that land on them and, in damp conditions, start to grow. They send out threads known as hyphae, which form a fine cobweb-like net – a mycelium – that penetrates the wood. Secondly, trees that have fallen down or are cut down are infected by the mycelium that is everywhere on the forest floor, living on the large amount of dead material – leaves, twigs and branches – which fall from the trees.

At certain times of the year the mycelium produces a fruit body – the mushroom or toadstool that we see. This fruit body distributes spores that land and develop into a new mycelium, starting the process again.

Penetrating the wood Once the tissues of the wood have been entered the mycelium often grows down the phloem and xylem, the sap and water conducting channels. Some fungi live off the food stored by the tree in its sap wood, while others actually absorb the substance of the wood, producing a condition known as heart rot.

An entire tree trunk can be full of mycelium, usually of one species, although some fungi

Above: Velvet shank *(Flammulina velutipes)* often persists through the winter to the spring when conditions are mild; it has been known to tolerate freezing temperatures. It has a tough, elastic flesh and a slimy appearance. The velvety texture of the stem gives it its name.

Left: The striking stag's horn fungus has a jelly-like texture and favours wet conditions, shrinking and losing colour in dry air.

Below: *Lycogala epidendrum*, a slime fungus, has a rather unpleasant appearance. It is usually found in autumn on dead wood and may vary in colour from pink to pale yellowish-brown.

extract all they can from the wood, leaving another to follow on and break it down further. One such example is the white, pear-shaped, stump puffball (*Lycoperdon pyriforme*) which attacks wood that has been broken down by other fungi such as the dark brown deer toadstool (*Pluteus cervinus*).

Fruiting times In general, the mushrooms and toadstools that grow in grassland fruit in late summer or autumn – earlier in the north and later in the south. Those that grow on wood tend to fruit later although there are exceptions. Autumn and early winter are good times to see interesting and attractive specimens in deciduous woodland.

Bracket fungi Species to look out for include the aptly named beefsteak fungus (*Fistulina hepatica*), which has a dark red, sticky upper surface and oozes a red juice when cut. It usually grows on oak, causing the wood to develop a deep, rich colour which makes it very popular with cabinet makers. Oyster mushroom (*Pleurotus ostreatus*), has widely spaced gills on its underside and a grey-brown cap. It grows mainly on beeches, attached by the stalk that appears on its side. The razor strop fungus (*Piptoporus betulinus*) has a smooth, greyish skin which develops a corky texture with age. It is widespread on dead birch trees in the south of the British Isles, while its place is taken in the north of Scotland by the hoof-shaped tinder fungus (*Fomes fomentarius*), which causes white rot in the trees which it infects.

Hardly any deciduous wood lies on the ground for long without producing a crop of the banded bracket fungus (*Coriolus versicolor*), which has a velvety upper surface banded with shades of yellow, brown and grey. Appearing at ground level, growing from the wood of the roots of beech tree

stumps, is a remarkably large fan-shaped bracket fungus, *Meripilus giganteus*, which can measure up to 80cm (33in) across. It often grows in tiers, forming very large and conspicuous colonies.

Toadstools *Pholiota* is a genus of yellow fungi with varying degrees of scaliness of the cap and stem, and is particularly common on dead beech trees, while charcoal pholiota (*Pholiota carbonaria*) grows in large numbers on burnt ground. These species are often confused with the beautiful golden *Gymnopilus junonius*, which is distinguished by the marked ring on its often swollen stem. It is generally found growing in dense clusters at ground level.

When the wood has been broken down into pulp or sawdust, some of the cup fungi, such as the wavy-edged *Peziza repanda* start to grow, the fruit bodies appearing in the autumn. If it is wet enough a remarkable species, *Lycogala epidendrum*, may appear. It is a slime fungus, which is capable of spreading out into a thin layer until it is ready to fruit. The thin film then actually

moves until it has gathered itself into pink balls about 1cm ($\frac{2}{5}$in) across which harden, turn brown and break down to reveal a powdery mass of spores in the centre.

Elms killed by elm-bark disease are subsequently broken down by the autumn fruiting *Lyophyllum ulmarium* or by the velvet shank (*Flammulina velutipes*).

Foresters dislike the honey fungus (*Armillaria mellea*) because it attacks living trees, spreading to them by long cords known as bootlaces (above), which may be found under the bark of infected trees causing extensive rot.

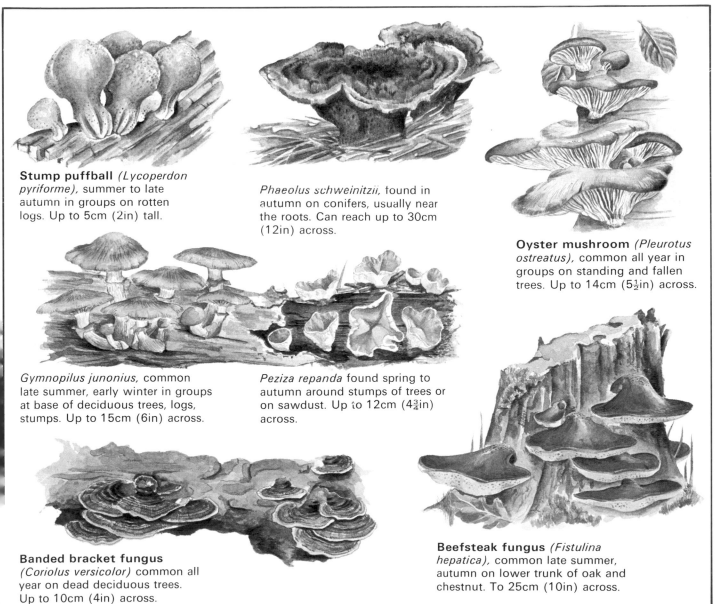

Stump puffball *(Lycoperdon pyriforme)*, summer to late autumn in groups on rotten logs. Up to 5cm (2in) tall.

Phaeolus schweinitzii, found in autumn on conifers, usually near the roots. Can reach up to 30cm (12in) across.

Oyster mushroom *(Pleurotus ostreatus)*, common all year in groups on standing and fallen trees. Up to 14cm (5½in) across.

Gymnopilus junonius, common late summer, early winter in groups at base of deciduous trees, logs, stumps. Up to 15cm (6in) across.

Peziza repanda found spring to autumn around stumps of trees or on sawdust. Up to 12cm (4¾in) across.

Banded bracket fungus *(Coriolus versicolor)* common all year on dead deciduous trees. Up to 10cm (4in) across.

Beefsteak fungus *(Fistulina hepatica)*, common late summer, autumn on lower trunk of oak and chestnut. To 25cm (10in) across.

Death cap (*Amanita phalloides*) appears summer-autumn on woodland floors, particularly beech. May also be found in pastures and on lawns.
Deadly poisonous.

DANGEROUS FUNGI

Most fungi are harmless to man and some have an excellent flavour, but there are those with deadly properties. Most notorious is the death cap; few people have survived eating it.

Mushrooms and toadstools have long been regarded with suspicion. Yet of the 6000 species recorded in the British Isles less than a score are known to be poisonous, and only a few of these have proved to be lethal. There are some delicious species which few people would even contemplate eating because they look so different from edible mushrooms sold in shops. Perhaps this is just as well, because some ghastly mistakes have occurred. No fungus should be eaten unless you are absolutely positive about its identification.

The infamous death cap, fairly common in the British Isles, is regarded as the most poisonous fungus in the world; all parts of it, even the spores, are toxic. The cap is usually an olive-green colour, but it can vary from a pale greenish-yellow to light tan. When it first appears it is rounded or egg-shaped, but it later opens out to become almost flat and up to 10cm (4in) across. A ring hangs loosely under the cap like a frill, partially covering the white stem which is 5-10cm (2-4in) tall.

Even just a quarter of a death cap can be fatal to humans. One of its most distinguished victims was Pope Clement VII in 1534. Together with its close relatives, the destroying angel and fool's mushroom, the death cap accounts for over 90% of all fatal fungi poisonings.

Destroying angel, very similar to the death cap, contains equally lethal slow-acting poison and is said to have killed Emperor Claudius of Rome. Fortunately it is rarely found in the British Isles, although it grows occasionally in broadleaved woodland. It has a white, rather sticky conical cap about 10cm (4in) across, and white gills, and is supported on a slender white stem up to 15cm (6in) long, which tends to be covered in flaky scales.

The fly agaric is so well-known that it hardly needs description. It is a beautiful species, and a firm favourite of illustrators of fairy tales. However it is poisonous, although not dangerously so unless taken in large quantities. In 1893 an Italian diplomat in the United States ate two dozen fly agarics for breakfast, and died the following day after a prolonged bout of violent convulsions. The species gets its name from its former household use against flies. The caps used to be mashed with milk and sugar and the mixture laid out as bait to attract and kill flies.

The fly agaric is a woodland species that appears in autumn, often in large groups and sometimes in rings. Typically it is found under birch trees with whose roots it forms a mutually beneficial relationship involving the exchange of nutrients. But it is also common in coniferous woods and plantations.

When young the cap is round and covered with a soft creamy white membrane or veil. As the fruiting body grows it pushes through the veil, patches of which are left sticking to the bright scarlet cap. As the cap expands and flattens out, the white spots form an evenly spaced pattern, although they are often washed off by rain. The gills and stem are white. It grows up to 20cm (8in) and the stem gently tapers from a swollen base.

Fly agaric contains small amounts of muscarine–a nerve poison–but the major toxins are ibotenic acid and muscimol, which cause headache, tiredness, nausea and intoxication. This latter property has been exploited for centuries by a wide variety of peoples. Several tribes in Siberia, notably the Koryaks, used to eat fly agarics in dried form to induce hallucinations and delirium. Recently, however, this practice has been more or less replaced by vodka drinking.

The panther is similar to the fly agaric but differs in that the cap is a smoky-brown colour. It is rather rare in the British Isles, appearing under deciduous woodland, especially beech. It contains muscarine in much higher concentrations than the fly agaric, and has been responsible for a number of deaths in Europe where it is more common.

The yellow-stainer often causes a violent stomach upset, although some people are immune, and is not fatal–with recovery in a few days. In some years it springs up in abundance and is often mistaken for the edible field mushroom. The cap is white when young, turning greyish towards the centre as it expands to about 10cm (4in) across. The gills mature from pale cream to a chocolate brown colour. To identify the species, cut the base of the stem; if it turns bright yellow instantly, then leave it alone.

The Inocybe species are a large group of fungi, some of which are poisonous. The red-staining inocybe is another species that has often been confused with the field mushroom, with tragic consequences, since its flesh contains a high concentration of muscarine. It appears rather infrequently along grassy paths, in woodland glades and in the shade of beech trees. The cap is up to 8cm (3in) across, whitish or pale brown at first, gradually staining red where the cap splits with age. The stem is fibrous and rather tough. It is white or creamy brown in colour, but if bruised during handling soon becomes spotted with red patches. The common white inocybe is a widespread poisonous species.

Should you eat it?

No fungus should be eaten unless you are absolutely positive about its identification. Never rely on the old belief that only edible species have a cap from which the skin can be peeled: the death cap peels easily, yet it is deadly poisonous.

Collect whole specimens that look fresh, and never think of eating anything until it is mature enough for the gills and spore colour to be visible. If you are really sure you have an edible species, cook it first. Some fungi can add a delicious flavour to soups and stews.

Red-staining inocybe (*Inocybe patouillardii*) appears summer-autumn by woods, in grass. Poisonous.

Fly agaric (*Amanita muscaria*) appears in autumn, often round birch trees or in coniferous woodland. Poisonous.

Destroying angel (*Amanita virosa*) appears in autumn in mixed woodland. Rare. Poisonous.

The panther (*Amanita pantherina*) appears in autumn in deciduous woodland. Rare. Poisonous.

Common white inocybe (*Inocybe geophylla*) appears in autumn in mixed woodland. Common. Poisonous.

Yellow-staining mushroom (*Agaricus xanthodermus*) common in fields, parks. Not deadly, causes discomfort.

THE TREE TRUNK PLAYS HOST

The trunks and branches of ancient trees in damp areas of the British Isles are often festooned with flowerless plants of intricate shapes and subtle colours.

Look at the trunks and branches of different trees in a forest or a dense wood, and you will notice that the bark surface is often covered with mosses or lichens. Look closer, and you will see that these growths are very small and beautifully coloured flowerless or 'lower' plants.

Their existence, when you think about it, is quite remarkable for tree trunks are continually shedding both their outer bark and the plants that live on it. Tree trunks are also dry places, so you might imagine that few plants could live on them. Nevertheless, many plants have evolved to cope with tree trunk living, probably to escape competition from the undergrowth on the forest floor.

These plants are collectively known as 'epiphytes'. Most plants draw up food and water from the soil, but epiphytes absorb their nutrients from the air around them; the lushest growths of epiphytes are therefore found on trees in the humid western parts of the British Isles where the air is often saturated with water vapour from fog or rain.

Delicate mosses and leafy liverworts form green mats on the relatively moist bark near the tree base; their minute leaves are often pleated or rolled to trap water. In the drier air higher up the trunk and on the branches, compact cushion-forming mosses–with upright stems (like a thick pile carpet) which trap water between them–are more common.

Lichens are either crustose and pressed to the bark or foliose–forming strange branching outgrowths. They festoon branches in woods of the West Country in particular, but most of them are too sensitive to pollution and aridity to thrive in many areas of the British Isles. Like mosses, they too absorb water over their whole surface, and anything dissolved in the water is absorbed with it, including pollutants such as sulphur dioxide and carbon monoxide produced by burning fuel or traffic fumes. In heavily polluted areas *Pleurococcus*, a tough microscopic alga which tinges tree trunks a dirty green colour, is the only epiphyte to be found.

Where epiphytes are abundant it is interesting to note how different species grow on different bark types. The trunks of old trees

Above: Tree lungwort (*Lobaria pulmonaria*) – one of the largest of the lichens – growing on a damp ash tree. Its presence often indicates ancient woodland.

Right: A heathland lichen, *Parmelia physodes,* growing on an old heather stem. It is common on trees, rocks, walls and soil.

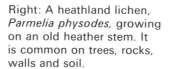

grow relatively slowly, giving epiphytes an opportunity to gain a strong foothold. You see many in the deep fissures of oak and poplar in particular, but only rarely in the rapidly flaking bark of sycamores.

On areas of damaged bark there is often a distinctive epiphyte flora because the tree is exuding nitrogen-rich substances. In the rain tracks running down the barks of beech and elm trees, epiphytes that can withstand the forceful water flow benefit from the extra nourishment such as bird droppings dissolved in water. Some rare mosses grow in the axils of large branches. If dust and humus collect there, then even non-epiphytic plants like ferns may grow.

A rich and prospering collection of lichens used to be a much more common sight when the British Isles were relatively pollution-free. This group is growing on a sessile oak tree at Dizzard Point in Cornwall.

WINTER-THRIVING WOODLAND MOSSES

Lowly, primitive mosses very often remain unnoticed, although they are everywhere around us in the countryside. They are most obvious in the winter months, when they are often the only green colour in a woodland shorn of summer vegetation.

Many mosses grow only in particular types of woodland, either because they are sensitive to the acidity or alkalinity of the soil, or because there is not enough light or space for them to flourish. This river bank in the New Forest (above) provides the ideal conditions for mosses, as well as for the ferns and primroses seen here. The running water and damp ground conditions encourage luxuriant growth.

Many mosses grow actively in the winter when the climate is cool and the moisture abundant, and they are at their most luxuriant after the winter's growth. In the spring they produce their spore capsules, and then gradually wither and dry as the summer progresses, repeating the cycle when damp conditions return.

A dry stone wall or a tree may appear to have an unchanging population of mosses. However, an interesting study of the rare moss *Grimmia stirtoni*, which has been known for eighty years at a site on a Scottish island, revealed that an apparently stable population of moss cushions was really a constantly changing one. The lifespan of the individual cushions was quite short—a matter of a few months only. This is probably true of a great many mosses, especially those living in harsh situations such as stone walls where new cushions appear each year.

Primitive characteristics Mosses are among the few plants still existing that retain some of the characteristics of the very earliest land plants. They have no 'true' leaves, stems or roots. The moss stem lacks the xylem vessels that are normally used to conduct food and water up a plant stem. Instead, mosses absorb water over their entire surface, and so every moss cell must be within reach of the growing surface to obtain its water supply.

Moss leaves are thin and flat and arranged spirally around the small flimsy stems. True leaves, such as those found on flowering plants, have stomata in their surface—these are pores bordered by special cells that can open and close according to the humidity, allowing air to enter the leaf. Moss leaves do not have these air holes, nor do they have roots, these being replaced by rhizoids—thin hair-like outgrowths that attach them to the ground.

Mosses also differ from flowering plants in reproducing by a system of alternation of generations. A moss plant carries both male and female organs and when the female part is fertilised, the second, or spore-bearing, generation is produced. The spore capsules dry and release spores which, pro-

Above: The distinctive spore capsules of this *Polytrichum* moss are covered with loosely fitting caps when young. Mosses such as these are often the first plants to colonize poor soil, helping to stabilise it.

Right: The attractive white fork moss, seen here in its preferred beech woodland habitat, varies in colour from blue-green to grey-green, and is often tinged with silver.

Spore dispersal

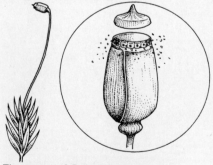

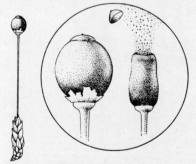

The spores of *Polytrichum juniperum* (found on heaths, moors and walls), are shaken out through pores at the top of the four-sided capsules, when the red cap has fallen off.

Spore capsules of *Sphagnum* moss (found in damp woods and bogs), have a tiny cap that flies off with a pop when the capsule dries, releasing showers of spores.

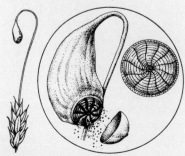

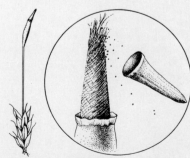

In dry weather *Funaria hygrometrica* (found in woods and gardens), releases spores through gaps in the top of the capsule. These close up in the damp, preventing dispersal.

Tortula muralis (found on walls in urban areas), has spores covered by spirally twisted hairs. In dry weather, the hairs unwind, exposing the spores to the wind for dispersal.

vided they land in suitable conditions, germinate to form a new moss plant.

Water-loving mosses As mosses need a constant water supply, they grow best in damp or wet places, although some species survive on stone walls or fences, provided the conditions in the spring are suitable for the production of spore capsules.

Some of the most spectacular mosses are seen in very wet places. Upland streams such as those found in Scotland and northern England often arise from springs; the water brings a constant supply of minerals and oxygen to the mosses and liverworts that grow on the ledges and terraces. *Philonotis fontana* forms a bright green carpet in such a situation, and it is often accompanied by the cushion-forming *Dicranella palustris* and many other mosses as well. On the banks of woodland streams species such as *Polytrichum formosum*, one of the hair mosses, and *Mnium punctatum*, grow along with many other mosses and liverworts. The genus *Polytrichum* includes some of the largest of all British mosses and *Polytrichum commune* may reach up to 30cm (12in) in length in very wet conditions among long grasses.

Favourite woodland habitats Not all woodlands contain the same species of mosses, for the vegetation growing in any one area is largely determined by the soil conditions. Beeches grow on a wide range of soil types from the shallow chalky soils of the Chilterns and the Weald to the acid sandy soils of Epping Forest or Burnham Beeches, and the moss population in these beech woods varies according to the soil types. For example, two mosses are common on the chalky soils of the beech hangers (wooded hillsides) so typical of east Hampshire. *Ctenidium molluscum* is restricted to the ground immediately around the bases of the tree trunks, and *Hypnum cupressiforme* grows on the bases of the trunks themselves.

In the woodland of the Chiltern Hills, the soil is often deep and fertile and so a greater variety of plants grows in these woodlands, frequently preventing mosses from growing at all, for at ground level there is little light. By contrast, the acid soil of the beech woods at Epping prevents the decomposition of the autumn leaves and here too, few plants grow in such deep leaf litter. One species, however thrives in these conditions – the great silvery cushions of the white fork moss (*Leucobryum glaucum*) form a beautiful feature of the woodland floor.

Oak woodlands, often regarded as the native forest of the British Isles, provide a greater variety of mosses than the beech woods. *Atrichum undulatum* and *Thuidium tamariscinum* grow in the damper spots together with several other slightly less common species. *Thamnium alopecurum* appears on chalky soils, while species of *Polytrichum* and *Dicranum* are characteristic of acid soils.

Above: The aptly named feather moss (*Thuidium tamariscinum*) is found throughout Britain in damp areas—in woodland, on rotting trees, and in shady places. It is a bushy plant, the bright green branched stems growing in thick, feathery tufts.

Pines and birches frequently grow together, particularly on acid heathland soils in Scotland and other upland areas. The ground beneath the trees is frequently covered with heather and other shrubs and, if the cover is dense, little else will grow. If the covering is fairly sparse, mosses such as *Hylocomium splendens* and species of *Rhytidiadelphus* are found. In very wet spots, *Sphagnum* and *Polytrichum* may form small areas of Sphagnum bog.

Tree trunk mosses The number and variety of habitats open to any one moss depends on the climate prevailing in the area. On a large scale, the climate is damper in the west of the British Isles than it is in the east, and so mosses tend to be larger and more common in the west where the conditions are more suitable.

On a tree itself, the distribution of mosses is determined by several factors. Mosses seem to grow more luxuriantly on the north side of a tree than on the south side, and the prevailing wind also affects moss growth, most mosses growing better on the lee side of the tree, out of the wind. A leaning tree trunk is an ideal moss habitat because the rainwater accumulates more readily on it than on a vertical tree trunk. However, once the upper surface of the trunk is covered by mosses, then the undersurface becomes quite dry. This is because the mosses themselves are perfectly structured to trap water between the spiralled leaves on their stems. As the mosses grow in cushions, these water-trapping stems are pressed closely together and the whole plant acts like a sponge. Indeed, in upland areas where the soil is thin and rocks protrude through the surface, mosses may provide an alternative medium for seed germination. It has been found that saxifrage seeds, for instance, germinate better in moss cushions than in soil because of the humus that is built up by the moss.

Colonizing mosses The water-trapping ability enables mosses to grow in some unlikely situations. Among sand dunes, mosses such as *Polytrichum piliferum* play an important role in the succession from the shifting, unstable main dunes to the vegetation-covered stable fixed dunes further inland. These mosses colonize the sheltered zone behind the main dunes where they are protected to some extent from the wind. They help to stabilise the sand and trap the water that helps other plants to grow. Lichens may already be present, and grasses and other plants follow, until finally pasture land is formed.

Mosses also play a significant part in other successions of plants, notably in the colonization of rocks and screes and of burned ground. Without mosses and lichens, such areas would be colonized far more slowly and would remain harsh and unsuitable for any other plants to grow for much longer periods of time.

Below: The glossy yellow or brown carpets of *Hylocomium splendens* are found on heaths, moors and sand dunes as well as in woodland. The transparent leaves are carried on red, branched stems.

WOODLAND FERNS

The damp, shady floor of deciduous woodland is an ideal habitat for many ferns. Hard to spot in winter, their fronds uncurl in spring to form a feathery summer carpet.

Woodland ferns die back in the winter, their dead fronds protecting the crown (or growing point) of each plant during the most severe weather. In late spring, the curled young fronds – known as croziers – begin to appear, different species unfurling at different times.

Typical woodland species include the buckler, shield and male ferns, and the delicate lady fern. They are seen at their best in midsummer, when their fronds are fully expanded. Looking rather like large green shuttlecocks, the plants form a feathery carpet on the woodland floor.

It is at this time of year that the contrast is most apparent between the abundance of these ferns in woodland – where they may form a lush, almost tropical, cover – and their scarcity in the surrounding fields and moorland. However, although typical of woods, these ferns are also found in similar, favourable conditions elsewhere – in damp, shady hedgerows for example, or on open, rocky hillsides or even on the coast. Bracken is a marked exception. A very invasive species, it is found not only along woodland edges and in clearings, but also spreading over the surrounding pastureland as well.

Young plantations of conifers or broadleaved trees are rarely carpeted with ferns, the conditions of light and moisture under the tree canopy being more suitable for grasses and other herbs. Mature conifer woods generally have only scanty undergrowth – or none at all – but where the trees are some distance apart, ferns are able to establish themselves.

Growth patterns The fronds of such woodland ferns as the male, scaly male, broad buckler, hard shield and soft shield ferns are arranged in a whorl on an erect stem. The lady fern also has an erect stem which may grow quite tall and look like a miniature tree trunk. It is the native species that comes close to the tropical tree ferns in appearance. In contrast, the stem of the narrow buckler fern is horizontal and only a few fronds arise from it at intervals.

The size and appearance of the fronds can vary considerably between one individual and another within any one species. About 50 varieties of the soft shield fern, 70 of the lady

fern and as many as 150 of the hart's-tongue fern have been identified. The varieties cover a remarkable range of form. The proportions of the pinnae or of the whole frond may be different, for example, and sometimes this produces a very feathery, dissected appearance. The fronds may even be branched and their margins incised or wavy. The lady fern exhibits a particularly striking variation in the colour of the frond stalk, which may be anything from pale green to dark brown, or even a bright reddish-brown.

Names and identification The indusium of a fern is the papery material that normally covers the groups of spore capsules (sori) seen on the underside of fern fronds. Its shape and

Above: Mature broad-leaved woodland can contain an almost tropically rich fern flora. Ferns such as this male fern are seen at their best in mid-summer, when their fronds are fully expanded, giving them the shape of a basket.

Left: The distinctive fronds of the hart's-tongue fern (*Phyllitis scolopendrium*) have striking, long, straight sori on their undersides.

Fern collecting

Many fern species, being very variable in form, were of great interest to the Victorian fern collectors, although several suffered from over-collection. Some 19th century fern books were illustrated by the process of 'nature printing' where fronds coated with ink were pressed on to the page. Large numbers of the delicate fronds were required as each could be used only a few times.

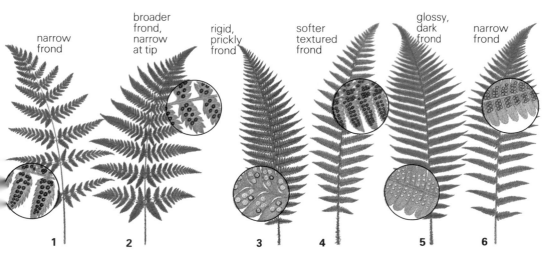

narrow frond

broader frond, narrow at tip

rigid, prickly frond

softer textured frond

glossy, dark frond

narrow frond

1   2   3   4   5   6

Fern identification
1. **Narrow buckler fern** (*Dryopteris carthusiana*).
2. **Broad buckler fern** (*Dryopteris austriaca*).
3. **Hard shield fern** (*Polystichum aculeatum*).
4. **Soft shield fern** (*Polystichum setiferum*).
5. **Scaly male fern** (*Dryopteris affinis*).
6. **Male fern** (*Dryopteris filix-mas*).
The details in circles show the sori on the underside of the fronds.

location is important not only in the classification and identification of ferns, but also in the origin of common names. The indusium's resemblance to a shield in *Polystichum* species has led to the name 'shield ferns', while the buckler ferns are also named from the shield-shaped indusium, a buckler being a small parrying shield. This name has been used as part of the common name for most *Dryopteris* species since about 1860. However, the two largest *Dryopteris* species in the British Isles are known as the male fern and scaly male fern. This allusion to masculinity conveys the way in which their robust appearance contrasts with the relatively delicate lady fern.

Differences in shape and texture are also indicated by common names, as seen, for example, in the soft shield and broad buckler ferns. Both shape and frond texture are reflected in the name of the evergreen hart's-tongue fern. Local folk names are given to ferns in different parts of the country, and so hart's tongue is also known as buttonholes (from the appearance of the young sori), seaweed fern, burntweed, Christ's hair, long leaf, horse-tongue and lamb-tongue.

Fern habitats Although woodland ferns are found throughout the British Isles, they may be locally rare or very abundant. For example, the hard shield fern is generally more common than the soft shield fern, but in the south of England the soft shield fern is the more abundant of the two. The hart's-tongue is less common in parts of Scotland where the winter temperature is very low, and where there is no suitably alkaline substrate for it to grow on. The narrow buckler and the lady fern are found mainly in wetter places.

A rare species of *Dryopteris*, the hay-scented buckler fern (*Dryopteris aemula*), also grows in deciduous woodland. It is distinguished by the scent of hay it exudes when rubbed, and by the frond stalk which is dark brownish-purple at the base and lighter above. Found mainly in the south-east and south-west of England, and in the west of Wales, Scotland and Ireland, it grows only in broad-leaved deciduous woodland where the tree canopy is high enough to keep the level of humidity high.

Above: The lady fern (*Athyrium filix-femina*) takes its name from the delicate appearance of its fronds. Although it can be variable in form, the J-shaped sori on the underside of the leaves are a good identifying feature.

Right: In late spring, the tightly curled young fern fronds start to appear, like these of the male fern. The brown scales protect the young fronds during the winter, before they begin to unfurl.

95

Insects of deciduous woodlands

The insect and other invertebrate life in deciduous habitats occurs in a bewildering array of forms. Every source of organic matter supports some kind of invertebrate, whether in the soil deep below the litter or on the topmost bud. These diminutive animals not only exist in a great diversity of forms; any one species can be extremely numerous. In some years the canopy of a large oak may accommodate about a quarter of a million caterpillars of the winter moth and these, in consort with, for example, green oak moth, mottled umber and spring usher larvae, may emerge from the buds in spring to defoliate their hosts almost entirely. Most deciduous trees defend themselves against such wholesale attack by producing tannins and other toxic compounds which make the leaves harder to digest. Some counter measure is crucial, for leaves are assailed from within and without–they are bitten and chewed by caterpillars and adult weevils, mined by moth, fly and weevil larvae, sucked by bugs and disfigured, sometimes grossly, by gall-forming midges, mites and wasps.

The flowers of most trees are wind pollinated, but some, like the sycamore, maple and lime, are regularly visited by pollinating insects, particularly bees, which therefore provide a valuable service. Much more prolific sources of pollen and nectar, however, are provided by the shrubs and flowering plants lower down, notably honeysuckle and bramble, which some moths and butterflies find especially attractive. Later in the year many insects make a final visit to feed on rotting fruits and tree sap.

Inside the trunk, another community of insects is busy, especially at any vulnerable points of decay. As many as 450 species of insects have been found to thrive in decaying wood. The first invaders are often specialist bark beetles whose 'softening up' process paves the way for woodlice, millipedes, centipedes, spiders, earwigs and flies. Later still, ants, bees and wasps may colonize the labyrinthine interior of the stricken timber.

Many of these invertebrates exist equally well in the leaf litter, the woodland 'basement store' of organic matter. Here earthworms, mites and springtails also abound, breaking down the waste products of everything above them–to the profound benefit of the woodland.

CHECKLIST

This checklist is a guide to the insects and other invertebrates you will find in broadleaved woodland. Although you will not see them all in the same woodland, you should be able to spot many of them as you walk through different woods during the changing seasons. The species listed in **bold print** *are described in detail.*

Apple blossom weevil
Banded snails
Bark beetles (Scolytidae)
Beeflies
Birch leaf roller weevil
Blood beetle
Brimstone butterfly
Brindled beauty moth
Bristletails
Centipedes
Comma butterfly
Dark green fritillary
Early thorn moth
Earthworms
Earwigs
Figwort weevil
Gall wasps
Green oak moth
Hazelnut weevil
High brown fritillary
Holly blue butterfly
Hoverflies
Ladybirds
Leaf beetles (Chrysomelidae)
Longhorn beetles

Millipedes
Mottled umber moth
Orange-tip butterfly
Pearl-bordered fritillary
Proturans
Purple emperor butterfly
Red admiral butterfly
Red oak roller weevil
Red soil mite
Sawflies
Silver-washed fritillary
Small pearl-bordered fritillary
Speckled wood butterfly
Springtails
Spring usher moth
Vapourer moth
Violet ground beetle
Winter gnat
Winter moth
White admiral butterfly
Wolf spiders
Wood ant
Woodlice
Wood wasps
Wood white butterfly

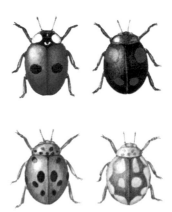

Above: Some of the many ladybirds inhabiting woodland.

Left: A magnificent brimstone butterfly pauses to sip nectar from a hawthorn blossom.

ANIMALS OF THE LEAF LITTER

Leaf litter is a world of living things, a place of dampness and darkness inhabited by a host of insects, arachnids, mites and other animals. Here we look at those dwellers in the debris of the woodland floor that are easily visible.

Above: Female mesh-web spider in her woodland lair. You can often hear the rustling sound this, and other, spiders make as they run over dry leaves. You may be lucky enough to see them, but you will have to look very closely—their brown colouring camouflages them well and protects them from such predators as birds.

Look at the debris on the floor of a well developed piece of mixed deciduous woodland containing oak, hazel and birch, with perhaps a little rowan and sycamore. In such a wood, on a medium loamy soil with reasonable drainage and no waterlogging, and with not too much disturbance, you stand a good chance of finding a rich and fascinating assemblage of animals.

The upper few centimetres of the woodland floor contain the most recently accumulated leaves, most of them still easily identifiable. This is the litter layer. The layer, or horizon, below has much more compacted leaves, bits of which are still recognisable, but most of which are already rotting. This fermenting layer, as it is called, may be several centimetres thick. Under it is a dark brown or blackish horizon—the humus—consisting of fully rotted plant, and some animal, remains. The distinction between the mineral soil and the three organic layers above it is sometimes blurred by plant roots and bits of twigs and stones.

Normally the three layers of the leaf litter harbour most of the visible plant life, but this area is also inhabited by millions of microscopic organisms—bacteria, one-celled animals, plants and fungal threads. These are the living things you cannot see, except with the help of a microscope. Here we describe some of the animals you can see with the naked eye.

Types of leaf litter The soil below leaf litter, and the trees above it, are both important factors in determining what kind of life can live within it. A well drained sandy soil is drier than one with a lot of clay, and is often acid, harbouring little wildlife in or on it. Under Scots pine on heathlands, for example, the needles may take up to nine years to decay because the acidity prevents the rotting agents, chiefly fungi, from doing their job properly. But a chalky soil, on the other hand, favours rapid bacterial action, and a great number of small animals can live in it.

The types of leaves are also important. The needles that drop from most conifers give a rather acid kind of humus, but oak, ash and sycamore leaves produce a much less aci medium. Beech, however, which favours a chalky soil, gives a rather acid humus, especially if it accumulates in large masses. However, if it is mixed with the top layers of soil and contains some chalk, it then forms a moister, better rotted type of humus.

Leaf litter hunters You can usually find a fair number of brown spiders of the Lycosidae family (hunting or wolf spiders) in leaf litter. They do not make webs, instead running down their prey by speed alone. They are often numerous on the floors of drier woodlands, and on warm days can be heard running about over the leaves. Some small web-spinning spiders also make their home in woodland leaf litter.

Only a few species of harvest spiders (harvestmen or Opiliones)–also arachnids–live in litter. *Oligolophus tridens* is one of the commonest and can be recognised by its dark brown body-saddle, sharply cut off at the back. Under the litter and among the humus, close to the earth, are two or three other species–all with the short legs that are an adaptation to the habitat. Harvest spiders are mainly carnivorous and feed on any small creatures they can capture, or on freshly dead bodies and animal droppings.

Multitudinous mites There is normally a vast population of mites in leaf litter. Most are visible to the naked eye, but young ones are extremely small. They live throughout all the organic layers. Many feed on fallen

leaves and plant debris and thus initiate the process of decay. In this they are helped by such animals as springtails. The process is finished by bacteria and fungi, by which time the material has been covered by new leaf fall and is approaching the state of humus. Eventually, chemical plant foods are released from this decayed matter into the mineral soil and taken up again by plant roots. This recycling is vital to the economy and successful functioning of the ecosystem.

Leaf litter insects Only a small number of our insect species are true litter dwellers, but one or two kinds can be very numerous there. Among these are some of the most primitive and least known of all the insects, none of

Above: Red soil mite. Vast populations of these animals live in leaf litter and feed on fallen leaves.

Below: Leaf litter appears everywhere on the woodland floor, even during the summer when the leaf fall from the previous autumn has not yet rotted. You also find it at the bottom of hedgerows, under scrub, and even in the proximity of rivers where it has been brought down as flood debris.

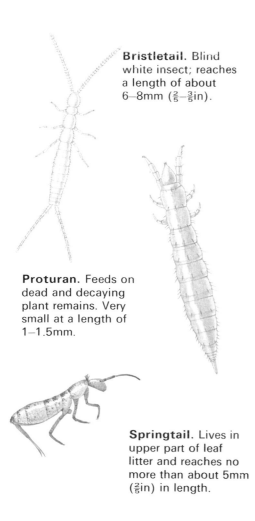

Bristletail. Blind white insect; reaches a length of about 6–8mm ($\frac{2}{5}$–$\frac{3}{5}$in).

Proturan. Feeds on dead and decaying plant remains. Very small at a length of 1–1.5mm.

Springtail. Lives in upper part of leaf litter and reaches no more than about 5mm ($\frac{2}{5}$in) in length.

them having wings or undergoing complete metamorphosis. They are the springtails (Collembola), proturans (Protura), two-pronged bristle-tails (Diplura) and three-pronged bristle-tails (Thysanura).

Springtails, living in the upper part of the leaf litter, are very active insects, rarely more than 5mm (⅖in) long and with grey or yellowish hairy bodies. At the end of its body a springtail bears a forked tail usually held underneath the abdomen by a small hook. When this tail is released and suddenly moved downwards and backwards, the insect springs vigorously forward – hence its common name. Springtails also have long antennae. They eat fallen plant material on the woodland floor.

Proturans are minute, pale, 1-1.5mm long insects that have no antennae. Their forelegs are held upwards and forwards and perform the same sensory functions as the antennae of other insects. The Diplura, or two-pronged bristle-tails, are also small, normally only 6-8mm long. They are white with long antennae but no eyes. The Thysanura, or three-pronged bristle-tails, have long antennae, compound eyes and scaly bodies. These three latter groups are thought to be mostly saprophytic in habit. That is, they feed on dead and decaying plant remains.

Beetles are also found in leaf litter. Some, like the pine weevil, use this habitat as a

Above: Ground beetles such as *Loricera pilicornis* are permanent inhabitants of leaf litter.

Opposite page: Rich, damp leaf litter such as this can house myriads of animals.

Right: Wolf spider *Lycosa lugubris*. These spiders are extremely numerous on the woodland floor.

Below: Longhorn beetle *Rhagium bifasciatum*. The larvae of this beetle feed on wood.

hibernating place, as do some ladybirds. Ground beetles and rove beetles, on the other hand, are permanent residents. Some are carnivorous while others feed on decaying plant remains or on roots and fruits. One of the most conspicuous carnivores is the violet ground beetle which is 22-28mm (about 1in) long and dark violet-black. This insect is also frequently seen in gardens.

Flies, and especially their legless larvae, frequently appear in leaf litter. Most are very small and live in the damper parts, usually in the less acid types of leaf litter. They are an important part of the food of such predators as beetles and centipedes.

Other litter dwellers Woodlice, despite their name, normally have little association with wood; they feed on leaf litter, seedlings, fungi and occasionally dung, and are decomposers helping, along with millipedes and other organisms, to break down dead plant remains.

Millipedes, familiar as long-bodied, many legged creatures, also make their homes in leaf litter. They are exclusively vegetarian and most species probably prefer living to dead plant material. Centipedes, on the other hand, are carnivorous and eat any living creature they can catch. Neither they, nor the woodlice and millipedes, have a waxy layer in their skins as true insects do and so they are liable to dry up. They must therefore remain in fairly moist places, emerging only at night when the air is damper.

WOODLICE: ARMOURED INVERTEBRATES

Since you are most likely to find woodlice in forests with chalky soils, it may come as a surprise to realise that these little animals are crustaceans–related to the crabs and lobsters inhabiting the sea. They are usually out and about at night when conditions are damp and cool.

Woodlice are recognisable by their seven pairs of legs, which are attached to the main part of the body. The head has eyes, a pair of antennae, and mouthparts for biting and chewing. At the rear end of the body is a short section with special limbs used in respiration and (in the male) for sperm transfer during mating.

Woodlice are isopods, which are a major group of crustaceans; in basic structure they resemble marine isopods such as the gribble, which bores into wood, and *Idotea*, which lives among seaweed. Marine isopods are found well back in the fossil record, but terrestrial species appear to be relatively recent (50 million years old!). It is thought

that when they moved on to the land, they lived at first on the seashore, where a number of species still remain, including the sea slater (see illustration).

Eggs in a pouch Woodlice mate when the male mounts the female and transfers sperm using his modified rear limbs. By twisting his body first to one side and then the other, he places sperm in the genital openings on her underside. Once fertilised, the eggs are laid into a brood pouch filled with liquid, forming a false 'floor' under the main part of the body.

In this protected environment the embryos develop and then hatch, but the young remain in the pouch until they are well formed,

Above: *Oniscus asellus*, and two of the lighter coloured *Porcellio scaber*. Woodlice are not actually lice at all; they have many local names, such as tiggy hogs, God's little pigs, and sowbugs.

Protective armour
Some woodlice are flattened with the heavily armoured top surface hiding the legs when looked at from above. Pill bugs are rounded and can roll up into a ball for protection (see below). Other woodlice have long legs and rely on running speed to avoid capture.

resembling miniature adults. In this way woodlice protect the early developing stages of their young from the worst rigours of the terrestrial environment. The number of eggs produced varies between species, and is also related to adult size, ranging from 4-5 in the small species to 300 or more in large adults of the largest species.

It takes between three months and two years for the young to reach maturity—depending on species and locality. Growth takes place during the warmer months of the year only, although woodlice remain active all year round. A few species have only one brood a year, but most manage a second brood in the autumn. Maximum life span is four years (in the common pill bug, *Armadillidium vulgare*) but usually it is no more than two years.

Mixed diet Woodlice eat decaying matter of all kinds, with leaf litter being the staple diet. This is eaten in large quantities, and woodlice in many habitats are key members of the community that breaks down dead plant material and return nutrients to the soil. Fungi, green algae growing on tree trunks, and carrion are consumed as well. Woodlice are unable to absorb all the essential nutrients from their food the first time it passes through their gut, so they eat their own faeces. The bacteria in these breaks down the food sufficiently during its second journey through the digestive system to release the nutrients.

Woodlice even eat each other. Such cannibalism is rare in the wild, but can be seen if woodlice are kept in captivity in large numbers. It is usually moulting or moribund animals which suffer. Woodlice which get into greenhouses can be a nuisance because they eat succulent young seedlings, particularly marrows and cucumbers.

A meal for others Predators of woodlice were once thought to be few, because of the distasteful and sticky fluids that woodlice can discharge from glands along the sides and rear of the body. However, recent research has shown that they are taken in large numbers by centipedes, spiders and beetles; while little owls, toads and shrews

also eat them readily. Any that die from other causes are rapidly scavenged by ants.

Well-developed behaviour Woodlice, unlike insects, do not have a waterproof cuticle and their chief problem on land is water loss. They have largely overcome this by developing a set of behavioural responses that make them instinctively come to rest in damp, dark and confined places. For instance, they move away from light, and they move more slowly the greater the humidity. The intensity of these responses varies with the degree of water stress experienced, and is reversed if an excess of water builds up in the body. Furthermore, response varies on a 24-hour basis, to allow escape from shelter sites at night to find food and mates (conditions in the open at night are generally much more humid than in the day).

Where to find them Woodlice occur almost everywhere in the British Isles and are usually more abundant in forests and ungrazed grassland where there is plenty of leaf litter and shelter. Densities of 500 per square metre are quite common. However, many woodlice require large amounts of calcium to make up the calcium carbonate which strengthens their hard outer surface (exoskeleton). So they are most abundant on calcareous soils. Most species are a good deal less common in the north than elsewhere because of the prevalence of acid soils which they do not like.

Above: *Oniscus asellus* shedding its exoskeleton. Woodlice grow continuously in life and, as with other crustaceans, insects and spiders, they have a hard outer surface (exoskeleton) which they must moult at intervals. They are unique, however, in moulting in two halves: the rear half of the body is shed several days before the front half. This ensures some mobility during this critical time, and so minimises the dangers from predators.

Facts about woodlice

There are currently 46 species of woodlice found in Britain but only 32 are likely to be seen away from greenhouses, and so can be regarded as native. One species, *Metatrich niscoides*, has just been discovered and is unknown outside Britain. Our largest woodlouse, *Ligia oceanica*, is 3cm ($1\frac{1}{4}$in) long, while the smallest, *Trichoniscus pygmaeus*, is 2·5mm ($\frac{1}{10}$in).

Sea slater (*Ligia oceanica*) 25mm (1in) long. Around coasts.

Philoscia muscorum 11mm ($\frac{2}{5}$in) long. Common, in hedgerows, grass, except in N England and Scotland.

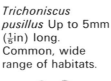

Trichoniscus pusillus Up to 5mm ($\frac{1}{5}$in) long. Common, wide range of habitats.

Oniscus asellus 16mm ($\frac{3}{5}$in) long. Widespread, on damp rotting wood.

Porcellio scaber 17mm ($\frac{3}{4}$in) long. Widespread, in dry places, sand dunes, walls and gardens.

Common pill bug (*Armadillidium vulgare*), 18mm ($\frac{3}{4}$in) long. Widespread.

WEEVILS: A VEGETARIAN LIFE-STYLE

Originally denoting almost any kind of beetle, the name weevil is now used for the 500 species of the family Curculionidae. Many are brightly coloured and all are vegetarians.

Most weevils are recognisable by the fact that the head is well drawn out into an elongated, beak-like snout, at the tip of which are situated tiny jaws. This elongation, called the rostrum, bears a pair of elbowed and somewhat clubbed antennae. In many weevils the antennae can be folded for protection into grooves at the sides of the rostrum.

Weevils are found on many kinds of plants, some being highly specific to their host-plant. According to their way of life, they may be leaf rollers, stem borers or bud eaters, and they may burrow into fruits and roots or just eat parts of the leaves. In fact, there is hardly any part of a plant that some leaf weevil will not eat. Because of this diet it is not surprising that some weevils are notorious pests of crops, and sometimes of stored food as well. Here we describe several species from four of the 26 British sub-families of weevils.

The leaf rollers The red oak roller, one of our larger weevils, is a conspicuous red colour, except for its legs and head which are black. The female is about 6mm ($\frac{1}{4}$in) long, while the male is slightly smaller. This species lives mainly on the foliage of young oaks and is rarely found on mature trees. The conspicuous coloration is a warning, indicating inedibility or the possession of some effective weapon of defence or offence against a potential enemy such as a bird. The female lays her eggs singly on oak leaves, then rolls the leaves up to form protective homes for

Above: The red oak roller (*Attelabus nitens*) is widely distributed in Britain, and can be found from late May onwards. This species is aptly named since the female lays her egg on an oak leaf, then rolls the leaf up to make a secure home—and provide food—for the larva. Like all weevils, this species has a hard, tough outer covering that is a useful protection against predators as well as against excessive loss of moisture.

the larvae.

The birch leaf roller is related to the red oak roller, but is rather smaller and of a shining dark bluish-black colour. This weevil has much the same shape as its relative, but is only 3-5mm long. Looked at with a hand lens the thorax of the birch leaf roller is decidedly hairy; the male can be distinguished by his puffed out black femora (the long leg joint nearest the body).

Like the red oak roller, the birch leaf roller is occasionally found on other trees—beech, hazel, hornbeam and alder for example. But it is essentially an inhabitant of birch woods and it, too, rolls up leaves to house its larvae. It is widely distributed and quite common in the British Isles.

A related, but larger and hairier, weevil also occurs chiefly on birch. It is called *Byctiscus betulae* and it can be a dark metallic blue, green, or shining red-brown in colour. This weevil is much more local than the other two and is commonest in the south of England. Although it is unlikely to be confused with the birch leaf roller, it can be precisely identified because the male has a small, forward-projecting spike on each side of its thorax. *Byctiscus* is also a leaf roller.

Figwort weevils There are seven species of weevils of the genus *Cionus*, all of them square in shape with a rather long rostrum on which the antennae are set well forward. The legs are short and stout, giving these weevils a

Rolling a home

The female red oak roller lays a single egg on the upper side of the midrib of a young leaf. She cuts a slit in the leaf from each side to the midrib and rolls the cut portions into a kind of tunnel, rather like a rolled up carpet. She then bites a little way into the stalk at the base of the leaf, which partly cuts off the leaf's supply of water and nutrients, causing it to turn brown. In time the leaf withers and drops off, but not before the larva has eaten the inner part of the leaf roll and turned into a pupa.

rolled oak leaf containing egg

cross-section of leaf roll

larva

ompact appearance.

Cionus scrophulariae is closely associated with common figwort, water figwort and the related common mullein. It is widespread over much of Britain. Its most distinctive feature the light colour of its thorax, which is covered with whitish or pale yellow scales. There are also a number of square black spots on its grey wing cases, the central ones being larger than the others. The antennae are reddish with darker clubbed ends, and the legs are black with brown tips. This weevil is 4.5mm long and one of the largest in the genus. The thorax of the closely related *C. tuberculosus* is much the same colour as its wing cases (not lighter). This species occurs on the same food plants as *C. scrophulariae* but is much rarer.

Cionus weevils feed on the leaves of their food plants, and a number of them are usually found together. The larva is a greyish, slug-like creature, heavily coated with slime, which produces from a gland near the end of its body. This slime undoubtedly helps to protect the otherwise rather vulnerable grub from bird predation, and especially from drying up. It is also used to form a tough cocoon, which is firmly attached to the food plant.

Inside the cocoon the pupa is well protected for the short period of a week during which it undergoes the transformation into an adult beetle, although it may be attacked by tiny parasitic wasps. The fully formed adult bites its way out, making a neat circular hole at one end of the cocoon. Ultimately it goes into hibernation at the base of a tuft of grass or among leaf litter in a hedgerow.

Fruit tree pests The apple blossom weevil is one of the best known members of its family. It is widespread in England and Wales and often very common where apples are grown. It is much rarer in Scotland and Ireland. The apple blossom weevil is a dark ashy red colour, with two broad oblique greyish stripes towards the end of each wing case—the two stripes together forming a somewhat flattened V shape.

Apple blossom weevils come out in spring from behind loose bark, leaf debris and other sheltered spots where they have hibernated. They live almost exclusively by feeding on young apple leaves, in which they make small holes. Occasionally they attack the leaves of pear trees.

The female bores a hole into an unopened blossom bud with her long rostrum, then turns round and deposits an egg into the hole. Each female lays about 50 eggs. Soon a pale grub with a dark brown head hatches and eats its way into the bud, gradually destroying it so that it turns brown and never opens. The grub then eats away the base of the flower and after about two weeks is fully grown and ready to turn into a white pupa. As with many weevils, the pupal stage is short; it takes only seven to ten days before the adult

Above: *Byctiscus betulae* is a leaf-rolling weevil that can be found on hazel and poplar as well as birch.

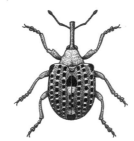

Above: *Cionus scrophulariae* can be found on figwort and is 4-4. 5mm long. It is common throughout Britain.

Above: The apple blossom weevil (*Anthonomus pomorum*) is widespread in England and Wales and is 3-4mm long.

bites its way out and starts to feed on the leaves. At this stage in its life the young adult does not make holes in the leaves but rasps at their tissues, skeletonizing them with its tiny jaws. This takes place mostly during the hours of darkness.

After about a month the weevil disappears to hibernate, emerging again the following spring to feed on the leaves, this time making the familiar round holes.

Birds, especially the tits, are important predators on apple blossom weevils. The ichneumon wasp *Pimpla pomorum* parasitises both the larvae and the pupae, but the proportion of parasites is never enough to make a really big difference in a concentrated population of weevils in an orchard. After all, it is not in the parasite's interests to destroy its host. Modern control of the apple blossom weevil is effected by careful spraying with one of the organophosphorus compounds.

Above: A figwort weevil (*Cionus hortulanus*) sitting on a figwort bud. If you examine the flower heads of common and water figwort (and the related common mullein as well) in summer you will probably be surprised to find that some of the 'seed boxes' fall off easily in the palm of your hand. Pause a moment and one may expand into six legs, a rostrum and a pair of antennae and start to crawl away. It is one of the compact-looking adult figwort beetles, which are decidedly like the figwort seed boxes in appearance.

Left: This rolled up birch leaf probably contains the larva of the birch leaf roller weevil (*Deporaus betulae*, or *Rhynchites betulae* as it used to be called).

NUT-BORING WEEVILS

If you look at acorns and hazel nuts in autumn you may find some with a small round hole bored in the shell. This is the work of weevils whose larvae live inside the shells and feed on the kernels.

The weevil, or Curculionidae, family has the distinction of being the largest in the animal kingdom; in the British Isles alone there are over 500 species of weevils. These insects are beetles (belonging to the order Coleoptera) and most are characterised by a long protruding snout (rostrum) and clubbed, 'elbowed' antennae. The majority are covered in fine scales, and all are vegetarians – both as adults and larvae. The long snout, with the mouthparts (mandibles) situated at the tip, is used for boring or piercing into plant tissue, especially stems, fruits and flowers, and for feeding on leaves.

Weevil antennae, situated about half-way along the snout, have a long first segment – the scape – which the insect can fold back into channels or grooves – the scrobe – on the sides of the snout. In the species described here – members of the genus *Curculio* – the sexes can be distinguished by the length of the snout: the female's snout is longer than the entire rest of her body and curves downwards, while that of the male is straight and shorter than his body.

Four nut-boring weevils The hazel nut weevil (*Curculio nucum*) has rusty coloured legs and antennae and a black upperside flecked with yellow-brown scales. The adults, out and about in May and June, feed on hawthorn flowers and are locally common in woodland and hedgerows in England and Scotland. This species lays its eggs in young hazel nuts.

Three other members of the genus *Curculio* lay their eggs in acorns. *Curculio villosus*, a black weevil with a red scape, frequents England and parts of Scotland and is about 4mm ($\frac{1}{6}$in) long with grey, hair-like scales. *C. venosus* is very similar to *C. nucum* in appearance, but is exclusively English, being found no further north than Nottinghamshire. Another English species, *C. glandium*, a rusty or brownish coloured weevil 4·5mm ($\frac{1}{5}$in) long, is found in counties south of Derbyshire.

Nursery nuts In early summer the female hazel nut weevil seeks out a hazel tree and finds a young green nut. She bores deep into the soft shell with her snout, then deposits a single egg into the hole.

The larva that hatches within the nut is a stout, limbless grub that is white or yellowish-white with a darker head. It spends the summer feeding on the nut kernel, moulting several times in order to increase in size. At this stage you cannot deduce the presence of the weevil larva in the nut because the small round hole bored in the shell by the female has healed.

In the autumn the nut falls to the ground and the larva gnaws its way out of the shell, leaving a neat round hole, and burrows into the soil to pupate. It stays in the safety of the soil throughout the winter, emerging in spring as a fully-formed adult (imago).

Above: *Curculio venosus* on an oak leaf. This species is about 7mm ($\frac{1}{4}$in) in length. The female lays her eggs inside acorns and the larvae that hatch have a ready-made store of food at their disposal.

Below: The female hazel nut weevil (*Curculio nucum*) (left) uses her long, narrow snout to bore a hole in a young hazel nut. Her larva feeds inside the nut (right) until the autumn, reaching a length of about 10mm ($\frac{1}{3}$in).

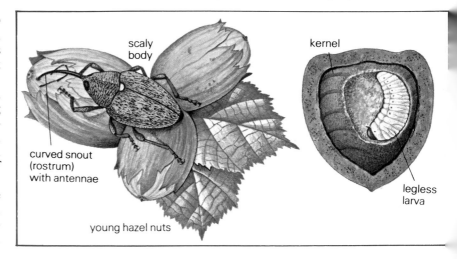

scaly body

curved snout (rostrum) with antennae

young hazel nuts

kernel

legless larva

HOVERFLIES: INSECT MIMICS

As their name suggests, hoverflies are expert at hovering and can often be seen poised over flowers or high up in a woodland glade. They are remarkable for their mimicry of bees and wasps—a mimicry that goes much further than mere similarity of colouring.

Above: Hoverflies are attracted to flowers and are important insect pollinators. Feeding on the pollen and nectar of this dandelion are two species, *Syrphus ribesii* (centre left) and *Episyrphus balteatus* (all others). As these insects hover their wings vibrate with extreme rapidity— perhaps 300 times per second or more. The males of some species seem to have a territorial instinct and make rapid darts at other males intruding on their air space.

Hoverflies are among the commonest and most familiar of the many flies you can see in garden and countryside. There are more than 200 species in Britain. Like all true flies (Diptera), they have only one pair of wings, the hind pair being greatly modified into small knobbed balancing organs (halteres).

Marvellous mimicry Many hoverflies are banded with yellow on a blackish or metallic background—colouring that gives them a superficial resemblance to wasps or bees. Some look extremely realistic, adopting even more of the appearance of wasps and bees. For instance, the wings of some have a dark front margin, suggesting the rolled wings of the common wasp; others have longer anten-nae than is usual in flies, again in imitation of bees and wasps; and most make a realistically bee-like buzzing sound if trapped.

Although such mimicry is widespread in insects, it seems to be particularly well developed in hoverflies. In their association with flowers—where they can easily be seen by birds and other predators—such a resemblance may give them a selective advantage. Predators will avoid the harmless hoverflies in much the same way that they avoid the stinging insects. The larvae of hoverflies, which do not have such mimicking colouring, are preyed on by birds and parasitised by ichneumon and other parasitic wasps.

A life-cycle centred on aphids A large group of hoverflies produce larvae that feed on aphids and are important in keeping down the numbers of these destructive insects. Some of this group are common garden insects, most of them blackish with yellowish bands or paired crescents (lunules) on their bodies. One of the best known is *Syrphus ribesii*; it is one of the larger species, at 12mm ($\frac{1}{2}$in) long and with a wingspan of 25mm (1in). Its abdomen is dark, with three orange-yellow bands and two crescents at the base. You can frequently see it sitting on flower heads or hovering near flowers in sunny weather from April to November.

S. ribesii, and its many allies, feeds at flowers; the females need to include pollen as well as nectar in their diet if their eggs are to

black hoverfly with creamy lunules on its abdomen, have successive generations throughout the year, and hibernate as adult flies in old trees, out-houses and similar sheltered places. In this case, however, only mated females hibernate; the males, their purpose accomplished, die. The females feed up in the autumn and fill their crops with nectar, increasing their body weight by as much as 50%. They are the first on the scene when aphid activity begins in the spring.

Another species, *Episyrphus balteatus*, a narrower insect with double bands on its abdomen, also overwinters as an adult fly. It is one of the species that regularly migrates, presumably to seek out fresh breeding sites. It is frequently found in huge numbers in coastal districts, suggesting that it has come from the Continent. It has even been found 25km (15½ miles) out to sea. Sometimes this species appears in unusually large numbers in gardens, but within a day or two they all disappear.

Nest invading hoverflies It is not only the aphid-feeding species that have a marked

develop. Males wait on projecting parts of plants for females to pass, then fly in pursuit. Mating usually takes place on vegetation. Females lay their eggs singly or in groups of two or three on plants infested with aphids. They are attracted to the aphids by odour and hover over the aphid colonies for a short time before landing to deposit their eggs. Each female may lay 100 eggs a day, with a total of perhaps as many as a thousand. The eggs, less than 1mm long, are white and hatch in three to four days.

The minute white larvae immediately start to feed, plunging their hook-like mouthparts into the bodies of the unfortunate aphids and sucking out their soft body contents. There are three larval stages, with moults in between – in all a 10-day growth period in which a single larva may consume over 800 aphids. The aphids make no attempt to escape, although the ants that attend the aphids to collect their honeydew often try to protect them. The *Syrphus* larva responds to this by exuding a protective slime which deters the ants.

When full-grown, the larva attaches itself by its hind end to a leaf or twig, and, as with all more advanced flies, turns into a pupa within its last larval skin, which becomes a hard, pear-shaped, brownish case. After a further 10 days or so, the adult fly emerges by splitting the upper side of the case or puparium.

Several generations of *S. ribesii* follow one another in this way, until autumn. At this time of year fully grown larvae seek out hiding places in the soil where they can pass the winter. They do not become pupae until March or April.

Overwintering and migration Other species, for example *Scaeva pyrastri*, a common blue-

Above: Hoverfly *Episyrphus balteatus*. This species overwinters as an adult fly.

Right: *Syrphus* larva feeding on an aphid. The larva pierces the aphid with its mouth hooks and quickly lifts it up, resting it in a hollow made by drawing the two front larval segments into the rest of the body. When moving about the larva, lacking eyes, waves its head from side to side in search of prey. It moves in a series of rippling undulations (like all Dipterous larvae, it is legless). The larva, pale orange-yellow in colour and rather slug-like, is 20mm (¾in) long when full grown.

Below: *Volucella pellucens*, one of five fairly large species belonging to the genus *Volucella*.

Left: The hoverfly *Scaeva pyrastri*. Mated females hibernate in winter in sheltered places such as old barns, outhouses or holes in trees, and are first on the scene when aphids begin hatching in spring.

Microdon eggeri (below left) is a hoverfly that shows quite a close resemblance to the honeybee *Apis mellifera* (above), especially in its antennae which are longer than is usual among flies. It is not a very common species.

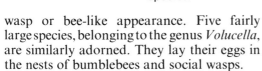

wasp or bee-like appearance. Five fairly large species, belonging to the genus *Volucella*, are similarly adorned. They lay their eggs in the nests of bumblebees and social wasps.

Volucella bombylans is a large hairy fly, 14mm ($\frac{1}{2}$in) long, with a wingspan of 3cm (1$\frac{1}{4}$in). It occurs in two forms, one with hairy yellow bands like a yellow-banded bumblebee, the other black with a red tail like the bumblebee *Bombus lapidarius*. The larvae of this species hatch from eggs laid in bumblebee nests where they act as scavengers, feeding on dead bees, dead larvae and any other rubbish.

The other species of *Volucella* are less hairy and scavenge in the nests of social wasps. The adults enter wasps' nests unmolested and lay their eggs on the paper envelopes. The commonest wasp nest-dwelling species is *V. pellucens*, which has a conspicuous whitish base to its abdomen. The young larvae that hatch from its eggs mostly fall to the midden below the nest. Here dead wasps and larvae, and any other rubbish that has accumulated, form their staple diet. Some manage to penetrate into the nest, squeezing into the paper cells with the wasp larvae, on whose secretions and excretions they feed. Late in the season the *Volucella* larvae penetrate the nest more fully and eat living wasp larvae and pupae.

In the autumn, the *Volucella* larvae become full grown, reaching a length of about 20mm ($\frac{3}{4}$in); they are broadly oval in shape and covered with spines. They become dormant and hibernate as larvae, either in the remains of the nest, or in soil nearby. They change to pupae in the following May and June and emerge as flies in July and August.

Ant 'guests' Other hoverflies, of the genus *Microdon*, show quite a close resemblance to the honeybee. They occur particularly in

old woodlands and in the heathlands of Surrey, Sussex and the New Forest. The two commonest species are *Microdon eggeri* and *M. mutabilis*; both are about 9mm ($\frac{1}{3}$in) long.

Microdon hoverflies are on the wing in June, flying low over the ground and around rotten tree stumps containing ants' nests, particularly those of the common black garden ant *Lasius niger*. The flies investigate holes in the stumps and eventually choose those suitable for laying eggs. The eggs hatch after 12 days and the larvae move actively into the ants' nests, where they become slug-like in shape and movement. The larvae seem to be present in fairly large numbers in the chambers where the ants are most numerous.

The larvae are ignored by the ants. They appear to feed mostly on the pellets of discarded food that the ants eject from a special pouch in their mouths. When fully grown the larvae travel to the upper and drier parts of the nest, where they remain until the spring. They change to pupae in April or May.

Volucella hoverflies, such as *V. bombylans* (above, and the mating pair below) are able to enter the nests of dangerous wasps and bees unharmed; their larvae also roam about the nests without being attacked. Experiments made by the French naturalist J. H. Fabre have shown that other hoverflies much more wasp-like in appearance, and also other social wasps, that he put into a wasps' nest were killed at once. Equally, *Volucella* larvae were not molested but other larvae were killed. Since all this happens in the dark below ground, it suggests that wasp-like coloration does not confer protection against wasps, although it may well deter vertebrate predators.

WOODLAND GLADE BUTTERFLIES

Although large and often vividly coloured, some woodland butterflies can be difficult to spot among the trees in which they live, but late summer flowers, and even the rotting fruits of autumn, may attract them down to feed.

Above: Recent research has shown that the delicate adult wood whites (*Leptidea sinapis*) live for only a week on average, although some individuals survive for up to a month. During their short lifetime the females lay 30-60 eggs, a large percentage of which are eaten by predators before they hatch. Although several types of larval food plant are used, the female butterflies prefer to lay their eggs on meadow vetchling, bitter vetch and bird's-foot trefoil.

An ideal butterfly wood is one with a mixture of open glades and mature trees, interspersed with sunny rides. Our ancient woods were of this type, with sunny glades and luxuriant undergrowth, and dominated by oak—a tree seldom planted today because it thrives only on deep, rich soils.

However, our current practice of planting woodland remnants with economically sensible, but alien, conifers is accelerating the loss of ancient woodland. Once the conifers have matured, the number of butterfly species to be found in these woods fall dramatically.

Although at least 20 of our native butterflies are associated with woodlands, four species—the purple emperor, white admiral, wood white, and comma—can be considered as true woodland butterflies.

The comma butterfly This is perhaps the odd one out among the four species as it is frequently found in gardens. It is, however, still considered to be a true woodland species, females preferring to lay their ribbed eggs on nettles in woodland clearings. Other larva food plants include wych and common elm hops and redcurrant.

Comma caterpillars resemble bird droppings, having black and white markings, the arrangement and shape of which change at each moult and help them to deceive vertebrate predators. When full-grown, the caterpillar selects a sturdy leaf and spins a pad of silk from which the chrysalis is suspended. This is brown, with small gold specks and blotches, and irregular in shape, like a dead leaf.

Eggs laid in April and May produce a generation of butterflies in July, which may include a number of specimens with pale undersides. This variety is called *hutchinson* and its colouring is thought to be genetically controlled. When the July brood lays its eggs the generation of butterflies produced from them in August and September are all normal comma butterflies.

In the autumn, the adults feed on the nectar of thistles and ragwort flowers before they go into hibernation for the winter.

Unique white butterfly The wood white

unique among British whites in being our only representative of the sub-family Dismorphiinae, an almost exclusively South American group. This delicate white butterfly can be recognised instantly by its slow, bobbing, fluttery flight. Both sexes have a black tip on each forewing, although this is rather paler in the females.

Female wood whites prefer to lay their eggs on vetches and bird's-foot trefoil in shady woodland rides. The caterpillars are green and blend in perfectly with the colour of their food plants, making them very difficult to find. They mature quickly and form chrysalids on the growing plant, in which they normally overwinter. Thus the wood white may spend up to 10 months of the year as a chrysalis, although in certain years two generations are produced – the normal one in May to June and a further brood in July to August.

Graceful white admiral Although strikingly black in colour on its upper wings, with white transverse bands, the white admiral is not as conspicuous as one might expect. The contrasting colours break up the outline of the wing, camouflaging it in the dappled light of the woodland.

A graceful butterfly, flying with a strong but elegant gliding motion, it feeds on bramble blossom and honeydew. The females lay eggs singly on wisps of honeysuckle growing in dense woodland.

The first two caterpillar stages feed in a very characteristic way, spinning a pad of silk along the main vein of a leaf and eating either side of this pad, camouflaged by their own droppings mixed with silk. As autumn approaches, the caterpillar forms a tent of leaf tissue called a hibernaculum. Before settling down in it for the winter, it secures the leaf to the honeysuckle stem with silk, so that it does not fall off with the other leaves.

The caterpillar awakes in spring and after a brief spell of feeding it moults to reveal a spectacular, spiny green skin. Eventually, it forms a green and gold chrysalis. Unfortunately, both the large caterpillars and chrysalids are eaten by birds and attacked by parasitoids, and many of them never reach the adult stage.

White admiral
(Limenitis camilla)
wingspan
6.5cm (2 1/2in)

Purple emperor
(Apatura iris)
wingspan 7.5cm (3in)

Comma *(Polygonia c-album)*
wingspan 5.5cm (2 1/5in)

Right: When the purple emperor caterpillar hibernates in the fork of sallow branches during the winter it is camouflaged perfectly, changing colour to match its surroundings.

Below: The comma butterfly takes its name from the white comma mark on the underside of its wings. The shape and sombre colour of the wings help the comma to resemble a dead leaf. This protects it during its winter hibernation among ivy.

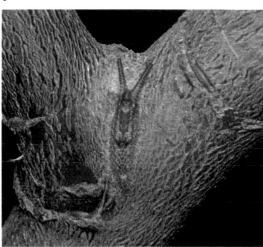

Life-cycle of the purple emperor

After its first moult, the small green caterpillar of the purple emperor resembles a velvety green slug, with prominent horns. It is well camouflaged on the sallow leaves where it feeds. In November, it hibernates in a fork on the sallow branches, moulting the following June to form a pale green chrysalis which resembles a leaf shoot. The adult butterfly is on the wing from mid-July.

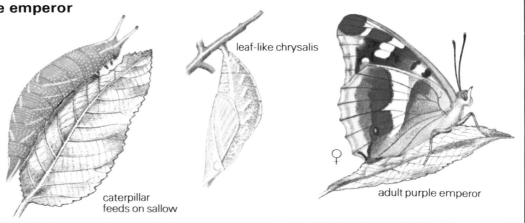

caterpillar
feeds on sallow

leaf-like chrysalis

adult purple emperor

Majestic purple emperor One of the earliest species to be recognised in the 17th century, the purple emperor was once known as the Emperor-of Morocco. The wings of the males have a rich purple-blue sheen which can only be seen from certain angles.

Female purple emperors are rarely seen for they spend virtually all their lives at tree-top level, particularly around oak trees. They come down only to lay their eggs singly on the upper side of sallow leaves. Males also spend much of their time in the tree tops, chasing off other males that approach their territory, although they sometimes come down to woodland rides to drink at puddles or feed on carrion or dung.

Fluctuating numbers All four species are linked by a common feature: they have all undergone dramatic changes in distribution over the past century. The best known case is that of the comma butterfly which, after occurring over most of southern England in the late 19th century, became restricted to the Wye valley in the early 1900s. Since then, it has gradually returned to its old localities and is now found as far north as Wales.

The most likely explanation for such fluctuation in numbers is a change in climate in the early part of this century. It appears that, in the early part of the 20th century, summer temperatures were cooler than average and corresponded with a period in which the range of these species contracted. When the weather is cool, caterpillars take longer to grow and are therefore vulnerable to predators for a longer period. Also, adult butterflies are relatively inactive in cool conditions and die before they have laid their full complement of eggs.

After this period of decline in the early 1900s, all four species mentioned above underwent a dramatic increase in numbers. This coincided with a series of warmer-than-average summers in the 1930s.

Unhappily, population numbers are now falling again and with the decline of suitable woodland, we can only hope that by the time these species recover and begin to spread again, enough of their habitats will be left to support them.

Above: The chrysalis of the white admiral is an unusual combination of green and gold. The gold, or occasionally silver, markings are believed to mimic drops of rain on the chrysalis, which resembles a withered leaf. If the chrysalis is disturbed by a bird, it is capable of violent wriggling movements.

Below: White admirals are commonly seen feeding on sunlit patches of bramble blossom along woodland rides.

What do butterflies eat?

Nectar is the food of many butterflies, but in woodland many flowers bloom in the spring before the tree cover shades them out—too early to provide a source of food. Such woodland species as the comma (below) and peacock feed on rotting fruit in the autumn, while other species rely on the honeydew which coats tree leaves in the summer. Apart from honeydew and bramble blossom, the white admiral has an unusual choice of food—cuckoo spit, which is rich in sugars and amino acids. The male purple emperor has rather unsavoury feeding habits—he visits muddy puddles, carrion, urine and dung for essential minerals.

SUMMER WOODLAND FRITILLARIES

Our five orange and brown-winged fritillary butterflies are insects of spring and high summer. It's easy to recognise a fritillary, but another matter to tell which is which.

All fritillary butterflies share a characteristic wing pattern: the upper surface is an intricate mixture of dark markings on a lighter background. The pattern, but not the colour, is similar to the snake's head fritillary flower after which the butterflies were named. Fritillary butterflies are insects of high summer and frequent sunlit woodlands.

It is easy enough to recognise a butterfly as a fritillary, but telling one species from another is more difficult. The best distinguishing features are size and the details of the underwing markings.

The five most widespread and common fritillaries in the British Isles feed, in their caterpillar stage, on the leaves of violets. The violet-feeding species are all members of one sub-family, Argynninae, and can be distinguished from other fritillaries by the warm, orange-brown ground colour of their wings. (The other species are darker brown with lighter brown markings.) You can also tell that a butterfly is one of the violet-feeding fritillaries by the silver marks on the

Above: A silver-washed fritillary of the variety *valesina*. This is a genetic form which occurs only in the female insect. It is found in the New Forest. The ground colour of the upper wings is silvery grey.

Pearl-bordered

Small pearl-bordered

Silver-washed

The spiny caterpillars of the five fritillary butterflies described here all feed on the leaves of violet plants, and come out of hibernation or hatch in spring when the new violet leaves are tender and succulent.

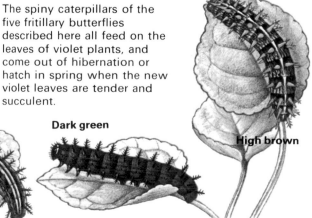

Dark green

High brown

underside of its wings.

Sight and scent The five violet-feeding species never interbreed with each other, so the butterflies must have ways of telling each other apart that do not involve looking at the underside of the wings. (When the butterflies are active the wings are open.) Sight, including colour vision, plays some part in this recognition process. Fritillaries always divert from their flight path to investigate another fritillary sunning itself on a flower, so experimenters in an Oxfordshire wood cut out paper models of pearl-bordered fritillaries on flowers. All the models had the correct wing pattern but only some of them had the right colour. Only those with the right colour (or a colour close to the natural one) got many visits from passing butterflies. These experiments showed that sight enables one butterfly to spot another from a distance and to identify it as a fritillary.

The males have special scent glands on their wings and it seems that at closer quarters scent is more important than sight. The females can identify the scent of the males of their own species and so find a suitable partner.

Hibernating caterpillars Only one generation of fritillaries is produced each year, and most species overwinter in the caterpillar stage in a shrivelled violet leaf. They wake up and begin feeding as soon as the violet leaves start growing in the spring.

The smaller fritillaries fly in spring and summer – the pearl-bordered in May and June and the small pearl-bordered in June and July. Both species frequent woodland with open rides where flowers such as bugle and thistles grow. The butterflies visit these for nectar.

You can often find the small pearl-bordered fritillary in the wetter parts of woods, and also in marshy areas away from woodlands. It does not occur in Ireland, while the pearl-bordered is found there only in County Clare, on the limestone pavements of the Burren. This is the only area where this species lives away from woodland.

Both these species of butterfly lay their

Silver-washed

Argynnis paphia is the largest species of fritillary, with a wingspan of 5.4-7cm (2-2¾in). The greenish-coloured undersides of the hind wings have silver markings running across them which look like a wash of silver. The other species have clearly defined silver spots on the underwings. There are several colour varieties of silver-washed fritillary, some darker than the ones shown here.

Above: The egg of a silver-washed fritillary. Other species lay their eggs on the leaves or stems of violets. The egg hatches in August and the caterpillar immediately goes into hibernation until spring.

Dark green

Argynnis aglaia and the high brown fritillary are almost identical when seen with their wings open. The dark green has a wingspan of 4.8-6cm (1¾-2⅓in). The distinguishing feature of the dark green, on the under-surface of the hindwing, is that there are no silver-centred red spots between the outer series and the big silver spots near the centre This under-surface is also greenish tinged.

High brown

Argynnis cydippe has a wingspan of 5-6·2cm (1¾-2½in). In contrast to the dark green fritillary, this species has a few small red, silver-centred spots on the under-surface of the hindwing between the silver wing border and the central spots. Like other fritillaries, it is most active on sunny days; it roosts in the top of tall trees on cloudy days, where it is well hidden among the leaves.

eggs on the leaves of violet plants. The eggs hatch in 10-14 days, and the caterpillars start feeding and growing immediately. They grow and moult their skins three times within five or six weeks. Each caterpillar then finds a shrivelled leaf at the base of the plant in which to pass the coming winter. Most pearl-bordered caterpillars begin hibernation at the end of July. In the following March the caterpillars, which have shrunk to half their size during hibernation, start feeding and growing again. They moult one more time as a caterpillar, then reach full size and pupate. The chrysalis stage lasts only 10-14 days.

The larger fritillaries fly in July and August, much later than the smaller ones. They are attracted especially to the flowers of bramble and thistles. The silver-washed and high brown are strictly woodland and wood-edge butterflies, and are most common in the south and west of England. The high brown does not occur in Ireland, and neither species breeds in Scotland. The dark green fritillary some-times flies in woodland, but is just as much at home in open areas such as cliff-tops or sand dunes where violets grow among the grass. It is much more widespread than the other large fritillaries.

All these three larger species of fritillary have life cycles that ensure that the young caterpillars, which do not feed at all before winter, are ready to start feeding as early as

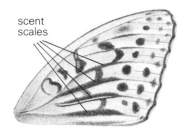

scent scales

Above: The upper side of the fore wing of a male silver-washed fritillary (*Argynnis paphia*) showing the scent scales (sex brands) that run along veins one to four. The scent from these scales attracts females and enables them to identify partners of their own species. The scales occur in other fritillary butterflies, but are particularly noticeable on the male silver-washed. Females never have scent scales. (Lepidopterists—butterfly specialists—number the veins in a butterfly's wing from the bottom to the top; the veins in the wings of other insects are usually numbered from the top to the bottom.)

possible in spring. But the way they survive the winter is different in each species.

The high brown lays its eggs low down on the stems of violets, but although the young caterpillar develops quickly within the egg, it does not eat its way out of the egg-shell until spring. The dark green fritillary lays its eggs a little higher up on the plant, on the leaves or stems. The young caterpillars hatch in just over two weeks, but they do not start to feed; they crawl down to the bottom of the plant and hibernate in a shrivelled leaf.

Strangest of all is the silver-washed fritillary. It is one of the few species of butterfly that does not lay its eggs on its caterpillar's foodplant. The female butterfly does find a good clump of violets—but then she lays her eggs on a nearby tree-trunk, sometimes as much as 60-90cm (2-3ft) above ground. The caterpillars hatch in early autumn but then hibernate in a crevice in the bark. In spring they have to make the long walk to the ground in search of violet plants. This is a long journey for a caterpillar only 2·5mm ($\frac{1}{10}$in) long which has lived for nine months with nothing to eat apart from the top of its egg-shell which it eats when it hatches.

Distribution All five species of violet-feeding fritillary are quite common in some years in the south and west of England. They often decline in numbers, and may then increase again. Even before World War I, entomologists were writing gloomily about

the declining numbers of fritillaries, and the situation has worsened since then.

In part, these declines may be natural—the fritillaries are at the edge of their range in Britain (they are more common further south in Europe), and a hard winter may kill many caterpillars, or a cold summer may prevent the butterflies laying all their eggs. Also parasitic wasps attack the caterpillars.

The usual pattern is that in good years the butterflies spread out and colonize the woods from which they had previously disappeared. Unfortunately, this does not always happen today because of the fragmentation of habitats by man. In dairy farming areas there are still flower filled fields and hedgerows along which fritillaries can fly when dispersing to new woods; but in the cereal-growing east of England fritillaries have almost disappeared. The few remaining woods in eastern England often have a very sharp boundary at a ploughed field, with little in the way of brambles and thistles at the edge, and the next wood may be a long way off across a flowerless barley field. Inside the woods, lack of coppicing and overgrown rides reduce the flowers for the butterflies.

One hopeful sign is that fritillaries seem to thrive in Forestry Commission conifer plantations. The wide, flower-filled rides are just what the butterflies require and, if the plantation was previously a deciduous wood, there are usually plenty of violets.

Small pearl-bordered

Boloria selene has a wingspan of 3·6-4·2cm (1½in). Across the middle of the underside of the hindwings there is a row of light-coloured spots; in this species they are all the same colour—usually all silver, but sometimes all yellow. There is some variation in the colour of the upper wings but the underside coloration is usually constant.

Pearl-bordered

Boloria euphrosyne is a little larger than the small pearl-bordered fritillary, with a wingspan of 3·8-4·6cm (1½-1¾in). Like the small pearl-bordered, this species has a row of spots across the middle of the underside of the hindwing; these spots are all yellow except for the middle one of the row which is a clear silver. The female has darker markings and more rounded wings than the male.

Birds of deciduous woodlands

The towering multi-layered structure of our woodland provides, in compact form, all the essential requirements of bird life–places to roost, nest and feed. Correspondingly, woods cater for a wide diversity of birds compared with more open, less structured habitats. The most densely populated zone is the shrub layer, the abundant insect life of which attracts tits, wrens and warblers in the summer. Some visit the high canopy which likewise harbours a rich store of caterpillars and aphids. The trunks and heavier limbs between these zones are the haunt of woodpeckers, nuthatches and treecreepers, while on the ground thrushes, robins, finches and jays rummage for fruits and invertebrates among the leaf litter.

Birds can often signal rather conspicuously the differences in woodland types. Redstarts, pied flycatchers and wood warblers, for instance, are quite common in the sessile oakwoods in western Britain, but are scarce or absent in the pedunculate oakwoods farther east. On a more local scale we can, with the passage of time, readily detect dramatic changes in the composition of birds in a given deciduous wood. Not least of these is the change wrought by the seasonal cycle of leaf production. Leaf emergence in spring is associated with a sudden and enormous increase in the insect food available, and a great influx of migrants, notably warblers, arrive from their African and Mediterranean winter quarters to swell the ranks.

At this time deciduous woods ring with bird song, the beauty of which, however, belies the earnest endeavour of the songsters to stake out territories, ward off rivals and attract mates. The bulk of the birds' efforts are concentrated in the dawn hours, often spearheaded before sunrise by the songs of the dunnock and robin. Many woodland specialists, such as the jay and redstart, sport a bright flash of colour, the better to spot one another in the dim light.

By June the summer flush of insects is at its peak, supporting a new generation of fledglings. Thereafter, breeding activity wanes and high summer finds woodlands silent. The insectivorous migrants drift south again, almost overlapping with a new wave of immigrants–redwings, fieldfares, bramblings and redpolls.

CHECKLIST

*This checklist is a guide to the birds you will find in broadleaved woodland. Although you will not see them all in the same woodland, you should be able to spot many of them as you walk through different woods during the changing seasons. The species listed in **bold print** are described in detail in this book.*

Blackbird
Blackcap
Blue tit
Brambling
Carrion crow
Chaffinch
Chiffchaff
Cuckoo
Dunnock
Fieldfare
Garden warbler
Great spotted woodpecker
Great tit
Green woodpecker
Goshawk
Hawfinch
Hobby
Jackdaw
Jay
Kestrel
Lesser spotted woodpecker
Long-tailed tit
Magpie
Marsh tit

Mistle thrush
Nightingale
Nuthatch
Pheasant
Pied flycatcher
Redpoll
Redstart
Redwing
Robin
Rook
Song thrush
Sparrowhawk
Starling
Stockdove
Tawny owl
Treecreeper
Tree sparrow
Willow tit
Willow warbler
Woodcock
Woodpigeon
Wood warbler
Wren

Above: The chiffchaff is a summer visitor to our woods.

Left: A great spotted woodpecker flying from its oak tree nest hole, chequerboard wings spread wide.

117

THE TAWNY OWL: NIGHT HUNTER

The tawny owl is most in evidence during the hours of darkness, when its exceptional hearing, sensitive vision and noiseless flight make it a particularly effective hunter.

Tawny owls are highly specialised nocturnal hunters. Although the head may seem disproportionately big, inside the skull are two large, asymmetrical ears so sensitive that they can pick up the rustling and high-pitched squeaks of nearby prey after dark. They can pinpoint a moving target like a mouse with such accuracy that a miss is rare. In addition owls have unusually large eyes. These are forward-facing—like human eyes and binoculars—for three dimensional vision, which enables owls to judge distance accurately.

The owl can turn its head both left and right (like a radar scanner) to inspect a full 360°, so the bird can search for and locate its prey while keeping its body still. The 'facial disc' of rather stiff, bristly feathers serves as a reflector, collecting sounds and focusing them on the ears.

Silent hunter The essence of effective nocturnal hunting is the silent approach—and again, in the tawny owl, evolution has come up with the necessary adaptations. The outer surfaces of the feathers have a velvety finish to deaden noise, and the feathers of the leading edge of the wing have a special comb-like fringe to silence the wing as it cuts the air.

Tawny owls will usually sit motionless on a branch, waiting for some unwitting meal to pass below. The owl then drops silently on to its victim, seizing it in the fierce grip of large, sharp talons. If this does not kill the prey instantly, the death blow may be administered by a sharp bite at the base of the skull.

Food supply Although the tawny owl is primarily a rodent killer (voles, mice and rats are all acceptable), shrews and small birds have good reason to be concerned by its presence, as their remains regularly feature in pellets. Owls often swallow their prey whole and the regurgitated pellets are made up of the indigestible remains of its prey such as bones, fur and feathers. These left-overs can provide valuable clues to its diet. In the case of the tawny owl, rodents and birds occur prominently, but the wide variety of its diet (and thus the adaptability of the species) can be gauged by the regular presence of fish, amphibian and reptile remains. Nocturnal observations show that invertebrates, particularly worms which do not leave easily

Opposite and right: A dark triangle on the crown of the head is a distinctive marking by which you can identify the tawny owl.

Above: Primary and secondary feathers are soft to deaden the noise of the owl's descent—giving it the element of surprise and enabling its sensitive ears to do their job without disturbance.

Holes in trees provide a safe nest for the round white eggs which fit compactly in a small area.

Tawny owl (*Strix aluco*) Also called brown or wood owl; 38cm (15in) from beak to tip of tail; 40-45cm (16-18in) high; distribution widespread but absent from Ireland and some Scottish islands.

upper left ear

lower right ear

Below: The tawny owl uses its disproportionately large feet to good purpose when hunting. The formidable talons often penetrate a vital spot to administer an immediate death blow and, because they are widely spread and can grip effectively, they enable the owl to carry even small rabbits.

Top: Asymmetric ears enable the owl to locate its prey.
Above: Ear holes are so large that a human finger can fit inside.

Above: Wedged into the tree hollow so they can't fall out, these chicks rely on their parents for food. The larger one is about two days older than the other.

recognisable remains in the pellets, also feature largely when more substantial prey is in short supply.

Family planning In some uncanny way tawny owls seem able to assess the likely food supply at the start of the breeding season. In years when small mammals are low in number, clutches of eggs tend to be small; the number of eggs increases when mice, moles and small rabbits are more plentiful. Tawny owls usually have a single brood of young each year—and this occurs from mid-March onwards.

Unlike small birds, which wait until their clutch of eggs is complete, the female tawny owl starts incubating as soon as she has laid her first egg, which is like a ping-pong ball in size, shape and colour. The chicks hatch at about two-day intervals, each egg taking 28-30 days to hatch. The chick waits fretfully in the nest for food—usually mice, shrews and sometimes even small birds. The first born tends to get more than its fair share of the food, the result being a considerable difference in size between youngest and oldest. If food is plentiful, then all is well. Should food fail, then the biggest chick eats the smallest one. It may sound unduly brutal, but for the survival of the species it is better that two chicks die to provide food for a third, than for all three to die of starvation. In exceptionally hard years when the shortage of food is acute, the tawny owl may not breed at all.

The owlets fledge (leave the nest) after five weeks, but for the next three months they continue to demand parental attention with hungry 'ku-wek' calls at their regular feeding stations, scattered through the woodland. After August, the parent owls begin to re-establish their territorial boundaries and the familiar calls, 'hoo-hoo-hoo' and 'tu-whit', are often heard. The youngsters finally move off or are driven away by the parent owls. This territorial activity increases in January and is probably at its height in February and March. Autumn and winter are the times when mortality is at its highest, particularly for the young birds, when cold weather and food shortages take their toll. Sadly, some also die in collisions with cars after dark on country roads, when the owls are dazzled by headlights.

Favourite nest sites are hollow trees, or cavities found in deserted buildings. One give-away sign of an owl's nest—or roosting site—is pellets around the base of the tree. Occasionally, eggs are laid in old nests of other birds such as magpies and carrion and hooded crows. If there is a scarcity of trees, tawny owls will even nest on the ground, perhaps choosing an old rabbit hole. Tawnies also take readily to nestboxes, and a barrel with good drainage holes, if slung at an angle beneath a high branch sheltered from direct wind and rain, will often tempt a pair of owls. The best time to go out and see tawny owls is on a clear night and at dawn, when they are returning to roost for the day.

The tawny is Britain's most numerous and widespread owl, though absent from Ireland; its place there is filled by a different species, the long-eared owl (*Asio otus*). We think of it very much as a woodland bird, and to a degree this is true. However, there are plenty of mice, rats and house sparrows in towns, plenty of parks and large gardens with trees large and old enough to have holes for nesting—and of course there are plenty of suitable buildings like churches in which to nest. Add to this the very catholic diet of tawny owls, and it becomes less surprising that these adaptable birds have taken to urban and suburban life so well.

Owl pellets

Pellets are found under a roost or nest site, usually at the base of a large tree. They contain the indigestible parts of a meal—mostly fur and bones—which have been compacted in the gizzard before being coughed up. The average length is 42mm (1¾in). The average width is 19mm (¾in).

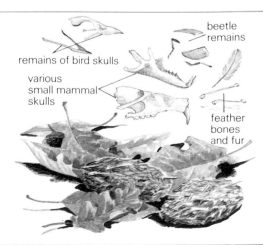

beetle remains

remains of bird skulls

various small mammal skulls

feather bones and fur

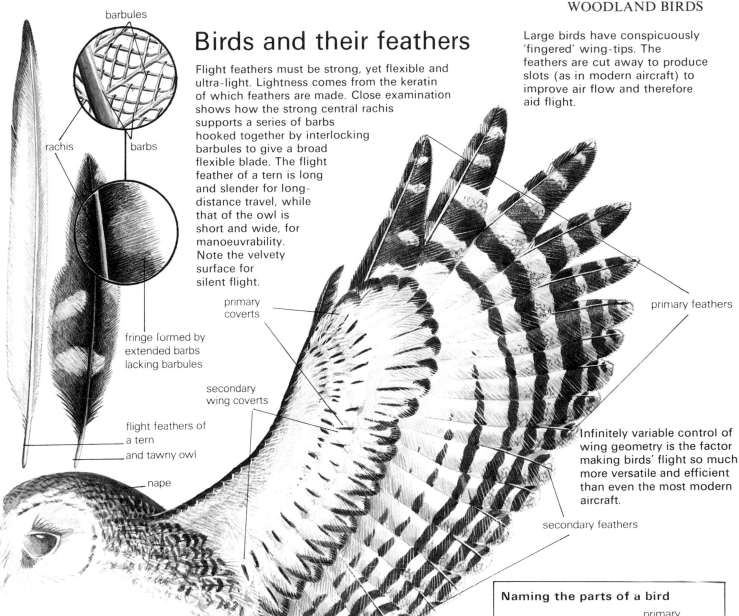

barbules

rachis   barbs

Birds and their feathers

Flight feathers must be strong, yet flexible and ultra-light. Lightness comes from the keratin of which feathers are made. Close examination shows how the strong central rachis supports a series of barbs hooked together by interlocking barbules to give a broad flexible blade. The flight feather of a tern is long and slender for long-distance travel, while that of the owl is short and wide, for manoeuvrability. Note the velvety surface for silent flight.

fringe formed by extended barbs lacking barbules

flight feathers of a tern and tawny owl

nape

primary coverts

secondary wing coverts

Large birds have conspicuously 'fingered' wing-tips. The feathers are cut away to produce slots (as in modern aircraft) to improve air flow and therefore aid flight.

primary feathers

Infinitely variable control of wing geometry is the factor making birds' flight so much more versatile and efficient than even the most modern aircraft.

secondary feathers

The streamlined outline of the owl is formed by stiff, specially shaped contour feathers. Between this surface layer and the body is a layer of down feathers—the bird's 'thermal underwear' —very necessary for survival through cold winter nights. This insulation may be provided by an aftershaft attached to the contour feather or by special down feathers.

Feathers are vital to a bird's survival. They power flight and supply warmth, and the colours and patterns used in courtship, aggression or camouflage are all in the feathers. Thus their maintenance is of utmost importance. Disarranged barbs must quickly be put straight to maintain flight efficiency, and this is the purpose of preening, which seems to occupy so much of a bird's time. Preen oil is applied by wiping the beak across a gland above the tail and then passing each feather through the beak, when rapid nibblings re-adjust any displaced barbules.

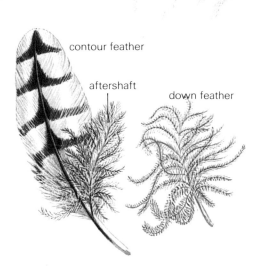

contour feather

aftershaft

down feather

Naming the parts of a bird

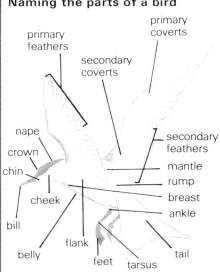

primary feathers

primary coverts

secondary coverts

nape

crown

chin

secondary feathers

mantle

rump

breast

ankle

cheek

bill

flank

belly

feet

tarsus

tail

Whether you want to describe a bulky bird like an owl or a slim tern, the same words apply to both. The parts vary in colour and shape, providing a means of identifying each species. To help identify an unfamiliar species, it is worth keeping a note book and making a rough sketch, labelling the colour of each part.

WADERS OF THE WOODLANDS

Bird watchers who know the woodcock as a shy retiring woodland bird are often surprised to learn that it is a wader, closely related to shore birds such as the curlew and sandpipers. The similarity is seen most clearly in its long probing beak.

Below: A female woodcock at her nest. Woodcocks seek out dry sites for their nests, preferably among leaf litter (left) near the base of a tree trunk. The nest is often a simple hollow scraped out of the ground.

The ideal habitat for a woodcock is a deciduous wood with plenty of leaf litter. The wood needs to have some dry areas where the woodcock can nest, and some wet areas for feeding–typically a patch of ground kept perpetually moist by seepage from an underground spring and rich in worms, the wood-

cock's major food source. Besides this mixture of wet and dry ground, woodcocks require a broken canopy and preferably also open glades for their display flights.

Despite having such particular requirements, the woodcock is widespread throughout both Britain and Ireland–more so than most bird watchers would imagine, as its secretive habits often keep it from view. In the breeding season it is absent only from the extreme south-west of England, the west of Wales and the northern isles of Scotland. In the south of England it is usually found in oak woods. Further north it is more likely to be seen in birch scrub (in Scotland) and in mixed plantations of deciduous and coniferous trees.

Judging from old records, the woodcock used not to be so widely distributed. Before about 1800 it was known to breed only in parts of England. One possible reason for this expansion is thought to be the increasing amount of commercial woodland being planted. Another factor might well be the

Above: Although the woodcock needs a dry site to nest on, it feeds in damp areas, probing the soil with its flexible beak to a depth of 8cm (3in) in search of worms and insect larvae such as leatherjackets.

Right: A typical clutch contains four eggs, coloured off-white to buff with brown markings for camouflage. They are laid at intervals of 2–3 days and incubated for three weeks by the female.

barred head

broad wings

Woodcock (*Scolopax rusticola*). Native resident, found in woodlands in most areas of the British Isles. Length 34cm (13½in), including its 8cm (3in) beak.

eyes set high in head

short legs

long beak

increase in pheasant shooting. The associated management of woodland for game rearing produces conditions well suited to the woodcock.

Like pheasants, the woodcock is a popular game bird and in many areas special shoots are organised during the winter.

Sedentary birds Ringing recoveries indicate that most woodcocks breeding in this country are relatively sedentary, moving only a few miles within their neighbourhoods. Some, particularly those from Scotland and northern England, move south or south-west to avoid the winter, sometimes travelling as far as France, Spain or Portugal.

Conversely, each autumn, large numbers of woodcock arrive in Britain from parts of the Continent that have severe winters, such as Russia, Scandinavia, Germany and Holland. In these countries, the ground can freeze for long periods and prevent the woodcock from feeding.

Effective camouflage The mottled rich brown plumage of a woodcock provides it with ideal camouflage against a background of dead leaves or bracken and makes the bird extremely difficult to spot. If you approach a woodcock it crouches down, completely immobile. Only when you come within a few feet (sometimes just a few inches) of it does it take off.

Once you do spot a woodcock, however, it is an easy bird to identify. The only other bird you are likely to confuse it with is the snipe. Like the snipe, the woodcock has a disproportionately long beak and its colouring is similar, though the snipe has pale bars on its head running from front to back, whereas on the woodcock they run from side to side. The woodcock also has much larger eyes, which it needs to help it feed and fly in the late evening. These eyes make the woodcock's head seem larger and more angular than that of the snipe. Another difference is in the way that they fly. The snipe is a swift and nimble flier. The woodcock, on the other hand, has a much heavier appearance and a strange, jinking flight that makes it a challenging target for a marksman. This partly explains its attraction as a game bird.

Sensitive beak The woodcock feeds by probing the wet soil for earthworms and insect larvae, though there are records of it eating seeds and other vegetable matter. To help it feed, its beak has a swollen tip containing numerous sensitive nerve endings that allow the woodcock to identify its prey.

Another adaptation allows the woodcock to avoid eating large amounts of mud with each creature. The top half of its beak is supported by long nasal bones, which are in turn attached to the skull. In most birds these bones are held rigid, but in the woodcock they are flexible. Special muscles can pull them back, allowing just the tip of the beak to open so it can grasp the worm but leave any mud behind.

Patrolling the glades During the breeding season male woodcocks perform a strange display flight known as roding. Usually a single woodcock, but sometimes two or three, patrol a lengthy but regular circuit across the open glades of the woodland, either at dusk or at dawn. As it flies it gives out a triple croak more reminiscent of a frog, followed immediately by a whistling 'tsiwick'. The wing-beats are very slow and owl-like, and belie the real speed of the bird.

Roding seems to be the only activity in which woodcocks are at all gregarious. For much of the year they are the most solitary of all the waders.

Simple nests The breeding season begins early in March with the building of the nest. This is usually a simple affair, a hole scraped in the ground, often among leaf litter, and lined with leaves. The nests are frequently close to the base of a tree.

As with so many waders, the typical clutch size is four, occasionally three or five. The eggs have a background colour of off-white to buff, with variable brown or red-brown markings making them nearly invisible against the woodland floor.

The female alone seems to incubate the eggs. Once hatched, the chicks' eyes are quickly open and within a few hours their camouflage-patterned down is dry enough for them to leave the nest on short forays. Although initially short-beaked they feed themselves from birth, under the watchful eye of the mother.

Do woodcocks carry their young? From time to time over a great many years bird watchers have reported seeing a woodcock in flight carrying a young chick between its legs. Whether or not this really happens has been debated among ornithologists for more than a century without settling the question.

The proponents argue that young chicks are sometimes found wandering with their parents a considerable distance from the nest. To get them there, or take them back, they have to be carried occasionally by one of the parents. It is thought that the adult clasps the chicks between its legs, holding them in place by depressing its tail and sometimes using its beak as well.

Sceptics say that what these people are seeing is simply a distraction display flight, a practice performed by many other waders to draw predators away from the young chicks. In the case of the woodcock, the flight is laboured and clumsy, the tail is held depressed and the beak droops. These flights usually end in a crash-landing, just as if the woodcock had been carrying a heavy burden.

There are now so many sightings of this phenomenon on record that most bird watchers have come to accept that it does occur, though rarely. But until someone can photograph it happening the question will remain open.

Below: The eyes of a woodcock are placed high up and on the sides of its head to allow it a complete 360° field of vision. With this, it can watch out for potential danger while probing deep into the soil for food.

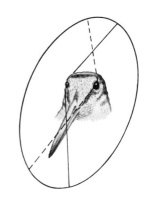

Below: Woodcock chicks in their nest. The young are quick to develop. Within a few hours of hatching they are capable of leaving the nest under their mother's guard for short journeys in search of food. At 15–20 days old they begin to make short flights. About three weeks later they become independent.

WOODLAND HAWKS

These two hawks—the supreme predators of our woodlands— are swift, silent and deadly in the hunt, specialising in the techniques of close encounter and surprise attack.

The sparrowhawk is well distributed throughout our more heavily wooded counties and is reasonably familiar to many people. But the goshawk is still a rare bird in the British Isles and its present status is poorly recorded and subject to much local secrecy.

What is surprising, making for great complications, is the considerable public confusion between the sparrowhawk and the familiar and conspicuous kestrel. People say that they have spotted a sparrowhawk hovering over a roadside verge, when this is the kestrel's main hunting method, and something which sparrowhawks never do. Unlike the kestrel (which is a member of the falcon family), the sparrowhawk or broad winged hawk (an accipiter), is a shy, inconspicuous bird and the goshawk even more so. This is because both are predominantly woodland birds, and spend most of their time in the cover of trees.

Apart from a period in late winter and early spring when their high circling displays make them more visible, you are most likely to encounter a sparrowhawk as it sweeps low over gardens, along a country lane or hedgerow, or as it crosses at grass-top level from one wood to another. It sometimes makes a series of 'kek-kek-kek' calls, and also has a short cry 'pew'.

Territory and display The annual cycle of establishing a territory, advertising it to likely mates and courtship, begins much earlier than the usual breeding season of other birds. Sparrowhawks begin to soar and spiral above the nesting woods from late February onwards, especially on clear and breezy days. Females are usually more active than males, and the intensity of their high circling displays reaches its peak as nest building begins in the second half of March.

At this time of year the display also frequently includes a series of exciting, bounding undulations above the nesting wood. These are often so vigorous that the bird seems to 'bounce' upwards from the base of each steep descent. This is the one time of year when the birds are regularly in evidence, and you can expect to look for them with some degree of success.

Goshawks stake out their territories even earlier in the year than sparrowhawks. The female can become vocal soon after the new year. She is notably noisy early in the morning –when you may hear a harsh chattering cry ringing through the breeding woodlands even before dawn.

Females call the tune Part of the reason for the louder, more noticeable female display is due to the dominant role that the much larger, more robust females play in each season's pairing. The females also tend to stay in or near their nesting territories throughout the year; this makes them sitting tenants when the new year comes. The females make the first moves in attracting a mate into the territory that they have kept exclusively as their own for the past three or four months.

The hawks probably seek new mates each year, since they go their separate ways at the end of the breeding season. Both the male and female usually remain solitary throughout the autumn and winter, each with its own hunting territory. The female stays in her nest and the male drifts away, or even sometimes migrates south.

The goshawk lays her eggs from early April onwards, and the sparrowhawk some three weeks later. Clutch sizes are surprisingly large; five to six is normal for the sparrowhawk, and three to four for the goshawk. The female is almost exclusively responsible for incubating the eggs while the male does all the hunting—calling the female off the nest to feed her once or twice each day.

Woodland cover Before the sixteenth century, when the British Isles were still heavily wooded, sparrowhawks and goshawks were abundant. Nowadays their presence and distribution are strongly influenced by the number of suitable woodlands still remaining.

The sparrowhawk survives just as well in a pattern of small woods and open fields as it does in extensive woods. The goshawk, how-

Female goshawk in flight from below

Above: The flight silhouette of the female goshawk is virtually indistinguishable from that of the sparrowhawk, but its head and tail are more prominent.

wider rounded tail

Female sparrowhawk in flight from below

Goshawk (*Accipiter gentilis*) about 50cm (20in) from beak to tail. Resident.

Sparrowhawk (*Accipiter nisus*) about 35cm (13in) from beak to tail. Resident.

Below: The juvenile goshawk has bolder streaks on its underparts and is more amber in colour than the adult.

Juvenile goshawk

bold streaks on underparts

Below and opposite: The adult goshawk has a narrow white eyestripe with a darker coloured crown and ear coverts. With its flame coloured iris the bird looks fierce and alert.

Adult goshawk

pronounced white supercilium (eyestripe)

conspicuous white undertail coverts

ever, requires a considerably larger territory, often in excess of 8000 acres. About a quarter of this area must be relatively undisturbed woodland. Although both birds once prospered in the former extensive deciduous cover, they are now equally at home in conifers or mixed woodland, provided the cover is not too close. The goshawk favours spruce or pine, while the sparrowhawk prefers larch plantations for nesting, as well as mixed deciduous woodland for hunting.

Falling numbers By the 16th century 90% of the former woodland cover in the British Isles had disappeared. The clearance of this native woodland was a major factor in reducing goshawk and sparrowhawk numbers.

By 1900 the ravages of game preservation had removed the last breeding goshawk from this country, and had taken a heavy toll of sparrowhawks throughout the game-rearing areas. In the 1960s goshawks began to re-establish themselves, helped by the release of falconers' birds. By this time, however, sparrowhawks were suffering from the serious effects of DDT and other organochlorine pesticides. They were virtually exterminated from south and east England, and their numbers were much reduced elsewhere in the country.

The sparrowhawk accumulates DDT through what it eats. Insects and earthworms are the first to take in DDT sprayed on crops, lawns or flowers; they are eaten by birds like thrushes which then fall prey to such predators as the sparrowhawk. DDT interferes with the breeding biology of the sparrowhawk, for example causing the female to lay thin-shelled eggs which break easily, and it also affects their general behaviour. Most of the DDT is laid down in the bird's fat. When

The predator – prey relationship

The phrase 'balance of nature' is well known, and the real meaning of the words is best examined in a predator-prey relationship. It is easy to become angry at the thought or sight of bird predators, such as sparrowhawks, goshawks, magpies or jays, taking garden birds or their nest contents. Such predatory birds are often accused of reducing the number of robins, blue tits and blackbirds. They do, of course, kill these small birds and reduce their numbers, but this is an essential part of the seasonal pattern and cycle of numbers.

The predators do not influence the basic numbers of breeding pairs; indeed the populations of many small birds are increasing. It is rather the numbers of prey that determine the population levels of the predators. So short-eared owls breed additionally well in a year of vole plague, while high numbers of magpies indicate healthy populations of small bird species and other prey.

Sparrowhawks feed almost exclusively on small birds, eating 700-800 in the course of a year. This may seem a great many. However, in 12 acres of woodland there may be, say, 12 pairs of blue tits. If each pair produces an average of 10 young per year, one pair and its successive progeny would multiply to a total of 7500 pairs in five years, if all survived. Together with other woodland species there is a huge surplus and hawks and other birds of prey help to keep the balance right.

it starts to use up the energy stored in the fat – for example, to keep warm on a cold day, or to power itself for a long flight – the DDT is liberated and poisons the bird.

The use of DDT has been restricted or even banned for several years, and the sparrowhawk has recovered some of its former numbers, but the poison is persistent and it is still having a marked effect on the sparrowhawk's nesting success.

Given protection from pesticides and gamekeepers, the prospects for both the sparrowhawk and the goshawk are good. The maturing of many forestry plantations will eventually help to provide the ideal habitat for returning goshawks.

Right: The male sparrowhawk is blue-grey on the upper parts and neatly barred underneath, while the female is much browner.

Left: A sparrowhawk and its half-grown chicks. Five or six eggs are usual, but not all the chicks hatch or survive. The female does almost all the incubating of the eggs while the male bird does all the hunting—finding food first for the female and then for the hungry chicks. The female feeds the chicks, tearing the prey into small pieces.

Hunting techniques

The hunting methods of the sparrowhawk and goshawk rely mainly on silent observation, stealth and final explosive acceleration. Both hawks exploit rich food sites within a territory, and return to them repeatedly as long as they remain productive.

The hawk sits silently on a perch, hidden in the cover of woodland, waiting for likely prey. It glides low to the ground, only as far as the next perch if necessary, until it singles out its victim. Then it approaches fast and low, using the cover of hedgerow or trees, flicks over the final hedge or bush at full speed and takes the unsuspecting prey with outstretched talons, either while the victim is still perched, or after a short and frantic pursuit.

The hawk's tenacity sometimes leads it to pursue its prey into buildings (even occasionally to fly through glass windows). Sometimes too it chases its victim on foot into bushes. Individuals have been known to take

Male sparrowhawk
catching prey

blue-grey above

orange underparts

Above: The sparrowhawk at close hand has a yellow eye of penetrating alertness, long legs, feet of almost disproportionately huge size and needle-sharp talons.

house martins from under eaves, and young moorhens off the surface of a pond, and sometimes a hawk prospects for prey by soaring high into the air, occasionally stooping (falcon-like) on prey on the wing.

After catching prey (with both feet if it is as large as a jay or wood pigeon), the hawk usually takes its victim into cover and perches on a tree stump, ant-hill or old nest platform to pluck the feathers off with its beak. You can easily identify such plucking posts by the scatter of feathers around them. The bird's sharp talons then make short work of tearing the meat to pieces.

The hawks' food includes game birds, wood pigeons and other woodland species. The goshawk, unlike the sparrowhawk, readily takes prey on the ground—attacking medium-sized mammals such as hares and rabbits.

Neither bird appears to be the specialised villain it is made out to be by gamekeepers, and game birds seldom form a substantial part of their diet. Some farmers and foresters today reckon that the increase in goshawk numbers will provide them with an ally against the destructive wood pigeon.

THE ACORN LOVING JAY

Jays, our most handsome and distinctive members of the crow family, are shy birds and you never find them far away from trees. In autumn they are busy collecting acorns.

The jay belongs to the crow family, but it has much brighter plumage than its relatives. At close range it looks quite exotic. Its crest, delicately spotted with white and black on the forehead, is raised when it is displaying to other birds. It has pale blue eyes and a broad black moustachial streak; most of the body is pale pinkish-brown. The flight feathers are black and grey, with a conspicuous patch of white, and the wing coverts are beautifully barred with pale blue and black.

Elusive bird Jays are shy and restless birds, and you may find it hard to get a good view. Most often you just see them flying away, when the large, white patch just above the black tail is very noticeable. They have broad, rounded wings and their flight often looks weak and laboured. At a distance, jays can be mistaken for hoopoes, an unrelated bird found in Europe which is fairly similar in size and shape and also has black, white and pink plumage.

Oak woodland is the jay's preferred habitat and you rarely find them far from trees. Unlike our other crows—magpies, carrion crows, rooks and jackdaws—jays seldom venture out into open fields. When they are searching for food in the trees or on the ground, they tend to hop and leap about, rather than walk or run.

Jays are often quite noisy, so you may hear them before you see them. The main call can be heard from far off. It is a loud, often twice-repeated, rasping shriek of alarm which they make when disturbed. People have also heard jays make a variety of chuckling and chirruping calls, a buzzard-like mew and even a low, warbling song.

Acorn hoarders The jay's favourite food is acorns. In September and October when the acorns ripen you can see jays searching methodically for them in and beneath oak trees. However, instead of eating only what they require and leaving the rest to fall to the ground where all kinds of animals and birds would find them, jays hoard them. By making their own private larder, they can be sure of enough food to last throughout the year.

Jays can hold up to nine acorns at once in their specially large oesophagus, but more usually they take just three or four. They

crest

wing coverts

white rump and black tail conspicuous in flight

flight feathers

Opposite: In its preferred woodland habitat the jay is well-placed to find a great variety of different foods. Its favourite food is acorns (above and below) which it hides in its own private larder. Each jay's larder consists of several thousand acorns, collected over about two months. A storing trip takes only a few minutes and jays fly back and forth all day. Jays also eat fruits and insects.

Above: An adult jay about to drink water. Jays thrive in most types of woodland, particularly oakwoods, but you occasionally see them in suburban areas and city parks where there are plenty of trees. Note the distinctive blue and black barring on the wing. You can sometimes find one or two of these blue feathers dropped by a jay as it flies over woodland.

The acorns are often 'planted' in suitable sites for growing and, when there is a surplus, those that are not retrieved grow into trees and provide food for future generations of jays. So the jay's storing habit ensures the survival of both the jay and the oak. It is probably also the most important method by which oaks spread uphill.

When eating an acorn, a jay usually holds it still against a branch or on the ground with its inner toes. Then with its strong, slightly hooked beak, it levers and tears off the shell to reach the nutritious core.

Jay 'marriages' In spring you may find gatherings of jays known as jay 'marriages'. These are probably courting birds trying to find mates. On some occasions up to 30 jays are present displaying and calling in great excitement.

Jays prefer to nest fairly low down in thick undergrowth—in bushes and small trees, and in evergreens such as ivy, or suckers next to a tree trunk. Occasionally they choose the outer branches of a large tree. Both male and female help to build the well-concealed, robust nest. They use numerous small sticks and twigs and a little earth, and then line the nest with a thick layer of fine roots.

The female usually lays four to six eggs at the end of April or in May, and does most of the incubation. She is very difficult to spot because she crouches very low in the nest, only leaving when her mate comes to feed her and can stay on guard.

The eggs hatch after 16 days but the female still has to brood her family for the first week or so, because the tiny, featherless chicks soon chill if left uncovered for long. At this time the male finds all the food they need. To start with, the chicks look all beak and belly—because they are eating as much

take each acorn to a separate place, usually within half a mile but sometimes up to 2 miles away from where they found it. Favourite hiding places are under leaves or roots, in small holes or amongst moss. Sometimes the jay actually makes a hole in the ground with its beak so the acorn is properly concealed.

Jays appear to have excellent memories, because they know every detail of their local wood and they remember where most acorns are hidden. Even when snow covers the ground, they know exactly where to dig. In the summer many uneaten acorns begin to germinate, but jays can also recognise the fresh oak seedlings and dig them up to find acorn remains below.

Anting: feather-care

Most birds replace their feathers once or twice a year, but without daily servicing the feathers quickly lose their warmth and waterproofing, and flight becomes inefficient. So birds regularly bathe, preen, dust and oil their feathers even—or especially—in winter when days are short and the water cold. Passerines (perching birds) have developed an additional feather-care technique—anting. In this country it is the jays, rooks, thrushes and starlings that most often do this. The anting bird crouches in a mass of ants, holding its wings out to the ground so the ants crawl over its plumage. Often it picks ants up in its beak and puts or rubs them on the feathers.
There are over 40 species of ants in Britain and most produce toxic chemicals to defend their colony, attack others or immobilise prey. Such poisons are effective against other insects and, while various explanations of anting have been suggested, it is now thought that the birds' behaviour encourages ants to release their 'insecticidal shampoo' on to their feathers, so reducing populations of parasitic insects living within the plumage. Subsequent bathing and preening removes the dead insects. Interestingly, birds never use ants that sting, even though these are common.

food as possible and growing quickly. By the time they are two weeks old, they are big and fat, and all the feathers are sprouting except perhaps the tail which is last to appear. When they leave the nest the young jays already have their adult plumage.

The jay parents collect a special diet for their nestlings. Mostly they choose leaf-eating caterpillars from nearby trees and bushes, storing them in their throats until they have enough to give each nestling a good mouthful. The chicks wait silently for a parent to land beside the nest, and then reach up and open their beaks wide. The parent carefully puts food down the bright orange-pink gape of each chick in turn. If one gets too much to swallow, some is taken away and given to another.

Nesting adult jays are secretive, and the nestlings are also fairly quiet, even when being fed – you may hear a few squeaks and squawks if you are close. Even the egg-thieving jay has to keep its nest-site secret from crows, magpies, squirrels and even other jays who rob the nest if they get the chance.

Just as small birds mob jays, so for the same reason jays mob their enemies.

Jays spend about three weeks in the nest but are not independent for another two months, so only one brood is raised each year. They can live for several years and some have been known to reach the age of 14. Throughout their lives jays tend to stay in one area, and most fly no more than four miles from their birth place. Very occasionally the British Isles is invaded by hundreds of jays from the Continent if food supplies there fail to support the jay population.

In the past, when Britain was covered in forest, jays were probably numerous and widespread. However, they were persecuted because of their egg-thieving habit, and many trees have been cut down to make way for agriculture, so jays became quite scarce early in this century. Since then they have benefited from being unmolested, and from extensive afforestation. Some have spread into suburban areas and city parks, especially those with a good collection of trees such as oak, beech or sweet chestnut, and shrubs.

Above: A pair of jays with their young in a rhododendron bush. Jay nests are small compared with the size of the well grown young, but they are well behaved and accidents are few.

Jay (*Garrulus glandarius*) about 34cm (13½in) from beak to tail; distribution widespread in woodlands of all types, particularly oakwoods, throughout the British Isles apart from northern Scotland. Resident.

WOODLAND DRUMMER-BIRDS

You can tell a spotted woodpecker by its frenzied activity even before you come close enough to recognise its brilliant colouring. Its persistent drumming against wood to attract a mate and proclaim territory is unique among British birds.

A male great spotted woodpecker removing wood excavated from its nest. In northern Britain nests are made in birch or pine, but in the south in hardwoods.

The great spotted woodpecker is both the most numerous and widespread of our woodpeckers, occurring in almost all areas where there are suitable trees. Strangely enough, the great spotted shares with its relatives a complete, unexpected, difficult-to-

explain absence from the whole of Ireland, even though there is abundant suitable woodland. There have been sightings in Ireland, but these seem to be of Continental migrants blown off-course in autumn, and none has stayed to breed. The lesser spotted woodpecker is much less common than the great. It does, however, share many characteristics of the great, and has all the same adaptations, though they are reduced in scale.

Woodland bird The great spotted woodpecker prefers stands of timber where at least some of the trees are mature, usually with a few dead or dying branches. It lives in both deciduous and coniferous woodlands or a mixture of the two, but is scarcer in closely planted coniferous plantations without old or decaying trees. Where good hedgerow are still common, it penetrates deep into agricultural land, feeding and nesting in the tall trees of the hedge, or in spinneys and copses linked by the hedgerow network. It is unusual to find great spotted woodpeckers in isolated clumps of trees.

The magnificent old trees of parkland offer an ideal habitat, and through parks the great spotted woodpecker sometimes penetrates into urban areas. It is a common species of large old gardens, with big trees, that meet the surrounding countryside.

Striking colouring With its pied plumage and scarlet patches, the great spotted woodpecker is a conspicuous bird. Its normal year-round call, a harsh and far-carrying 'tchack', or its staccato breeding-season drumming, quickly draw attention to its presence. Its deeply undulating method of flight, too, is conspicuous and characteristic, consisting of a few flaps of the rounded wings, followed by a deep swooping glide, before the next series of flaps helps it gain height again.

The wings are boldly barred black and white, with a striking white oval patch on each wing near the body–a feature lacking in the lesser spotted woodpecker. The back is plain black (again, different from the lesser spotted, where the white bars cross the back as well), and the underparts are white save for a bright scarlet patch beneath the tail of both sexes. In addition, the male has a small block of scarlet feathers on the nape of his otherwise black crown.

Woodpeckers perch, or rather cling, to the sides of tree trunks and branches in a characteristic head-up position developed in the course of evolution as the tail feathers have become specially strengthened and inflexible, serving as a third leg, or prop, to use in climbing in much the same way as we balance on a shooting-stick. This adaptation assists a particularly powerful grip. Wood-pecker legs are short but muscular, with strong toes tipped with long, sharp claws which give an effective hold even on the smoothest-barked trees such as beech.

Unusually for a bird, the toes are arranged with two pointing forwards and two back, (a condition called zygodactyly), which gives optimum performance on a vertical surface. Thus woodpeckers move vertically or often in a spiral up the trunk, and occasionally laterally. When they have finished searching for food on one tree, they swoop off to the base of another tree or branch and begin to ascend once again.

Woodpecker headaches? The most obvious wood-pecking adaptation is, of course, the beak. In the great spotted woodpecker this is relatively short, stout and sharp, with a squared-off end like a small chisel–an appropriate simile: rather than bludgeoning its way into the wood by sheer power, the woodpecker uses its beak as a combination of hammer and chisel, inserting the tip into the crack it has made and using its powerful neck muscles to twist the beak and prize off flakes of wood.

One obvious question relating to wood-peckers is: why don't they get splitting head-aches? The answer lies partly in the robust

scarlet nape-patch

♂

white shoulder patch

plain black back

Great spotted woodpecker

scarlet under-tail coverts

nest chamber

Below: A female great spotted woodpecker can be distinguished because she does not have a red nape patch like the male. Note the red under-tail coverts.

bone structure of the skull, especially in front of the brain, and partly in a layer of shock-absorbing cartilaginous material that forms a cushion between the bones within the beak and the rest of the skull.

Long-tongued feeder The diet of the great spotted woodpecker is varied, and includes seeds, fruit and nuts. Nuts are often removed to a well-used cleft in a favourite piece of bark, and hammered open while they are held in position in this natural vice. Insects and larvae are another important food item. During winter these are often found sheltering under easily lifted flakes of bark; the great spotted woodpecker is also a specialist at extracting wood-boring larvae that have tunnelled into trees. The bird senses the approximate location of the grub, perhaps hearing minute sounds of movement or chewing. After a few swift pecks an opening is hacked into the tunnel, and then the woodpecker's enormously long tongue comes into play. In the case of the great spotted, the tongue can be extended for a couple of inches up the tunnel. The luckless grub is harpooned by the sharp, barbed horny tip of the bird's tongue, and dragged out to be eaten.

At rest the phenomenally long tongue is far too bulky to lie in the floor of the bird's mouth: a thickened tube runs out of the lower jaw, backwards beneath the hidden ears and then up the back of the head to the top of the skull. It is here that the tongue is retracted when it is not in use.

The natural all-year-round diet is augmented at various times by rather surprising items. The great spotted woodpecker has a marked taste for the nestlings of other birds, and is adept at catching them. As they grow, the nestlings of most hole-nesting birds, such as tits, alerted by the shadow of their parent falling across the hole, jump up to the nest hole entrance. Woodpeckers have capitalised on this: as their shadow falls across the hole a young tit jumps up to be the first to be fed, and the woodpecker reaches in and grabs it, dragging it out to hack up and eat on a more suitable perch. Sometimes woodpeckers learn to associate this food supply with nestboxes put up for tits, and they chisel their way through the back of the box to get at the eggs or young.

In rural and suburban areas from late summer through the winter great spotted woodpeckers are regular visitors to garden bird tables. They come particularly for fat, suet and peanuts. Even if the peanuts (or the fat) are suspended on a string, the woodpecker quickly cuts through it with its sharp beak, dropping the food to the ground where it is easier to eat.

Excavated nests Great spotted woodpeckers excavate their nesting chambers in the trunk or a stout branch of a tree. The nest is usually at least 3m (10ft) above ground. The entrance hole is circular and about 6cm (2in) in dia-

Great spotted woodpecker *(Dendrocopos major)*; 23cm (9in) from beak to tail. Common in both coniferous and deciduous woods in England, Wales, Scotland. Resident.

Lesser spotted woodpecker *(Dendrocopos minor)*; 14·5cm (5¾in) from beak to tail. Found in parks, orchards, gardens, copses, in England. Uncommon, but numbers have increased slightly in recent years. Resident.

scarlet cap in male

♂

Left: A male great spotted woodpecker at the nest of its young. Nests are made at least 3m (10ft) above the ground. The young birds have a red cap, like the adult male lesser spotted woodpecker.

Right: A male lesser spotted woodpecker at his nest hole. The female bird lacks the red patch on the crown of the head.

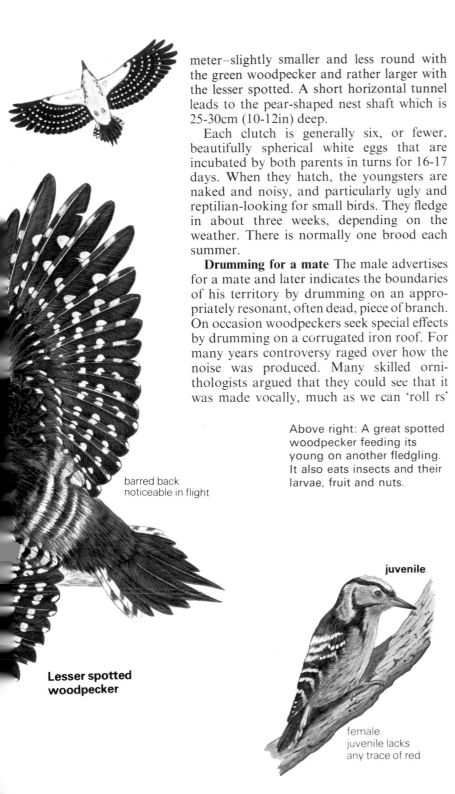

meter—slightly smaller and less round with the green woodpecker and rather larger with the lesser spotted. A short horizontal tunnel leads to the pear-shaped nest shaft which is 25-30cm (10-12in) deep.

Each clutch is generally six, or fewer, beautifully spherical white eggs that are incubated by both parents in turns for 16-17 days. When they hatch, the youngsters are naked and noisy, and particularly ugly and reptilian-looking for small birds. They fledge in about three weeks, depending on the weather. There is normally one brood each summer.

Drumming for a mate The male advertises for a mate and later indicates the boundaries of his territory by drumming on an appropriately resonant, often dead, piece of branch. On occasion woodpeckers seek special effects by drumming on a corrugated iron roof. For many years controversy raged over how the noise was produced. Many skilled ornithologists argued that they could see that it was made vocally, much as we can 'roll rs'

Above right: A great spotted woodpecker feeding its young on another fledgling. It also eats insects and their larvae, fruit and nuts.

barred back noticeable in flight

Lesser spotted woodpecker

juvenile

female juvenile lacks any trace of red

with our tongues curled. The issue was only settled in the 1930s by embedding microphones in regularly drummed branches, which showed that a rapid succession of physical taps by the beak against the tree caused the noise.

Compared with the short and powerful bursts of drumming of the great spotted, the lesser spotted woodpecker drums at a noticeably higher pitch and in drum-rolls lasting twice as long.

The lesser spotted woodpecker shares the pied, barred plumage of the great, although it lacks the scarlet beneath the tail. It is the smallest European woodpecker. The circular nest hole is only about 4cm (1½in) wide and the nest is usually situated on the underside of the dead branch. There are normally four to six white eggs, and incubation and fledging take much the same time as in the larger bird. The eggs are incubated by both the male and the female parent, and both birds also feed the nestlings.

The lesser lives in similar habitats to the great spotted, although it penetrates less into agricultural and urban surroundings other than in old orchards which it particularly favours. It is nowhere very numerous. Old county reports and Victorian bird books, however, indicate that in the latter half of the last century the lesser spotted was the commoner, the greater spotted the rarer woodpecker. It would be fascinating to know the reasons for the change. Perhaps they are similar to the causes of the current increase in lesser spotted woodpecker numbers. For some reason they seem to have profited particularly from the Dutch elm disease outbreak, feeding off the numerous insects that live beneath the dead bark and nesting in the rotting wood: at least some small benefit from the disease.

THE GREEN 'YAFFLE'

The green woodpecker is the largest of our three British species of woodpeckers, and the most colourful. Unlike the two smaller species it is not a frequent drummer, but you can recognise its call among the trees for it sounds just like someone laughing.

Green woodpecker (*Picus viridissima*); resident in England and Wales, spreading into Lake District and Scotland since 1950s. Call resembles a human laugh, a loud 'gua-gua-gua-gua-gua' from which its country name, the yaffle, derives. Length 32cm (12½in).

The main difference in appearance between male and female is in the 'moustache'. The female has a full black stripe, while the male's stripe has a red centre.

stiff tail feathers

crimson crown

female has black moustache

greenish yellow rump

male's moustache has red centre

Of the three woodpecker species in Britain the great spotted and less common lesser spotted are black and white; in length they are about 23cm (9in) and 14.5cm (5¾in) respectively. But the green woodpecker, as its name implies, is mainly green; and it is comparatively large at about 32cm (12½in) long. At a distance it appears generally green, but closer examination reveals that its back is darker than its buffish green belly, and that its rump is bright greenish yellow. The crown is a contrasting crimson, and the sexes can be distinguished by looking at the moustache-like stripe, which is all black in the female but is red with a black border in the male. Young birds are less brightly coloured, with pale spots on the green and black streaked underside.

The green woodpecker is a resident bird, rarely undertaking journeys of more than a few kilometres. This may explain why it has not colonized Ireland. It has only recently invaded the Lake District and Scotland. In Scotland, breeding was first recorded in 1951 and the invasion was two-pronged. Birds from north-west England moved into the counties across the Solway Firth, while their range in the north-east extended from Northumberland to the central lowlands of Scotland and up to Aberdeen on the east coast. Their progress northwards may still continue in future.

Green woodpeckers prefer open (and often deciduous) woodland to the denser stands of conifers. The open parklands and landscaped gardens that man has created in much of Britain are particularly favoured, so that people who regularly walk in such areas are familiar with the bird. It also commonly visits bird tables, and in doing so it adds conspicuous flashes of colour, appearing suddenly and moving jerkily in its yellow, green and red plumage.

Varied diet Its long and highly manoeuvrable tongue is useful for searching under loosened bark for grubs, but the green woodpecker also uses it to probe into short turf, or into ant hills, in search of the abundance of food that these contain. In recent decades a number of open conifer woods have reached maturity in Scotland; these are inhabited by dense populations of wood ants, and this may have been one factor that made it possible for green woodpeckers to invade Scotland.

Ants are significant because they help to extend the range of the green woodpecker, but the birds have an extremely varied diet. They eat a large number of tree-inhabiting insects, especially the larvae of wood-boring beetles and gall-producing insects, and many caterpillars as well. Green woodpeckers have also been known to prey on other birds, especially nestlings. Tits, house martins,

before 1945
by 1965
present day

Below: A young green woodpecker. The parents continue to feed the young for several days after they leave the nest hole, until they are independent.

Above: An adult female green woodpecker, with some of her plumage standing on end to dry in the sun, perhaps after a bathe. Dead wood, on which she is perching, often contains a wealth of grubs and other forms of prey for woodpeckers.

Above: Female feeding her young. The entrance to the nest is a passage about 5-7cm (2-3in) long, leading to the top of a chamber 30-40cm (12-16in) high, and up to 18cm (7in) wide.

Right: Woodpeckers made this hole in an ants' nest and were frequently seen plundering ants from it. Green woodpeckers benefit from the presence of sheep and rabbits, whose grazing creates good conditions for ants to thrive.

How the tongue sticks out

Most vertebrate animals possess a pair of hyoid bones supporting the base of the tongue. Woodpeckers have extended hyoids that curve up behind the head. Muscles pull on the hyoids, giving a powerful thrust to the very long tongue.

bones anchored near right nostril

muscles pull on hyoids

tongue is thrust forward from base

barbed tip

copious sticky saliva

house sparrows, starlings and even lesser spotted woodpeckers are occasionally eaten. They also eat eggs as well as acorns, hazel nuts, rowan berries and a variety of other seeds, berries and fruits.

New nests each year Out of the breeding season, green woodpeckers continue to use tree holes for roosting at night; one member of the pair roosts in the former nest hole, and the other bores a new hole which it uses solely as a roost. Even though the birds have kept the previous year's nest hole in use throughout the winter, they generally bore a new one for nesting each spring.

Both the male and female take part in the work of boring the nest hole. They normally cut their holes in decaying, rather than living, timber, although they often use decaying branches of living trees. The nest contains no lining material, except for a few wood chips that the birds do not remove, and the eggs are laid directly on the floor of the cavity. The eggs are white and oval, and normally number between five and seven.

Green woodpeckers breed between the end of April and June, but starlings pose a serious threat to those that nest early in the season. The starlings, in their search for convenient nesting places, evict the woodpeckers forcibly from their hole, and proceed to occupy it themselves.

In nests that escape these most unwelcome visitors, the green woodpeckers (both male and female) incubate their eggs for 15-17 days. After hatching, both parents feed the young, and it is during this period (about 20 days) that you can most easily detect a green woodpecker nest by the raucous calling of the noisy young.

Woodpeckers and man It may seem surprising that woodland birds such as green woodpeckers should have an important effect on the activity of man, but their habit of boring holes does cause difficulties. They sometimes damage shingle roofs by boring into joists and weakening them at least enough to cause a partial collapse. Telegraph poles, being made of dead wood, have obvious attractions for green woodpeckers; and where electricity cables are carried by wooden poles, the birds can damage them sufficiently to bring them down and cause a power failure.

On the credit side, some foresters believe that the green woodpecker is useful in removing insect pests from trees. Besides this, their preference for boring into decaying wood provides an early warning system for the forester – their activity shows him where to cut off dying branches. To the wider public, their colours and laughing call bring excitement to gardens and town parks.

WOODLAND NUTHATCH

Nuthatches look like small woodpeckers but, unlike them, can walk down trees head first, and instead of chiselling out grubs, they hunt for insects and split open nuts.

Nuthatch (*Sitta europea*); resident tree-creeping bird found in woods and parks with mature trees; feeds on hard seeds and nuts, as well as insects and larvae; length 14cm (5½in).

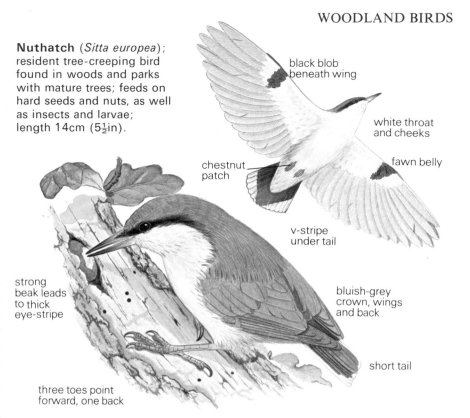

black blob beneath wing

white throat and cheeks

chestnut patch

fawn belly

v-stripe under tail

bluish-grey crown, wings and back

short tail

strong beak leads to thick eye-stripe

three toes point forward, one back

Although superficially similar to our woodpeckers in its choice of habitat and in its behaviour, the nuthatch is generally thought to be more closely related to the tits and treecreepers. True, it climbs with great ease even on the trunk of the smoothest-barked beech tree, but the nuthatch's toes are arranged three forward, one back, as in the other families of birds within the passerine order, not two forward, two back as in the woodpeckers. It is also true that the nuthatch has a large, dagger-shaped beak just like a woodpecker's, but this is the result of 'parallel evolution' (in other words it has evolved over the ages to do the same sort of work, but in a totally different bird), and the nuthatch lacks the extremely long tongue that the woodpeckers use to extract their insect food.

There are other, subtler differences. Woodpeckers always move head-up on a tree-trunk, leaning back on their stout tail feathers as if these were a shooting stick. But nuthatches can move with similar ease head-up, head-down, or horizontally across a trunk. Their tails are short, and the tail feathers are of normal shape, flexibility and toughness: only rarely do they come into contact with the bark at all, and nuthatches are able to rely on their strong claws alone to maintain their position on the trunk.

Nuthatches are attractive woodland birds, slightly more than sparrow-sized, neat but not gaudy. They are dove-grey above, white on the throat and the sides of the face, and a rich, cinnamon-tinged fawn on the belly. On each flank, and extending up under the wing, is a rich chestnut patch, considerably more extensive in area and darker in colour in the male than in the female, so with a little practice it is possible to separate the two sexes. The effective-looking beak leads to a striking long narrow black patch, running through the eye and backwards on to the nape.

Nuthatch distribution This is rarely the case, for nuthatches are among the most sedentary of our birds, rarely moving more than a mile or two from the area of their birth. Their distribution is an interesting one: over an area roughly south of a line from the Wirral to the Wash they are widespread – except in a few lowland areas, principally in Cambridge-

Above: The larger and harder nuts, such as acorns, beechmast, hazel cobs and chestnuts, are often carried in the nuthatch's beak and wedged in a crevice in the bark of a tree, or perhaps in a wall. The nut is then hammered and split open with the beak (right).

Below: The nuthatch's toes are arranged three forward, one back, unlike those of a woodpecker, two of which face forward, and two back.

20,000, which compares unfavourably with 50 times that number of coal tits, but is rather more than the breeding populations of the lesser spotted woodpecker and the long-eared owl.

Patient plasterwork The nest is built in a natural cavity, usually in a decaying broad-leaved tree but sometimes in a little-used or deserted building. Most are within a few metres of the ground, but nests at least 20m (60ft) high are on record. Nuthatches take readily to nestboxes, but other, more extraordinary sites include disused woodpecker and sand martin holes, an old magpie nest and even a series (reported from Sussex) in haystacks. Neither the size of the cavity nor that of the entrance hole seem to influence their choice, and nuthatches have a habit—unique among British birds–of cementing up the entrance with mud until the hole is of the right size. When using nestboxes, they also plaster round the lid, from the inside.

Inside the cavity, the nest itself is also of a unique type. The eggs are laid on the floor of the cavity, on top of a layer of flakes of bark (especially of yew or larch if this is available), or of oak or other leaves. When the incubating bird (always the female) departs to feed or drink, she covers the eggs with similar debris, so on a superficial inspection the occupied nest looks like the long-deserted winter lodging of a field-mouse or dormouse.

shire, which is probably because there are few suitable woodlands. North of this line, there is an outlying area, mostly in Yorkshire, where they occur, but very few other breeding records.

Their range seems to have contracted southwards, as the birds left their northern English haunts, during the 19th century, and at the same time it was noted that they had deserted the parks of central London and some other large urban areas. One suggestion is that this might have been due to increasing atmospheric pollution in industrial areas, reducing the insect food supply. This is borne out by the gap between the present-day Yorkshire outpost and the main area of distribution, this gap corresponding with the location of much of south Yorkshire's heavy industry. Other species sensitive to industrial pollution–such as the kingfisher–are also missing from this area.

Though well-distributed in Wales, the nuthatch is another of those birds (such as the tawny owl and the woodpeckers) whose complete absence from Ireland seems so puzzling. One possible explanation is that being sedentary birds, and having poor powers of long-distance flight, nuthatches were unable to reach Ireland during the re-colonization period that followed the last Ice Age, before the rising seas formed what is now the Irish Sea and created an insuperable barrier.

Nuthatches are birds of mature, or even old, deciduous woodland; they sometimes occur in mixed deciduous and coniferous areas, but rarely in woodland that is predominantly coniferous. They particularly favour areas where beech, oak, sweet chestnut, hazel and hornbeam occur, for these provide winter food. Open parkland and, in many parts of England and Wales, large gardens with very old trees, also appear to be attractive to them.

Although the species is widespread within its area of distribution, the nuthatch is not a numerous bird in Britain. There are many sites that seem highly suitable, but where there are no nuthatches at all. Recent estimates put the number of pairs at about

Above: Nuthatch eggs, resting on a bed of yew bark flakes. The usual clutch is of six to nine white eggs, heavily spotted with dark reddish brown. Occasional clutches of as many as 13 eggs may well be the product of more than one female.

Below: Both parents share in feeding the young, which fledge after about three weeks or rather longer if the weather at the time is poor. Like the tits, nuthatches produce only one brood.

TREE TRUNK CLIMBERS

The treecreeper can be seen in woodland, spiralling up tree trunks and clinging to the bark with sharp claws. It pauses to seize insects with its fine, down-curved beak.

The birdwatcher's first impression of a treecreeper is of a small, brownish bird, fluffy in appearance and furtive and jerky in its movements. It is often seen feeding in its characteristic manner – it creeps up the trunk of a tree in short stages, searching for insects, and when it cannot usefully hunt any higher it flies across and down, to start again at the base of another trunk.

Adult treecreepers are brown above, with various darker and paler streaks, and off-white below; the sexes are alike in plumage and general appearance. In good lighting conditions and during dry weather, this white can appear almost silvery, shading to fawn on the flanks, but in damp weather, when the belly has been pressed close against the bark of damp tree trunks, it can appear brownish or even greenish, smeared with material such as algae rubbed off the bark. The tail is long and brown, and the wings are short and rounded, with a conspicuous pale crescent-shaped wingbar in flight. Climbing up a tree trunk, treecreepers seem long, slender birds, but seen in flight – which is deeply undulating and looks rather feeble in character – they appear much fatter and almost moth-like, so rounded are the wings.

Young birds are if anything slightly fluffier than their parents, particularly around the white under-tail coverts, and the feathers of

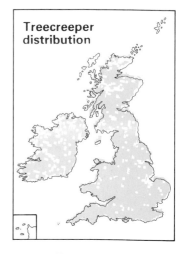

Treecreeper distribution

Below: Treecreepers nest in slender cavities in tree trunks, or behind a flap of peeling bark on a dead or dying tree. The cavity usually has two entrances – or rather, one of them acts as the emergency exit!

the head and back each have a yellow-buff fringe, giving the upper parts a scaly appearance. This lasts only from when the chicks fledge in the summer until September, when the moult of body feathers is completed.

Head, tail and toes Treecreepers feed mostly on small insects, spiders, other bark-living invertebrate animals, and their eggs and larvae. Their long, slender, finely pointed beaks are down-curved, and are ideal for extracting such tiny items from the crevices in the bark in which they are hidden. The eyes are large, and protected by unusually prominent eyebrows for a small, slow-flying bird. The advantage of these 'beetling' eyebrows is not known, but a close-up view through binoculars reveals that they give to the otherwise docile-looking treecreeper an extremely bad-tempered expression, additionally emphasised by the long, bold white eyestripe.

The long tail closely resembles that of the woodpeckers, with the shafts of the central feathers specially strengthened. As in the case of the woodpeckers (to which, however, treecreepers are not related), the tail is used as a prop, the treecreeper normally moving head-uppermost on trunks and branches.

Compared with the powerful claws, toes and legs of the woodpeckers, treecreepers seem poorly adapted to their arboreal habitat. Unlike the woodpeckers' toe arrangement (two facing forward, two behind for maximum grip), the treecreepers have the same pattern as almost all other passerine birds – three in front, one behind. The toes and legs seem slender and feeble, but the long and sharp claws can cling easily to the bark.

Above: Once they have left the nest, the brood of young follow their parents from tree to tree, clambering up the bark in a comical train. If they are disturbed they tend to 'freeze', beaks pointing skywards, hoping to escape detection with their excellent camouflage.

Tree-dwelling birds

1 The coal tit is typically found in the upper crown, feeding on tiny insects under leaves. **2** The willow warbler also feeds on insects that it finds among the foliage in the outer crown. **3** The nuthatch eats nuts and seeds – fresh or windfalls – as well as insects and small creatures in dead wood. **4** The treecreeper searches upwards from the base of the trunk for insects and other small creatures. **5** The great tit is typically a ground or lower branch feeder, eating a mixture of invertebrates and seeds. **6** The great spotted woodpecker often nests in holes in the dead wood and eats insects and larvae beneath the wood surface. **7** The hawfinch is a seed eater and often feeds in the outer crown, where it takes the ripe seeds direct from the tree. It is particularly attracted to hornbeam seeds – the tree shown here is a hornbeam. Those birds that feed mainly on insects (**1**, **2** and **4**) have long, fine beaks, while those mainly eating seeds (**7**) have large beaks.

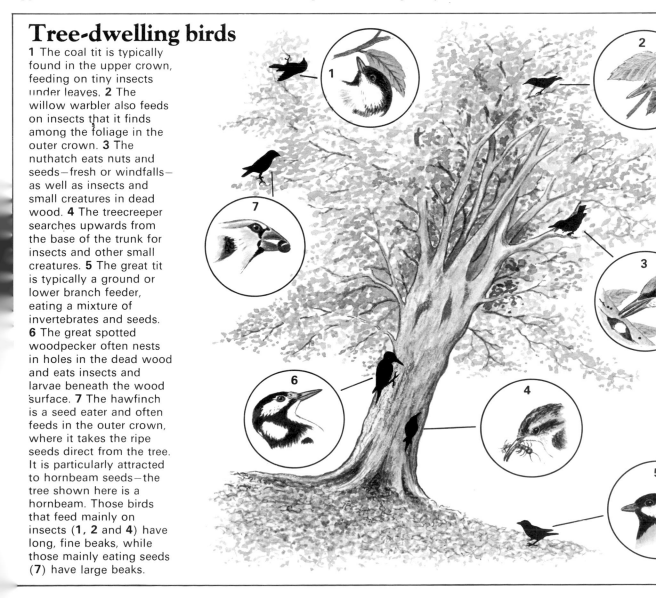

Song and display The birds are most vocal, and most easily seen, in late winter and in early spring, when there are few leaves on the trees. The song, high-pitched and silvery in tone, is a descending trill with a small last flourish of three clear notes, recalling the songs of willow warblers and chaffinches. It is at this time of year that treecreeper pairs display: a novel performance as the birds chase each other in spirals up tree trunks.

Single brood The first eggs are laid early in April, but the peak laying period is in late April and early May. It seems that the majority of pairs are single-brooded, and that the eggs found freshly laid in early June are replacements for clutches lost to predators.

A hollow in the bark An intriguing feature of the treecreeper is its use of winter roosting sites in enormous Wellingtonia trees. The bark of these North American introduced trees—relatives of the redwood—is thick and papery, and easy even for the slender beak of a treecreeper to excavate. Close inspection of almost any Wellingtonia anywhere will show some of these roosting sites a few feet from the ground. They are cavities, roughly the size and shape of a hard-boiled egg cut lengthways, and usually there is a give-away trickle of white droppings running down from them. The treecreeper snuggles down into this hollow, fluffy feathers bristling for the best insulation, and becomes almost invisible, so good is its camouflage.

Treecreeper (*Certhia familiaris*); resident in woodland and parkland. Length 12.5cm (5in).

Below: The typical feeding route—working up each tree in turn.

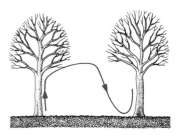

Opposite: In their well-protected nests, treecreepers suffer relatively few losses of their young to predators. The fewer losses may explain why single-brooded treecreepers can maintain their population with a clutch size of five when the tits, also usually single-brooded and also hole-nesters, need average clutches at least twice as large.

Below: Bringing food to the nest—the recipients are completely hidden from sight.

Change of habitat In Britain and Ireland, treecreepers seem to be most numerous in deciduous woodland and quite scarce among conifers. On the Continent of Europe, there are two treecreeper species: the one that is common in Britain and Ireland, and the short-toed treecreeper. There are very small differences in some anatomical measurements, and equally small differences in plumage, but these are not reliable for identification. Their songs, though, are quite different, and so too are their habitats. Astonishingly, it is the short-toed treecreeper that is found in deciduous woodland on the Continent, while 'our' treecreeper is almost confined to upland conifers.

The explanation for this is thought to be that after the last Ice Age (which ended about 10,000 years ago) the two species recolonized Europe at different rates. 'Our' treecreeper spread northwards with the coniferous forest, which was its natural habitat, and which grew in Britain and Ireland some centuries before the deciduous woodland.

The English Channel and the North Sea formed during the period of recolonization, isolating Britain and Ireland before the deciduous woodland—and the short-toed treecreeper—arrived. When, subsequently, the conifers were mostly replaced by deciduous species, the treecreeper was able to adapt itself to the changed habitat in the absence of competition, as the Channel proved an effective barrier to the short-toed treecreeper.

WARBLERS OF THE TREE CROWN

Three warblers of the leafy treetops come to Britain in the summer to breed. They are the willow warbler, the wood warbler and the chiffchaff.

Above: A willow warbler sings amid the opening buds. Besides the warbling song, the bird has a faint 'hoo-eet' call. The chiffchaff also has a similar call, sung slightly faster.

Below: Plentiful down surrounds the eggs in a willow warbler's nest. All three leaf warbler species usually lay 6 or 7. Only the females incubate, and this takes 13 days. The young fledge within 2 weeks, so sometimes there is time for a second brood.

Three species of leaf warbler are found in Britain and Ireland: the willow warbler, the chiffchaff and the wood warbler. Many people find warblers of any kind difficult to identify because they are invariably well camouflaged, retiring birds. Leaf warblers provide additional problems because they look so similar to one another. A leaf warbler can generally be described as a small, greenish-brown, lightly built bird with a fine, insect-eating bill, a pale stripe above the eye and yellowish underparts, flitting about in the canopy of a tree. This description applies to virtually all the *Phylloscopus* (leaf warbler) species that occur in the Old World (there are about 30 of them). It certainly applies to

Britain's three species.

The chiffchaff This, the dingiest of the three, has olive-brown upperparts and yellowish-buff underparts, an indistinct eye stripe and, usually, black legs. In keeping with its plumage and its name, its song is the least varied, alternating between two monotonous squeaky notes – 'chiff' and 'chaff'. Sometimes one note predominates as the bird 'misses' the other.

The chiffchaff is the earliest of our summer migrants: the harbinger of spring. The first birds arrive in early March, the last in April or May. However, this pattern is complicated by the tendency of an increasing number of chiffchaffs to overwinter in southern England. Although these hardy individuals may fly north to Scandinavia and beyond to breed, they are usually still here when the British breeders arrive.

The chiffchaff requires both bushy undergrowth for its nest, and tall trees as songposts and feeding sites. While it can therefore live in well-grown deciduous and coniferous woodland, it is excluded from many areas where tall trees are uncommon, particularly parts of northern England and Scotland.

The willow warbler This bird is greener above, and more yellow below, than the chiffchaff; it has a stronger eye-stripe and, usually, pale legs. The overall impression it gives is of clearer colours and a 'cleaner' appearance.

The first willow warblers to arrive, usually in mid or late March, signal that the spring influx of visiting birds is under way. Their song is one of the most welcome country sounds, especially as it typically rings out from the heart of a colourful pussy willow tree on a bright sunlit morning. Starting quietly, the musical warbling gains volume and pitch and then descends back down the scale to a deliberate final flourish.

In its choice of habitat, the willow warbler is the least fussy of the three leaf warblers. Almost any wooded or open bushy area is suitable, provided the canopy is not too dense. Ideal habitats range from damp areas with willows (as its name suggests) to young conifer plantations and small copses. The

willow warbler is the commonest and most widespread of all our summer visitors, breeding throughout Britain and Ireland, even in sites close to built-up areas.

The wood warbler Of the three leaf warblers, this is the most brightly coloured, having yellowish-green upperparts, a sulphur-yellow throat and breast, a white belly, a noticeable yellow eye stripe and pale legs. At 12.5cm (5in) long, it is also noticeably larger than the other two leaf warbler species, for they each measure only 11cm (4¼in) in length.

The wood warbler is the last of the three leaf warblers to arrive, mainly between mid-April and mid-May. Full appreciation of its song is certainly only achieved when you can both see and hear the bird in action. Starting with a steady 'stip, stip, stip', it accelerates to a marvellous, far-carrying trill which sets the whole bird quivering with the effort involved. The wood warbler also has a second, less well-known though equally distinctive song: a piping 'piu' repeated several times in quick succession.

The wood warbler is very particular in its choice of habitat: it prefers mature oak, birch, beech and chestnut woodland with little or no undergrowth. The sessile oak-woods of the valleys of western Britain are ideal, but this type of habitat is not common elsewhere. Consequently this species is the least widespread, being scarce or absent from wide tracts of England and Scotland. For every one of our breeding wood warblers, there are about ten chiffchaffs and a hundred willow warblers.

The breeding season Males of all three species typically arrive to set up territories a week or two earlier than their mates, often in the same area in which they were raised. Their beautiful, domed nests, almost spherical with the entrance at the side, are solely the work of the females. Leaves, grass, stalks, moss and perhaps bracken comprise the main structure, but whereas the wood warbler lines its nest with fine grass and hair, the other two use feathers. Each species hides its nest among low-growing plants and bushes. The chiff-chaff builds its nest a foot or two above the ground in most cases, while the others make

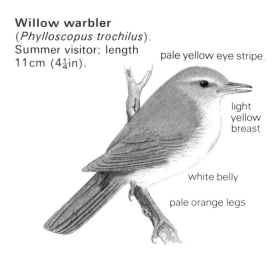

Willow warbler (*Phylloscopus trochilus*). Summer visitor; length 11cm (4¼in).

pale yellow eye stripe

light yellow breast

white belly

pale orange legs

Willow warbler distribution

Chiffchaff distribution

Chiffchaff (*P. collybita*). Summer visitor; 11cm (4¼in).

white eye stripe

yellowish-buff breast

white belly

blackish legs

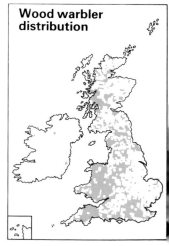

Wood warbler (*P. sibilatrix*). Summer visitor; 12.5cm (5in).

yellow eye stripe

yellowish-green upperparts

bright yellow throat and breast

white belly

brown legs

Wood warbler distribution

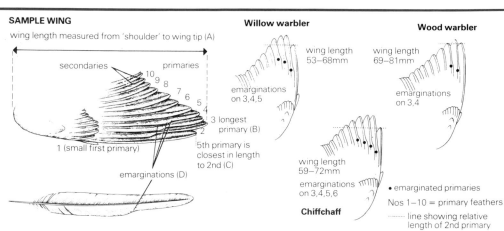

Wing formulae

Wing formulae are a series of measurements made to prove the identity of a bird such as a leaf warbler. In some cases, the first measurement alone is sufficient, but in others as many as four are necessary:

A How long is the wing?
B Which primaries (or primary) are longest?
C Which primaries have the same (or nearly the same) length as the second?
D Which primaries have an emargination?

SAMPLE WING

wing length measured from 'shoulder' to wing tip (A)

secondaries   primaries

1 (small first primary)

emarginations (D)

Willow warbler

wing length 53–68mm

emarginations on 3,4,5

3 longest primary (B)

5th primary is closest in length to 2nd (C)

Wood warbler

wing length 69–81mm

emarginations on 3,4

Chiffchaff

wing length 59–72mm

emarginations on 3,4,5,6

• emarginated primaries
Nos 1–10 = primary feathers
······ line showing relative length of 2nd primary

Above: The chiffchaff is the least colourful of the three leaf warblers: its upperparts are olive brown.

Left: The wood warbler has brighter plumage than the other two species. Its nest is made at ground level and is domed, with the entrance at the side.

Below: The chiffchaff's nest is normally sited above ground level in the shrub layer; the bird is dependent on bushy undergrowth for nest sites.

theirs at ground level among grass and dead leaves.

Moult strategy One of the most distinct differences between our three leaf warblers, though perhaps the least obvious to the casual observer, is the timing of their feather moults. The only feature they share is that the young birds of all three species undergo a partial moult in autumn before they leave this country. (A partial moult is when the birds replace their body feathers, but not their wing or tail feathers.)

After this stage, chiffchaffs undergo a partial moult each winter and a complete moult each autumn; wood warblers undergo a complete moult each winter and a partial moult each autumn; and willow warblers undergo two complete moults, one in winter and one in autumn. To moult the entire plumage twice in each year is highly unusual, and so the willow warbler is in a class of its own in this particular respect. Curiously, there seems to be no obvious advantage in this behaviour, for all three strategies are demonstrably successful.

End of the season Late summer is the time when each individual bird must find extra food to fatten itself. This facilitates the growth of new feathers after the moult, and then fuels the bird's migration journey south. Leaf warblers are quick and agile birds, hopping to and fro to pick up tiny insects and caterpillars from twigs and leaves, hovering

to catch those out of reach or darting out to intercept them in flight. At this time of year, berries provide additional variety, and those chiffchaffs that stay for the winter occasionally visit bird tables for fat, meat, bread and other household scraps.

It is remarkable that such tiny birds, weighing some 10g ($\frac{1}{3}$oz), are able to fly to winter quarters as far away as Africa. Migration begins as early as the end of July. The first to leave are willow warblers, which migrate to tropical west Africa, some even crossing the equator. Most wood warblers migrate up the Nile valley to southern Sudan. The last to leave are the chiffchaffs, many of which fly no further than the Mediterranean.

THE PIED FLYCATCHER

In the western oakwoods of Wales, the pied flycatcher is a familiar breeding species, and often it is the commonest bird there during the summer. But it is slowly expanding its range, especially with the help of extensive nestboxing schemes.

Over most of Britain, pied flycatchers are not nearly as common as their near relatives, the spotted flycatchers. Only in the western oakwoods of Wales are they a really common breeding species. They are small birds, about the size of great tits; the breeding males, in full plumage, are absolutely unmistakable with their striking black and white markings.

During their summer visits to Britain, pied flycatchers prefer woodland with a good tree cover at the canopy level, but without much of a shrub layer. Such open woodland is typical of the grazed sessile oakwoods of the south-west, much of Wales and some other parts of upland Britain. The males arrive on the breeding grounds in mid-April, often while

Above: The vivid breeding plumage of the male pied flycatcher: black upperparts are interrupted by striking white wing stripes and a white throat patch extending to the sides of the neck.

Right: The female is brown and white. This is also the appearance of both sexes of pied flycatchers in autumn.

Pied flycatcher (*Ficedula hypoleuca*). Summer visitor to woodland with nest holes and little or no shrub layer. Length 12.5cm (5in).

the weather is still cold, and immediately start to defend territories and advertise nest sites. These are always holes–generally in trees–and the pied flycatchers sometimes try to displace resident tits. Although they are often able to defeat blue tits, great tits are generally more than a match for them. The females start to arrive four or five days after the first males, and pairs are quickly formed.

The birds build their nests of the soft outer bark stripped from honeysuckle stems, and can complete them in less than 48 hours. The female does most of the incubation, which takes about 12 days starting with the penultimate egg. The young remain in the nest for 14-16 days and fledge as spotty young birds looking like young robins or spotted flycatchers. Although they seem to stay within a few miles of the breeding site for several weeks, while the adults complete their total moult, both young and old birds are almost impossible to see, and probably spend their time high in the tree canopy.

Catching 'flies' For most of the time, pied flycatchers feed on flying insects, which they take on the wing. They use convenient perches in the woodland, from which they make athletic, darting forays to catch moths and flies, returning quickly to the perch to watch for more prey. The early arrivals may find the weather so cold that hardly any insects are flying and have to feed on the ground, catching such creatures as spiders and ground-

dwelling insects such as beetles, bugs and many larvae.

The young, in the nest, are fed almost exclusively on insect larvae. These may be moth caterpillars feeding on the oaks, or they may be sawfly larvae. In many years there seems to be a super-abundance of these creatures, so that the oak trees may even be partly defoliated: in such circumstances, the youngsters invariably fledge successfully. In other years, when there are few caterpillars or larvae, or if there has been heavy rain washing them off the trees, fledging success may not be very great.

Ringing results It is easy to study breeding pied flycatchers in great detail, for they very readily breed in conventional nest boxes, and many studies have been undertaken in Britain and abroad. In addition, they can safely be handled by ringers and marked to make the different individuals recognisable. Recaptures of adult birds in later years have shown that the males are very faithful to their breeding areas, and may come back to nest in exactly

Above: This alder wood in Dumfries, with its delightful stream, has a regular summer population of pied flycatchers. The habitat is extremely suitable, with virtually no shrub layer.

the same nest box or one very close by. Many females do the same, but they are much more likely to nest in a completely different place: in a few well-documented cases more than a hundred miles distant from the previous year's nest. Recaptures of birds ringed as nestlings show that the young often disperse very great distances: one Yorkshire-reared youngster was found in a Dutch nest box in a later year!

Ringing has also made it possible to chart the birds' migration routes in some detail. Birds from Britain, Scandinavia and even Russia are found in the autumn in northern Iberia, mostly in northern Portugal. Obviously this is the important stop-over point on the migration southwards. Here they set up defended feeding territories for a few weeks as they put on weight for their further flight south to tropical West Africa.

Autumn migrants Many eastern European pied flycatchers fly westwards at the start of their autumn migration, and some of these wander off course into Britain. Light south-easterly winds over the North Sea can cause large numbers of them, with other small migrants such as redstarts, garden warblers and whinchats to occur in eastern Britain, together with such exciting birds as wrynecks, barred warblers and Icterine warblers. Almost always these erratic arrivals are associated with cloudy weather which obscures the stars, for these provide the most important navi-

Pied flycatcher distribution (recent years)

Pied flycatchers in summer

black wings with conspicuous white patches

white outer tail feathers

brown upperparts

dull white underparts

pure white spot in male only

dark brown wings with small white wing patches

pure white underparts

Pied flycatcher distribution in 1938

:: Local or sporadic

▢ Regular

The peculiar distribution of the pied flycatcher in Britain, with hardly any breeding records in the south-east, has long puzzled birdwatchers, for there are many pairs breeding in woods in the Netherlands. Various reasons have been proposed, but the true explanation has yet to be proved. The author favours the theory that the woodlands remaining in south-eastern Britain are probably, on the whole, too thickly grown, with too rich a shrub layer to attract the species. In many areas where they do breed, the nest box schemes run by conservationists and naturalists' trusts have helped to maintain the numbers. At the same time the range has expanded.

gational information for the migrants.

It has been proved that there are hardly any adult birds among the autumn arrivals, so that it is young and inexperienced birds that are involved. Ringing has shown that they are not doomed to die, for a number of them have been seen in later years in their normal range.

Hunted birds Even such a small bird as the pied flycatcher has, in the past, been hunted by man. In parts of Spain and Portugal, specially constructed spring traps were (and sometimes still are) used to catch them for people to eat. Each bird weighs about 15g ($\frac{1}{2}$oz) and they are fried, whole, after the feathers have been singed off them. International conventions on bird protection have had considerable effect

Above: A pied flycatcher in autumn plumage, in flight.

Left: The nest is made of strips of honeysuckle bark. Eggs are usually laid in May. Once an early pair have their eggs, the male may desert the female and start a new territory and nest a short distance away.

over the last few decades, and this distressing practice is dying out. When Spain and Portugal have joined the European Community and the various EEC bird directives are enforced in the two new member countries, these attractive little birds will be able to undertake at least the European part of their long annual journey without fear of hunters! This could lead to the prospect of further expansion of the range.

Extensive nestbox schemes

Many people put up nestboxes in their gardens, but you can achieve even better conservation results with extensive nestbox schemes in the countryside. Many hole-nesting species of birds take readily to properly constructed nestboxes. Often these are just the species that are losing nest sites as old trees are 'tidied up'. Nestbox schemes are usually designed to provide a variety of boxes within managed woodland. In such cases there should be some 10 or 20 of the small hole-nesting boxes for each of the larger ones. Ideally, you should keep a record of the occupancy of the boxes from year to year, and regularly inform the British Trust for Ornithology (BTO).

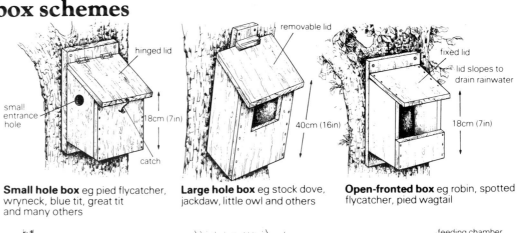

Small hole box eg pied flycatcher, wryneck, blue tit, great tit and many others

Large hole box eg stock dove, jackdaw, little owl and others

Open-fronted box eg robin, spotted flycatcher, pied wagtail

Open-fronted box (pole mounted) for kestrel

'Chimney' box for tawny owl, stock dove

Large tray for barn owl

MARSH TIT, WILLOW TIT

Marsh and willow tits are so similar that they were not recognised as distinct species until 1900. Stuffed museum specimens showed the willow tit wasn't a newcomer – it just hadn't been identified before.

The most fascinating thing about marsh and willow tits is the problem of identification. Since the year 1900 when the two species were positively distinguished, much has been found out about the birds and field recognition skills have improved greatly, but the two still present one of the greatest challenges to British bird watchers. It is not too difficult to separate marsh and willow tits from other tits: they are slightly smaller than a blue tit, they are our only two truly black-capped tits (both the great and coal tits have white marks on the crown), and their plumage is a subtle mixture of delicately toning beiges and browns. The problems all start when it comes to deciding which is which.

A ruffled-looking marsh tit feeding a beakful of grubs to its chick. The nesting site in the apple tree probably started out as a natural hole, and was then widened and deepened by another bird before being taken over by marsh tits who almost never excavate.

Marsh tit *(Parus palustris);* 11cm (4½in) from beak to tail; distribution widespread in dense deciduous woodland up to the borders of Scotland, but absent from Ireland.

153

Sight and sound The black crown of the willow tit is not as glossy as that of the marsh tit – but this characteristic is influenced by the quality of the light and requires an exceptionally close view, so is risky to rely on. A better guide is the pale patch visible on the closed wing of the willow tit, which is lacking in the marsh tit. This patch is often conspicuous and, if present, is a clear indication that the bird is a willow tit. Unfortunately for bird watchers, damp feathers or the wear and tear caused by the bird scrambling in and out of a nest hole during the hectic summer nesting season can obscure the pale patch, and the lack of it does not necessarily confirm that the bird is a marsh tit.

These differences are so small that it is difficult to identify the birds with any certainty. Fortunately, however, there is another feature which is of great help: the two birds have distinctly different calls, in addition to a variety of sharp notes to keep in contact with each other. Only the marsh tit produces a rather explosive 'pit-chu' sound, and only the willow tit a scraping 'dee-dee-dee' or 'chay-chay' reminiscent of a squeaking gate hinge.

'Marsh' a misnomer The marsh tit is rather inappropriately named as it is the willow tit which shows a preference for swampy woodland and copses. This mix-up probably dates from the days before the two species were separated.

The marsh tit prefers dense deciduous woodland, generally with oak, hornbeam, hazel and beech trees; these produce a prolific and nutritious seed crop which forms a valuable part of the tit's winter diet. Some hibernating insects, plus their eggs and larvae concealed in cracks in rough bark, are eaten in winter, but insect food becomes most important as spring advances. The chicks are often fed almost exclusively on caterpillars – the green winter moth caterpillars which usually occur in enormous numbers in oakwoods are specially favoured. As autumn comes and the supply of insects dwindles, berries start to feature in the marsh tit's daily menu.

Its pale wing patch and bull necked appearance identify this willow tit, which is bringing caterpillars to its young hidden deep inside the nest hole. The strong neck muscles enable the willow tit to excavate a sizeable hole in softwood.

Willow tit *(Parus montanus);* 11cm ($4\frac{1}{2}$in) from beak to tail; distribution widespread in damp deciduous and conifer woodland including lowland Scotland, but absent from Ireland.

What is a species?

A species is a term used to classify similar looking individuals that can only breed successfully with others of their own kind. This means that offspring retain the particular characteristics of their parents which fit them to their special place in the complex web of life. Similarities in appearance, calls, song and behaviour patterns and courtship rituals help individuals to recognise others of the same species, differences in these things keep species apart: for instance, though willow and marsh tits look extremely similar, they do not interbreed. However, since nature is versatile, there are exceptions. Two different species of duck can mate, but their offspring – hybrids – are usually infertile. Individual varieties can exist within a species – hence the different colours of pigeons – and these varieties can breed together successfully.

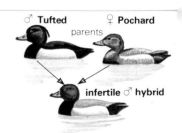

In winter marsh tits may join any large mixed flock of tits that moves through their area, but this is only on a temporary basis and they will not move far, deserting the flock as it passes on. It seems probable that many pairs remain in the same territory, winter and summer alike. The territory is large compared with that held by other tits, and sometimes exceeds 10 acres in extent. It is noisily and fiercely defended by the male throughout spring and summer.

Pairing takes place in February and March when the territory has been established by the male, and the search for a nesting site then begins. Competition for a suitable nest site is intense between all the tits; the marsh tit can hold its own against blue tits but will usually give way to great tits. The squabbling over nest sites is accompanied by a lot of aggressive calling, and even by fighting.

Marsh tits choose a natural hole or crevice, usually in a tree or where a branch has broken off, but occasionally in a bank or wall. Sometimes they take over a second-hand nest hole of another species, and chip away the wood to modify the entrance, but they will only very rarely excavate their own nest in rotten timber. The nest cavity is floored with moss and usually lined with hair or fur. In April or May five or six white eggs with red spots are laid (up to a dozen may sometimes be produced). The female incubates the eggs for 13 or 14 days, with only brief excursions from the nest for food. After hatching, the young remain in the nest for 15 days before fledging, being fed by their parents for the whole of that time. In cool, damp summers this period may be extended by several days until a settled spell allows the youngsters to emerge with a reasonable chance of learning to fend for themselves within a few days.

Willow tree dweller The willow tit is more aptly named since the willow is one of its favourite nesting trees. Willow tits often breed in damp woodland, usually ones with many old, moss-covered tree stumps. The essential requirement in their breeding area is a supply of live, dying or decaying softwood stumps. Birch and elder are often used for nests, as well as willow.

The willow tit pair excavate their nest – a striking difference, not just from marsh tits but also from other British members of the tit family. It is often impossible to separate male from female willow and marsh tits by sight (the female may be very slightly smaller), but studies of colour-ringed birds have shown that the female does most of the excavating work. Unlike woodpeckers, which leave a conspicuous pile of chippings below their nest hole, willow tits usually carry their debris 10 to 15m (11-16yd) away, and for good measure may pulverise it too, leaving no tell-tale traces at the nest.

Excavating naturally demands strong and bulky neck muscles if the beak is to be effectively used as a combined hammer and chisel.

Marsh tit

glossy crown extending only a short way down the back

small bib

Willow tit

dull black crown

larger bib

thick neck with powerful muscles for excavating nest hole

pale patch

marsh   willow

These muscles give the willow tit a distinctly bull-necked appearance which can be one of the best ways of separating willow from marsh tits in the field.

The nest chamber is 20-30cm (8-12in) deep, with a carpet of fine roots, grasses and other fibres supporting a nest cup lined with fur or feathers. Unlike the marsh tit, willow tits very rarely use moss. The willow tit's eggs are very similar to those of the marsh tit but the average clutch is rather larger, at eight or nine eggs. Incubation and fledging times are also similar to those of the marsh tit. Once the chicks have left the nest, it is very difficult to tell parents of either species from the young, although the young may look fluffier.

The eggs of both marsh and willow tit are very similar in appearance, both tending to have a ring or cap of reddish-brown spots at the larger end. The marsh tit's egg, about 16.2mm long, is slightly larger than the egg of the willow tit, which usually only reaches 15.5mm in length.

NIGHT-SINGING NIGHTINGALES

The nightingale is justly praised for its tuneful singing, but it cannot excel in all things: despite its wonderfully varied musical performance, it is an unobtrusive, dull brown bird, here for a short breeding season spent hiding in the thickets.

The nightingale combines the extremes of delightfully melodious singing and a generally uniform, unremarkable plumage. It is about half way in size between the robin and the song thrush, two fellow members of the thrush family. In its general posture the nightingale is comparable to these two birds. Its plumage, however, is considerably less colourful than that of other members of the thrush family, being chestnut-brown all over the upperparts and paling to a rufous fawn beneath.

Most nightingales breed to the south of a line between the Severn and the Humber, preferring habitats with a well-developed and dense undergrowth. Thus most are found in woodland areas, usually of deciduous trees and very often of oak, with the mature trees widely spaced. Towards the north-western fringe of this breeding range, the wooded slopes of river valleys are favoured.

Over the last few centuries, the distribution of the nightingale right across Europe has contracted considerably. Possibly this is partly due to wholesale trapping (particularly on the Continent) of nightingales for caging as song birds or, even more unpleasantly, for

Nightingale distribution

Top: A nightingale with a good catch of caterpillars.
Above: The nightingale breeds only in the south and south-east of England.
Opposite: Note the rich brown rump and tail plumage.
Right: The nest is always well-hidden from predators.

sale in delicatessens. Though this does still occur, it seems more likely that the major factor in the decline is the loss of the appropriate type of deciduous woodland. This is due both to modern farming, with its demands for full land usage and increased field sizes, and to modern forestry practice, in which broad-leaved woodland is replaced by dense plantations of conifers.

Watching for nightingales Generally, nightingales are shy, rarely venturing into the open, so for many of us this is a bird far more often heard than seen. Considerable patience, and quiet watching from semi-concealment in an area with several nightingale pairs – and preferably with some paths to provide open ground – is required to obtain even fleeting glimpses. If you are lucky, a male nightingale may choose to sing from a perch in your line of sight, head thrown slightly back, throat bulging, giving you a chance to see the performance as well as hear it.

More often, apart from the song, much of what you hear in the undergrowth is the surprisingly varied repertoire of 'chack' and 'churr' noises with which the nightingale deters intruders from approaching its place of concealment. You may also hear the soft 'weet' call that the pair use to keep in contact.

Our best night singer The voice of the nightingale, heard solo at dead of night, comes through the clear, warm early summer air as one of the most delightful bird songs in the world. The song period is, however, short, generally spanning the second half of May and the month of June, but rarely continuing as late as July.

For quality, range and versatility the nightingale's voice cannot be matched, even among British birds with their exceptionally rich songs. Part of the enjoyment stems from

broad, rounded wings   'wing-fanning' display

white breast

adult ♂

large dark eye

mottled head

underparts look 'scaly'

juvenile ♂

fanned tail

the sheer variety–from throaty chuckles to far-carrying whistles–and part from the quality of the tonal range, from rich, deep phrases to the purest of treble-like trills and flourishes.

Special adaptations In the shelter of its habitat of thick undergrowth, the nightingale spends much of its time concealed from view. It is one of the more terrestrial birds in the thrush family. Strong legs and large eyes are adaptations to this mode of life, as also is the beak. Though not so stout as the conical beaks of the finches, nor so fine as that of insect-eaters such as the pied wagtail, the well pointed but strong beak of the nightingale allows it to tackle most soil and litter-dwelling invertebrates. These range from tiny insects and spiders to caterpillars and worms. The beak is also suited to feeding on berries as they become available later in the month. At this time they are invaluable as a sugar-rich resource to help the nightingale put on fat as a fuel reserve for the long migration south.

The breeding season Nightingales perform a pairing display which is rarely seen because of the dense cover in which it takes place. It involves much ritualised posturing, with wings drooping and fluttering, and with tail fanned. After the display, the nest is built low in the vegetation or, quite commonly, on the ground. It is always well concealed from disturbance by humans and large predatory mammals or birds, although it is not safe from such predators as weasels or mice. The nest is basically constructed of dead leaves, usually those found lying nearby. Those found in England are most often held together by fine twigs or stout grasses. The lining of the cup is of fine grasses and hair, and the normal clutch is four or five (occasionally six). The eggs are brown, so densely speckled as to

appear almost uniformly coloured. Because of their early departure on migration, there is normally time for just a single brood each season.

Long-distance migrants Nightingales desert their breeding woods from late July onwards. Ringing results indicate that most nightingales cross the Mediterranean in autumn and fly over the western margins of the Sahara Desert. Their wintering areas are in tropical West Africa. As with many other migrants, individual breeding birds often return to precisely the same patch of dense cover in successive years, for unless the site has been cleared by man, nightingales keep to their traditional nesting grounds.

Nightingale (*Luscinia megarhynchos*). Summer visitor breeding in thickets. Splendid song audible at night. 16.5cm (6½in).

Right: The wooded slopes of a river valley are much favoured as breeding habitats by nightingales.

Below: After an incubation period of about a fortnight, the brood hatches. In their earliest days the chicks have the same speckled appearance as young robins.

Night singing birds

It is interesting to note that nightingales sing a great deal during the day as well as the night, but in the daytime their song tends to be drowned by the richness of other birdsong heard at this time. However, *why* they sing so much at night is intriguing, and by no means well understood. Few other songbirds sing at night, but two that do, the grasshopper and the reed warblers, are both birds of dense cover, like the nightingale. Also like the nightingale, they are summer visitors to this country, migrating by night to and from wintering areas in Africa.

One theory is based on the observation that males usually migrate some days in advance of the females. On arrival, they set up territories and defend them by song, and then it is thought that they sing to the night skies to attract the females as they pass over. Although plausible in this context, the theory leaves unexplained the fact that all these species continue their nocturnal singing until well into the breeding season.

Mammals of deciduous woodlands

In keeping with its status as the most elaborate habitat we have in Britain, deciduous woodland supports the most diverse community of mammals. Most of them lead secretive lives, foraging under cover of darkness, but with practice we can interpret much of their daily lives by observing their tracks, runways, droppings and the leftovers from their meals.

Unlike birds, woodland mammals live in a largely two-dimensional plane and, though some mice and voles are accomplished climbers, only squirrels and, of course, the bats are found at any height. Mammals are also creatures of habit, their comings and goings typically following familiar, well-worn paths at regular times of day. Although their hearing, and especially their sense of smell, are acute, their vision is at best not exceptional and at worse (as in shrews and badgers) quite poor, so we can, with care, observe them quite closely without being detected.

The mammal community of woodland is a good illustration of a food 'pyramid', with a broad base of herbivorous and insectivorous rodents, at relatively high density, serving as prey species for top carnivores such as the weasel and stoat which defend large territories and are thus thinly spread. Typical of the small prey species are the wood mouse and bank vole. Both supplement a diet of fruits, nuts, seeds and the green parts of plants with a certain amount of insect food. Shrews devour a wide variety of invertebrates and are the arch exploiters of the rich earthworm population that lurks beneath the leaf litter, a resource also tapped by hedgehogs, moles, foxes and badgers. It is not hard to see why, in this hazardous environment, the small mammals have sought safety by confining their activity to the hours of darkness—and many of their predators have had to follow suit.

Woodland deer—the fallow, roe and introduced muntjac—though largely exempt from this food chain, are also mostly dusk foragers, an adaptation to bygone times when they too had natural predators. Though most woodland mammals hunt throughout the year, a minority—the hedgehog, dormouse and the bats—hibernate over winter, while some others, such as the badger, merely become less active.

CHECKLIST

This checklist is a guide to the mammals you will find in broadleaved woodland. Although you will not see them all in the same woodland, you should be able to spot many of them as you walk through the different woods during the changing seasons. The species listed in **bold print** *are described in detail in this book.*

Badger
Bank vole
Chinese water deer
Common shrew
Dormouse
Fallow deer
Grey squirrel
Hedgehog
Long-eared bat
Mole
Muntjac deer
Noctule bat

Pipistrelle bat
Pygmy shrew
Rabbit
Red fox
Roe deer
Sika deer
Stoat
Weasel
Whiskered bat
Wildcat
Wood mouse

Above: Rough-and-tumble play between two badgers.

Left: A roe deer stands poised and alert—its sensitive ears pick up the slightest sound that might mean danger.

THE MAMMALS OF DECIDUOUS WOODS

Although deciduous woods can seem to be uninhabited, tucked away in the different layers of vegetation are many of our mammals, from large badgers and foxes to small mice, shrews and voles. Each has a special niche within this rich environment.

Deciduous woodland supports a greater variety of mammals than any other natural habitat. Many of today's woodlands are remnants of the great broadleaved forest that once stretched across the whole of northern Europe. Two thirds of our deciduous woodland is either native beech or oak, usually combined with species such as birch, ash, hazel, sycamore and various shrubs.

Layered habitats Deciduous woodlands consist of four main layers of vegetation, each providing living space for different species. Some, such as common and pygmy shrews, spend their entire lives at one level; others, such as squirrels and woodmice, move between the layers. Competition for space is not as great as it is in the less complex habitats of fields or moorlands, and many more species are accommodated into the woodland environment.

The highest point is the tree or canopy layer, comprising the branches of mature trees from 6-18m (20-60ft) high or more. Young trees, shrubs and bushes form the next

Right: A badger sett at dusk on a summer's evening. Badgers are one of the most common mammals of all types of deciduous woodlands, advertising their presence by evidence of their vigorous digging outside the sett. The best kind of site is one that is well protected – often by elder trees which have grown up from seeds contained in the droppings.

Below: A vixen and her cubs. A vixen will move her cubs to another location if she feels threatened, often taking over an old earth. Many foxes spend days lying up above ground.

level, the shrub layer, a dense growth sometimes called the lower canopy. Here such species as blackthorn, buckthorn, dog rose, elder, hawthorn and spindle flourish. Below is the field layer which extends to about 2m (6ft) above ground level and consists of low woody and herbaceous plants, flowers, ferns and mosses. This is the richest level in the variety of wildlife it supports, and most woodland mammals live or feed here. Below is the litter and soil layer.

Most mammals are more dependent on the general structure of deciduous woodland than on any individual plant species contained there. Important factors are the height of the vegetation, the presence or absence of field and shrub layers, and whether there are areas of open land, scrub and old trees. The bank vole, for example, is most common in woodlands with dense herbaceous areas, while the woodmouse is the common rodent of woodlands with an open field layer.

The canopy This layer attracts mainly insects and birds. Oak trees, in particular, are noted for their rich insect life – well over 200 species may live on a single tree during its life-span of up to 250 years. This activity not only draws numerous birds, but some mammals spend much of their lives high in the branches. Several species of bat hunt around

The red squirrel has lived in the British Isles for over 9000 years, particularly in the native Scots pine forests of the north. Today it lives mainly in pine woods, but in some parts of the British Isles it has adapted to deciduous woodland, above all to areas containing hazel and oak. Because of its arboreal nature, it has few predators, although it is occasionally pursued by the pine marten in areas of mixed natural woodland in the Scottish Highlands. In general the red squirrel population is declining in deciduous woodlands, although in some areas it co-exists well with the grey squirrel.

Shrub layer This layer consists of the lower branches of mature trees, saplings and shrubs, and it is often entwined with such climbers as ivy or honeysuckle. Indeed, stripped honeysuckle stems are a sign of the presence of the common, or hazel, dormouse, an increasingly rare mammal which lives mainly in the shrub layer, although it also climbs into the canopy. It prefers woodlands with plenty of dense secondary growth and scrub, where hazel, beech and sweet chestnut are the dominant tree species. It makes its daytime roosting nest in the undergrowth or in the cleft of a sapling.

The dormouse is a solitary, nocturnal animal and one of the best times to look out for it is the twilight of late summer and early autumn evenings when it emerges from its daytime sleep to eat all the fruits and nuts it can find so as to gain weight before its long winter hibernation from October to April. One sign of its presence is discarded hazel nuts with smooth, neat, round holes; other rodents leave a more ragged hole.

Deer are creatures of the shrub layer. They remain hidden during most of the day, moving from cover in the evening to graze, and returning at dawn. In undisturbed areas they may be active during the day, but usually all you will see is a disappearing rump as the animal runs off into the trees.

Sika deer have established feral herds in

the tops of trees for flying insects and some, notably the long-eared bat, specialise in picking insects off the foliage. Bats often inhabit holes in the upper reaches of the trunk. In beech woodland during the day you can sometimes hear the noctule bat chattering in a tree hole, and nursery colonies are also found in tree holes.

The most common mammal of the tree canopy of deciduous woodlands is the grey squirrel. It thrives particularly in oak and sweet chestnut woodlands, feeding on nuts, bark (especially that of sycamore), shoots, fungi and birds' eggs. In winter it is quite easy to spot its untidy spherical drey of twigs and dead leaves high in the branches, or at the junction of a branch and the main trunk.

A mammal sometimes confused with the grey squirrel is the fat dormouse, also known as the grey, edible or squirrel-tailed dormouse. It is confined to an area around Tring in the Chilterns, where it was first introduced earlier this century. However, it is smaller than the squirrel and entirely nocturnal, spending its day in a nest built close to the trunk of a tree or in a tree hole. It has a similar diet to the grey squirrel, and can cause damage to trees. Both species are accomplished acrobats, making great leaps between branches, using their tails to help with balance.

Below: The stoat lives in most areas of the British Isles but particularly in deciduous woodland where there are good supplies of food. It takes fruits and berries as well as rodents and rabbits. Apart from man, the stoat has no natural predators.

Above: The roe deer is much more conspicuous during winter when its white rump shows up clearly in the bare woodland. It is a browser, preferring bramble and twigs.

Below: A hedgehog with its young in autumn leaves. The hedgehog tends to live on the edge of deciduous woodland, as well as in copses and farmland. Litters may be born as late as October, but the young are unlikely to survive the winter.

Dorset, Hampshire, West Yorkshire and parts of Scotland. They prefer deciduous or mixed woodland with an undergrowth of hazel, bramble, blackthorn or other shrubs. Sika are grazers, feeding mainly on grasses and sedges in fields and open land within easy distance of protective cover.

Roe deer are mainly browsers, taking leaves, branches, shoots and bark of broad-leaved trees including ash, hazel and oak. In many areas they are considered a serious pest. Fallow deer and muntjac are both grazers and browsers, depending on the availability of food. Fallow deer have the widest distribution of all the deer species in England, while muntjac are mainly confined to the south-east.

Lower layers Dwelling in the field layer and at ground level are woodmice, bank voles, shrews, hedgehogs, rabbits and hares, and their predators the fox, stoat, weasel and, in Wales, the polecat. The badger, largest of the woodland mammals, eats small mammals occasionally but its main diet includes amphibians, slugs, snails, grubs, insects and earthworms (probably its most important food item), as well as fruits, roots, tubers and nuts.

Some of these species, such as shrews and bank voles, are active day and night. The common shrew makes runways and tunnels through the litter and soil and can sometimes be heard making a soft twittering sound as it searches for invertebrates to satisfy its voracious appetite. It eats at a furious rate for two hours or so, then rests, and then eats again, for it must take in its own body weight each day. The pygmy shrew also lives in woodlands, but it is less abundant than its relatives. The bank vole builds a nest of grass and moss under roots and in tree stumps. It is an active burrower, but most of its food is obtained from the field layer.

Moles are also both nocturnal and diurnal, although mole hills are likely to be the only evidence of their existence, for adult moles are seldom seen above ground. The mole digs its complex tunnel system underground, pushing the loose soil upwards to form the characteristic molehill. People do not always realise that deciduous woodlands have abundant mole populations because the large nest mound or 'fortress' is usually built in dense undergrowth.

Of the woodland's mammal predators, the stoat and weasel are the most active during the day. They are mainly ground-level hunters, following regularly revised paths and feeding on locally available small to medium sized mammals such as mice, voles and rabbits.

Night life Towards dusk, when truly diurnal mammals such as the grey squirrel are eating their last meal of the day, a night-shift begins to appear. Bats, including the noctule, pipistrelle, Bechstein's and serotine, emerge from their roosts in tree hollows or beneath foliage in the upper canopy, and can be heard squeaking and chattering as they chase insects, including moths.

Around dusk the badger emerges from its sett. It has no predators apart from man, and its conspicuous colouring serves as a recognition sign for other badgers at night, although it appears grey from a distance. Its ideal habitat is a beech wood on light, well-drained gravelly soil, with pasture and arable land within its home range, although it is well adapted to all types of deciduous woodland. Another carnivore, the fox, is one of the most successful of all our mammals, managing to live in almost all types of habitat in the British Isles. In woodlands its diet includes small rodents, rabbits, hares, birds, insects and carrion.

The most nocturnal mammals are the hedgehog, fat and common dormouse, woodmouse and yellow-necked mouse. The hedgehog sleeps in undergrowth during the day, changing its site frequently during summer. It searches at night for ground level invertebrates.

Cold weather The deciduous woodland in autumn provides a rich supply of food for its inhabitants. Nuts and pulpy fruits, as well as fungi, are eagerly seized. Even the highly carnivorous fox takes its share. To some species the autumn harvest is of special long-term importance. The grey squirrel stores surplus nuts in the ground, in tree hollows and in dreys. In times of shortage it can remember the general area where the caches lie, but damp conditions are needed before it can locate, by its sense of smell, the exact position of a hoard. Many of these caches remain unused or undiscovered, and the seeds and nuts may germinate to become new trees.

In years of poor mast harvest many mammals, especially those with specialised or restricted diets, such as the edible dormouse, die before their first winter. Many young mammals leave home in autumn, and the available food supply from trees and shrubs can be a vital factor in their survival. Many mammals reduce their activity, but in the British Isles only a few truly hibernate: hedgehogs, bats and the two species of dormouse. The metabolism slows right down, the heart beats much less often, the animal breathes more slowly, and its temperature drops. In

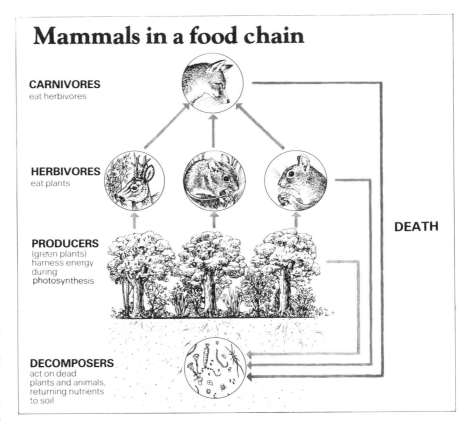

Mammals in a food chain

CARNIVORES
eat herbivores

HERBIVORES
eat plants

PRODUCERS
(green plants) harness energy during photosynthesis

DECOMPOSERS
act on dead plants and animals, returning nutrients to soil

DEATH

this way it conserves its energy. Warm days in mid-winter can be disastrous for hibernating animals, for their body temperature heats up and they use their vital stored energy too fast, with no means of replacing it until spring.

For the deer on the other hand, autumn and winter are the most strenuous period of the year. For the fallow deer, in particular, autumn is the time of the 'rut', a period of tremendous activity for the males, which mark out their territories by fraying trees and shrubs with their antlers and by scraping the leaf litter and soil. Rutting areas, which are usually beneath trees, can be recognised in autumn by the well-trodden paths around the bases and by the musky scent of the bucks.

Below: A mole making an appearance above ground. The mole takes nearly all of its food underground, for worms are its main diet and on a clay soil in a deciduous wood they will often fall into the mole's tunnels. The mole sometimes builds a fortress, an enormous molehill that is usually concealed in the undergrowth. Since it spends most of its time underground the mole is relatively secure from predators, although some are killed by foxes.

FALLOW DEER – GRACEFUL GRAZERS

By the early summer the male fallow deer is growing a new set of impressive and distinctive antlers in readiness for the autumn rutting season. After this mating period, the female deer gives birth to a single fawn in the following June.

Fallow are the most widely dispersed deer in the British Isles, including Ireland – where roe deer are absent. Their natural habitat is deciduous or mixed woodland with thick undergrowth.

Fallow deer existed in the British Isles more than a million years ago, but died out during the Ice Age. The Normans reintroduced them to Ireland in 1244, and almost certainly to England before that date. Since then fallow deer have been widely kept in special deer parks – of which there are currently just over 100 – partly for their attractive appearance and also for their venison. You have a good chance of seeing these deer at close quarters in many town parks, such as Richmond Park in London, as well as zoos; in both locations they have learned to tolerate humans.

Wild herds that are found in areas such as Epping Forest, The Forest of Dean, Cannock Chase and the New Forest are descendants of those deer reintroduced by the Normans; but many wild herds have a closer ancestry to park deer which escaped during the two World Wars. Deer parks were neglected and fences fell into disrepair at these periods, and this enabled large numbers of deer to escape. Left alone in the wild, these herds flourished and multiplied.

Signs and tracks In the wild, fallow deer are shy and elusive creatures. Unless you move very quietly, they will take fright and you will catch only a fleeting glimpse of them as they run away. So it is best to look for signs which give away their presence in a wood; these are provided by the outline of the trees.

Fallow deer feed on leaves and twigs. The branches of the trees are cropped off in a

straight line about two metres above the ground—the highest the deer can reach—giving them a flat-bottomed shape. In muddy ground you may see cloven hoofmarks; these are, however, similar to those of sika, roe and red deer and even sheep, so you will find it difficult to tell them apart.

The droppings of these deer species are also alike, with some variations in size between the species and the sexes. Fallows' are glossy, black, striped cylindrical pellets, pointed at one end. The pellets of an adult male (buck) are about 12mm ($\frac{1}{2}$in) square; those of the female (doe) are slightly smaller.

Coat colour Although fallow deer vary considerably in colour, you will most likely see the dark-dappled 'Bambi' coat. This summer coat is a rich, glossy brown with white spots. Before winter it changes to grey-brown with barely discernible spots. The white rump patch is edged by a black horseshoe-shaped line. The tail, which is about 18cm (7in) long, is white below and black on top—a continuation of the black stripe that runs down the mid-line of the back. The deer shows its white scut with a flip of the tail to warn other members of the herd of any danger.

There is a paler variety, with black markings replaced by brown and the main body colour a lighter fawn. In winter the spots remain distinct. The so-called black variety has a glossy jet-black coat in summer, with elephant-grey belly and legs; the spots are indistinct and dappled. The coat becomes duller in winter.

The other main variety you are likely to see is white or pale ginger; these deer are partial albinos and have orange hooves and a pale nose. They are sandy coloured at birth, becoming gradually whiter during their first few months. You will see many intermediate shades, since deer of different colour varieties can interbreed, and the offspring are not necessarily the colour of either parent.

Elegant heads Both the buck and doe fallow deer have a gracefully curving neck. Their brown eyes are set in the side of the head to give wide-angled vision and the large ears can be swivelled in the direction of the slightest sound. The deer's acute sight and sensitive hearing alert them to any hint of danger.

From late summer through to spring the bucks sport magnificent antlers which they later shed. These can measure up to 80cm (31in). The long spikes growing from the broad, flat palms distinguish these deer from all other British species.

Rutting season During the long days of summer, while food is plentiful, the deer eat well and build up reserves of fat to stand them in good stead for the leaner days ahead. They not only have the rigours of winter to face, but also the rut or mating season—a time of intense activity for the bucks.

Having spent the summer away from the does and their fawns, the bucks return before

The annual cycle of antler growth

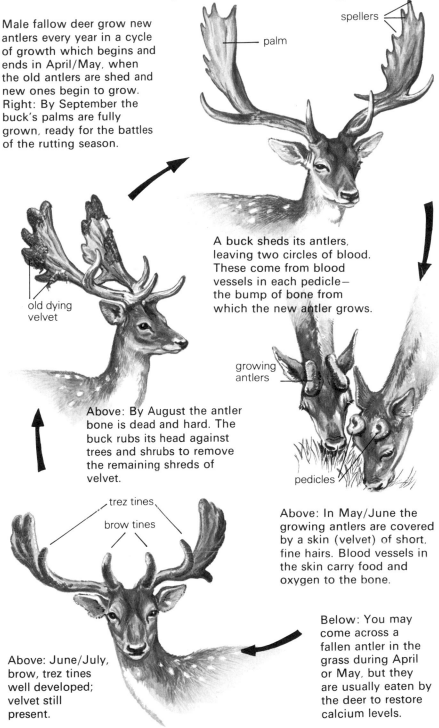

Male fallow deer grow new antlers every year in a cycle of growth which begins and ends in April/May, when the old antlers are shed and new ones begin to grow. Right: By September the buck's palms are fully grown, ready for the battles of the rutting season.

palm

spellers

old dying velvet

A buck sheds its antlers, leaving two circles of blood. These come from blood vessels in each pedicle—the bump of bone from which the new antler grows.

growing antlers

pedicles

Above: By August the antler bone is dead and hard. The buck rubs its head against trees and shrubs to remove the remaining shreds of velvet.

Above: In May/June the growing antlers are covered by a skin (velvet) of short, fine hairs. Blood vessels in the skin carry food and oxygen to the bone.

trez tines

brow tines

Above: June/July, brow, trez tines well developed; velvet still present.

Below: You may come across a fallen antler in the grass during April or May, but they are usually eaten by the deer to restore calcium levels.

FALLOW DEER (*Dama dama*)

Size of adult male about 95cm (37in); weighs 50-95kg (121-209lb). Female 35-55kg (77-121lb).

Breeding (rutting) season autumn; young born following summer (June).

No of young one

Lifespan uncertain, at least 10 years in parks.

Food Tree foliage, acorns, beech mast, grasses, herbs, bramble, ivy.

Predators man; foxes occasionally take fawns.

Distribution Throughout England, Wales and most of Ireland; more isolated in Scotland.

Right: Tree bark fraying is common in woodlands with fallow deer—the buck rubs his head against the tree to remove the shreds of velvet from his antlers.

Below: The 'black' variety of fallow deer has a very much darker coat than usual.

the rut starts in October. They parade around their territories and advertise their presence to other bucks by groaning loudly and thrashing bushes and trees with their antlers. Sometimes they will strip the bark of older trees, rub the trunk smooth and anoint it with secretions from glands below the corners of the eyes.

They also scrape the ground with their forefeet, and at this time of year you will often come across bare patches of muddy ground with hoofmarks, hairs and the unmistakeable pungent smell of rutty urine. On a still night the deep belching noise of the rutting cry can carry a long way. With their massive antlers, enlarged necks and prominent Adam's apples, the bucks are an impressive sight.

Does are attracted into a buck's territory, where he chivvies and herds them. He defends them fiercely and will fight off any rivals, groaning at and chasing them. Well-matched rival bucks size each other up and often pace the ground shoulder-to-shoulder before wheeling to meet with a tremendous clashing of antlers. Very occasionally antlers may become inextricably entangled–leading to the death of both animals.

Fawning Eight months after mating the doe seeks out a quiet place well away from other deer to give birth to her fawn. This is usually in June, when the bracken and long grasses of the woodland floor provide good cover. After licking the fawn clean and suckling it for the first time, she will move back to the doe herd or feed alone, returning a number of times each day to feed her youngster.

Does and fawns spend the summer in a separate part of the wood from the bucks. The does and their offspring often form herds after the fawns are a few weeks old, when the youngsters will gambol about, chasing one another playfully.

Maturing fawns When the fawns are about three months old, the first difference between the sexes becomes apparent: a tuft of hairs growing from the male's penis sheath. This brush becomes a characteristic of mature bucks. By the time they are six months old, some of the male fawns have quite noticeable bumps on their foreheads. These are pedicles from which the antlers will grow. When the fawns are about one year old their first antlers–stubs or slender 15cm (6in) spikes–will have formed on top of the pedicles.

In the second year the young bucks leave the doe herd and join the older bucks, to whom they are subordinate. The youngest does to be mated are about 16 months old; they will give birth to their first fawn by their second birthday.

Diet and feeding During the summer fallow deer eat the grasses and herbs in woodland glades and rides or in open pastures. You are most likely to see them feeding at dawn or dusk, although in undisturbed areas they may spend much of the day lying in a sunny field chewing the cud. Usually they choose a spot

with woodland nearby. If danger threatens they will quickly run for cover, led in single file by a doe. Sometimes when they are alarmed they adopt a strange gait – the pronk – in which they bound stiff-legged on all four feet, stop, stare around them and run off again.

Come autumn the deer move into the woodland and seek out acorns, beech mast and sweet and horse chestnuts. A good crop will help the bucks regain condition after the rut. If there is heather available on adjacent heathland, as in the New Forest, they will often move out into the open to eat that in winter.

Selective culling The bear and the wolf – once the two great natural predators – have been extinct in the British Isles for centuries. So adult deer have little to fear today except Man, who hunts them for sport and venison. However if a fallow deer herd were left alone in the wild, it would increase by about a third every year. So selective culling is sometimes necessary to protect both the deer population and the valuable woodland timber.

Above: The fawn weighs 4.5kg (9½lb) at birth. Although it takes its first faltering steps within a few hours, it tires easily and spends its first days resting. It follows close to its mother when it is two weeks old, and begins to supplement an all-milk diet with vegetation until it is completely weaned – although a fawn may be still taking some milk at seven months.

Left: If you find a young fawn lying in the grass, do not make the mistake of thinking its mother has abandoned it – you can be sure she is nearby. She will not return to suckle her offspring until you have gone.

ROE DEER

The roe deer, smallest of our native species, is a shy animal, hiding away for most of the time in woodland thickets.

The graceful roe deer, smallest among our native species of deer, is found in most of the forested areas of Great Britain with the exception of Wales and Northern Ireland. It is as much at home in the sombre conifer plantations of the Scottish highlands as in the open hazel thickets of southern England.

Without practice in spotting them, roe deer can be difficult to see, even in the open. This art of remaining 'invisible' is one of the qualities that has earned them the nickname, 'Fairies of the Woods'. A single thistle can be enough to break up the deer's outline and, once suspicious, the roe may stand motionless until quite certain that its presence has been discovered. Only then will it bound away, displaying a prominent patch of light-coloured hair on the rump. This hair can be puffed up as an alarm signal to other roe in the area.

Identification The actual size of these little deer is deceiving. Although the bucks weigh less than a large dog, and are little more than 60cm (24in) in height at the shoulder, they often give the impression of being much larger, possibly because of their graceful build and fine bone structure.

The roe can be distinguished from the similar-sized muntjac (barking deer) by its lack of spots and absence of tail. The bony points (pedicles) from which the antlers grow are short by comparison with those of the muntjac.

A typical adult roe buck has antlers with three branches or points on each side, making six points in all. The total length may be as great as 30cm (12in). The size and the number of points depend more on feeding and health than age and heredity.

In the early part of the year, while the antlers are still growing, they are covered in furry skin (velvet). When growth is complete, the antler hardens; the velvet dies and is rubbed off by the buck. He does this by scraping his antlers up and down on a tree of a suitable size; this action, which is known as fraying, damages the bark and may distort or even kill the tree. Even after the antlers are cleaned of velvet the buck persists in this activity, which is ritualised into a demonstration of aggression.

Telltale signs In woods inhabited by roe, signs of their occupation are everywhere for those with eyes to see them. Their cloven hooves leave tracks (slots) in muddy places and on their favourite paths. Well-trodden

tracks may sometimes be seen around a single tree or bush, especially in summer. These are known as 'roe rings' and may be related to courtship behaviour.

When the deer have been running or jumping, the marks of the two dew claws, vestigial digits slightly above the hoof, may also register on the ground. If disturbed, roe make off in a series of terrific bounds and up to 16 metres (17 yards) may be covered in a single spring.

In forest rides, your eyes may be attracted by the peeled stem of a small tree or shrub where a buck has been marking his territory. At the base of the tree there is often a triangular scrape where his flailing forefeet have dug into the earth. If you look more closely, you may see his signature in the shape of a hoof mark stamped clearly into the centre of the scrape.

Other bushes and low-growing herbage of all kinds may have been nibbled. If there seems to be an inexplicable lack of leaves up to a certain height from the ground, the reason is that deer have eaten everything within their reach. This is called a browse line, and whenever you come upon one that is about one metre (roughly three feet) high, you can be fairly sure that roe are numerous in the area.

Territories Unlike the larger breeds of deer, roe do not normally form herds but live on their own or in small groups, unless they are forced in winter to congregate in the limited areas where there are food reserves. From about April to August the doe and buck each have their own territories, which may overlap or be quite separate. The doe's territory may overlap with that of several bucks and vice versa. Parts of the doe's territory may also be shared with other females.

The buck defends his territory vigorously against other bucks by aggressive displays of barking, fraying and scraping up moss and leaves with the forefoot. Fighting between two evenly matched bucks can occur in

Above: The fawn is born with a sandy brown coat flecked with black and blue and liberally splashed with white. The spots gradually fade, and disappear after about three months. The adult coat (opposite) is a sandy or foxy red in summer.

ROE DEER (*Capreolus capreolus*).
Weight Male (buck) 26kg (57lb). Female (doe) 24kg (52lb).
Height (to shoulder) Male 64cm (25in). Female 63cm (24in).
Colour Winter: greyish brown. Summer: sandy/foxy red.
Breeding season young born mid-May to mid-June.
Gestation 5 months, preceded by 5-month period of delayed implantation.
No of young (fawns) 1-3.
Lifespan Average 3 years.
Food Brambles, broad-leaved tree twigs, herbs.
Predators: Adults: Man. Fawns: dogs, foxes.
Distribution Widespread in Scotland and north of England. Also present in south of England and East Anglia. (See map below.)

Roe deer in summer and winter

In winter the coat is greyish brown. The rump patch is a distinctive white or light buff. In the male, this patch is oval. In the female, it is an inverted heart shape and includes a small brush (anal tush). Some adults also have light patches on the neck.

distinctive brush of hair

indented rump patch

♀

pedicles (growing points)

rump patch

neck patches

♂

In summer the coat varies from a sandy to a foxy red. The rump patch is an inconspicuous pale lemon yellow, and the new growth of antlers distinguishes the buck from the doe. A typical roe buck has antlers with forward and rear points on each side, making six points in all.

rump patch inconspicuous

♀

clean antlers

♂

rump patch inconspicuous

more open moorland, where visibility may be several hundred yards, he can defend a much larger area from incoming bucks.

Eating habits Like all deer, roe are ruminants. They generally feed at dawn and dusk, resting between these times to chew the cud. In undisturbed areas, feeding and ruminating take place throughout the day.

Roe are primarily browsing animals rather than grazers, preferring twigs to grass. They are, however, far from fussy in their choice of foods. Probably their favourites are the twigs and leaves of brambles (or roses, if they can get them!), and the leaves of willow, rowan, hazel and other broad-leaved species. They also eat conifer needles and buds, especially the softer varieties such as cypress and Douglas fir.

Roe deer can also be seen grazing in fields, particularly in spring when food in the woods is still scarce. They have been known to eat mushrooms and hedge fruit, as well as many herbs.

Breeding cycle The mating season or rut of the roe is in late July and early August. One of the strangest features of the breeding cycle, unique to this species, is that the fertilised egg does not immediately implant in the uterus wall, but stays free-floating, increasing only gradually in size, until December when implantation takes place. After that, development at the normal rate leads up to the birth of the fawns in late May or early June. The total gestation is therefore 10 months, although the female is only visibly pregnant for about half that time.

Does usually give birth to twins, but triplets are not uncommon, and singles occur in areas of poorer feeding. The fawns are born with spotted coats which camouflage them as they lie motionless in the dappled shade of the trees. By the time they are about

summer. Although this usually takes the form of a pushing match, with the loser soon disengaging and bounding away, fights to the death sometimes occur. The victim is nearly always stabbed repeatedly, even after he is lying prostrate on the ground. In spite of the simple form of their antlers, two roe bucks occasionally become entangled during a fight and, if they are unable to disengage, death for both adversaries is inevitable.

Ideally, a roe territory should contain ample food and cover, with some open space. The size of the buck's territory depends not only on the density of deer in the area, but also on visibility. In thick woodland, he may have only a couple of acres, while in

First antlers may be simple spikes, as in the case of this yearling buck, or have forward points. Occasionally, they may have rear points as well. Usually, six-point antlers are not grown until the second year of life. The nubbly effect (pearling) is particularly pronounced in the roe deer.

three months old, they have acquired the normal adult coat and, apart from being lighter in build, may be difficult to distinguish from their parents.

Male fawns sometimes grow tiny spikes or buttons of antler in December of their first year. These are hard and clean in January and are shed early in February, when the regular yearling antlers begin to grow.

A heavy toll The survival chances of the young roe are poor. Mortality in the first year may be as high as 50%. Some fawns, particularly young ones, fall victim to foxes and dogs. The doe defends her young vigorously against these predators, but she can do nothing to protect them against disease. In areas heavily populated by roe, parasitic pneumonia, caused by lung-worm, can kill large numbers of fawns in early spring.

In May, when the new season's fawns are due to be born, the buck and doe drive out their young of the previous year. The banished yearlings then have to wander about until they find somewhere else to live. In the meantime they are exposed to increased risks from cars, dogs and, not least, from people who have shooting rights over the land they cross.

Friend or foe? The roe's liking for newly-planted forest trees, for both fraying and browsing, has brought it into sharp conflict with landowners. In the past, the deer population was kept in check by bears and

wolves but, with the absence of these natural predators, this is now the job of the forester.

If roe deer were to become completely protected they would soon become an unbearable pest. As it is, with careful management, we can expect these graceful creatures to inhabit our woods for many years to come.

Above: Two high-spirited young bucks engage in a harmless winter sparring match. In summer, when the adult bucks are armed with antlers, these contests cease to be playful and sometimes end in death.

Below: Growing antlers are covered with furry skin (velvet), which the buck removes by scraping on wood. He persists in this activity even after the antlers are cleaned.

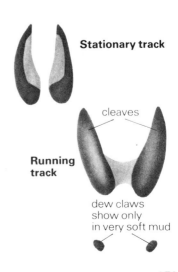

Stationary track

cleaves

Running track

dew claws show only in very soft mud

THE FAMILY LIFE OF THE RED FOX

Fox cubs are born deep in the earth in spring and pressure then mounts on the adult foxes to find enough food to go round the ever-hungry family. In some family groups, non-breeding vixens lend valuable assistance in rearing the young and by the end of the summer the young are able to fend for themselves.

Below: A pair of half-grown fox cubs near the earth where they were born. Four or five cubs to a litter is usual, and a vixen does not bear more than one litter each season. As autumn approaches the cubs, which by then have learnt how to hunt for themselves, disperse —the dog foxes are likely to travel further from the home earth than the vixens.

During the winter dog foxes and vixens often shelter underground in an earth. Normally each fox regularly uses only a few earths within its territory.

With the approach of spring, however, the behaviour of the vixen changes. She is pregnant, having mated in late January, and carries her young for an average of 53 days. As her pregnancy advances, she excavates many disused earths–sometimes old badger or rabbit holes–throughout her home range, and makes exploratory diggings at potential sites for new earths.

These burrows, begun along sandy banks and ridges, often reach no more than 10-20cm (4-8in) into the ground. You can spot where they have been started from the surrounding soil, which bears deep gouges from the vixen's claws. These exploratory diggings are often abandoned, but why is not always obvious. Sometimes the fox encounters a sturdy root which impedes progress, but at other times she simply seems to change her mind about the site.

Birth in the earth The earth the vixen eventually chooses to house her cubs–which are generally born at the end of March–usually has two or three entrances and may stretch for several metres underground, through a series of ramifying tunnels.

When the cubs are born the vixen is confined within the earth, staying there for several days and sometimes for more than a week. During this time, the dog fox's behaviour may be critical to the vixen's well-being. On the whole the dog fox is a conscientious father and regularly provides food for his mate. You can sometimes find a small offering of food lying outside the entrance to the earth, where the dog fox has left it.

Non-breeding vixens In some areas, foxes live in social groups made up of one dog fox and several vixens. By radio-tracking it has been possible to discover that each of these group members shares roughly the same range of territory. There is little overlap with the range of similar neighbouring groups.

Although vixens are reproductively mature in their first year, it seems that where social groups develop some vixens within the group –particularly the younger members–do not breed.

In some places, perhaps as few as one third of those able to do so actually breed. This figure varies greatly from place to place. World-wide research shows that in certain areas well over 90% of vixens conceive and give birth in their first year.

From observation of fox groups in captivity it seems that the dog fox mates with only one vixen, showing no interest at all in any others in the group. In the wild it is likely that more vixens mate and conceive than in captivity, but only a minority succeed in reaching a full-term pregnancy or rearing offspring.

In a survey in which radio-tagged non-breeding vixens were followed at night, it appeared that these individuals visited the vicinity of the breeding earth each night–and several times in some cases. The 'barren' vixens were apparently participating in rearing the cubs, sitting and playing with them and even providing them with food.

At first sight, this seems to be an extraordinary act of altruism. The vixens which do not have the opportunity to bear young themselves instead help to rear those of another vixen. Since the success of an individual, in evolutionary terms, is measured by the number of offspring which survive to

A villainous predator?

Foxes, long accused of preying on poultry and lambs, have always been sought out and killed. The debate continues to rage about the extent of damage done and the effectiveness of fox control in reducing that damage. Free-range hens are not so often kept now, so fox depredation on poultry is no longer a vexed issue.
There is some evidence that foxes take poor-quality, weak lambs, but many of these are probably dead before the fox finds them. There is also irrefutable evidence of lamb-worrying. However, only a minority of foxes in sheep-farming regions ever kill lambs. If this were not so, losses would be enormous.
Spring, when fox cubs are out and about, is also the time when farmers and gamekeepers seek to destroy them.

Below: A family of cubs at play. If you want to watch cubs in the open, position yourself downwind and keep still. Any adult foxes about are likely to bolt at a gust of wind or crack of a twig.

Cubs and the earth

The night or two before giving birth, the vixen tours round several earths before choosing one – which will usually be in a bank or ridge of sandy, easy-to-dig soil. The vixen bears one litter of 4-5 young in a season; these are born blind but covered with short, dark fur. She does not make a nest with bedding material; the cubs lie on bare earth in a hollowed-out cavern deep inside the earth. A high-pitched whimpering sound will betray the presence of suckling cubs. If you can hear this, you'll probably already have disturbed the adults enough to make them move the cubs to another earth.

breed subsequent generations, this behaviour is paradoxical.

A clue to the reason for this apparently selfless behaviour may lie in the observation that all the vixens in a given group commonly look alike. They may share features such as a blaze of white on the legs or a heavily marked muzzle. It seems that the female members of fox groups are at least sometimes close relatives – daughters, sisters, aunts. This provides a possible explanation. They have a stake, an evolutionary investment, in the survival of their relative's cubs, since those cubs will carry some of the genes shared by the whole family. Helping to rear a relative is breeding by proxy.

Social controls Why don't the helpers simply breed themselves? The answer may be that they have no choice. Evidence suggests that helpers are often socially subordinate to the breeding female. It may be that their failure to breed is a direct consequence of low status and thus beyond their own control. The mechanism could be equivalent to a sort of inbuilt family planning.

The young vixen may be faced with the dilemma of staying at home, with no opportunity of breeding, or of leaving home in the hope of surviving long enough to find a territory of her own. Staying at home as a helper – at least for a time – may be the best compromise. There is, after all, a chance

Right: As a fox cub grows older, it wanders off on foraging expeditions of its own, mainly catching worms and beetles. At this stage, the cub is less wary than its parents and is therefore easier to watch.

that she will inherit the territory when the dominant vixen dies. There may even be opportunities to breed before then, since not infrequently there are cases of two vixens within one group breeding, and even sharing the same earth.

Feeding the cubs Up to the age of about three weeks, fox cubs are fed on their mother's milk. After that they begin to gnaw at scraps of meat. This heralds a change in the behaviour of the non-breeding vixens. They start to spend much more time with the cubs, grooming them and sometimes even splitting the litter up into two or three hiding places, each guarded by a different vixen. The most striking thing of all is the extent to which non-breeding vixens aid the young cubs by feeding them. In some cases, they carry more food back to the cubs than the real mother. On one occasion, it was found that when a vixen, the mother of a litter, was taken seriously ill, her cubs survived with the help of several non-breeding females .

It is a major task for the adult foxes to provide enough food for the growing cubs, even though the labour for parents which have the benefit of helpers is reduced. In areas where foxes maintain large territories—some well over 400 acres—the task of carrying the food home is substantial. There is some evidence that the diet of growing cubs comprises more large prey than does that of the adults during the same period. This could

Above: By autumn, when the young foxes start to disperse, they are able to hunt down and kill prey for themselves. Dog foxes probably wander further afield than the stay-at-home young vixens.

result if parents were deliberately economising on travel by carrying larger prey to the cubs. Certainly, it is more efficient to carry back one hare than to make several dozen trips with mice and voles.

Gaining independence By early summer the cubs have grown sufficiently to follow the adults out of the earth. It often looks as though the adults lead a cub deliberately on a tutorial expedition. Every time one adult fox sniffs at something, a cub rushes up and also sniffs at it, closely imitating its parents' behaviour in everything. Sometimes the cubs wander away from the earth by themselves and this when they are out in daylight—is a good time to see them.

As the cubs grow increasingly independent, they forage more and more for themselves, often choosing quite different prey from that fed to them by their parents. Three or four-month-old cubs scour the grass for beetles and at night, if weather conditions permit, they catch earthworms. Adults catch the worms without difficulty, but the cubs seem to take a while to learn the technique of stabbing the snout down into the vegetation to grab the worms. At first they are more inclined to try to catch them by the so-called mouse leap—a movement the cubs exhibit almost as soon as they can run. The fox leaps high off the ground, then lands on a mouse with both forepaws. This may be an adaptation to thwart the escape response shown by wood mice which leap upwards when threatened. By landing from above the fox forestalls the mouse's escape. Cubs trying to catch earthworms with such leaps fail miserably because the worms slip away between their paws. However, the correct technique is soon learned.

Some young dog foxes begin to disperse in early autumn, although others wait until midwinter. Although members of a group may spend little time together as the summer draws to a close, and even though they rarely hunt together, they may well still be in close contact. As they criss-cross the territory by night, members of a family not only meet quite frequently, but can also keep in touch through scent and sound.

BADGERS–EXCAVATORS OF THE WOODLANDS

Badgers spend most of the day out of sight–underneath a sloping hillside covered with plenty of undergrowth. Inside this hidden lair they are either resting or busy digging to improve and enlarge their chambers and passages. At dusk they are up and about, hunting, playing and searching for new bedding.

Below: A badger emerges from its sett at dusk, ready for a night of hunting. The badger's prey consists principally of earthworms but it also eats a variety of insects (particularly beetles), rabbits, carrion, fruit and even cereals. Shallow untidy holes in the vicinity of a sett indicate where the badger has been digging for food, and well-worn paths show the extent of its territory.

Badgers have been described as the oldest land-owners in Britain. There is little doubt that long before Britain was an island they were here rooting among the vegetation of ancient deciduous forests. They belong to the family of mammals that have musk-bearing scent glands under their tails: these are chiefly carnivorous and include the otter, polecat, stoat, weasel and pine marten.

Many millions of years ago the earliest forms of this family group were rather simple land-dwellers, but they have gradually become adapted to their different ways of life and habitats. Thus the otter has become an accomplished swimmer and the pine marten a trapeze artist; the polecat, stoat and weasel are streamlined for speed and the badger has become a skilful excavator.

You can tell from its appearance that the badger is a digger. Its body is wedge-shaped and carried rather low on the ground on short but immensely strong legs—excellent for working in confined spaces. The muscles of the forelimbs and neck are particularly well developed and the five claws on each foot are long, especially those on the front ones.

The badger's digging activity is geared to enlarging and improving its home: a large underground burrow system called a sett, which consists of several sizeable chambers where the badger sleeps and breeds and a few smaller ones which sometimes serve as latrines. These chambers are linked by a complex network of tunnels.

When enlarging one of its tunnels a badger will loosen the earth with rapid strokes of its forelimbs, using its claws as rakes and for winkling out stones. The loose earth collects under its body, but by arching its back it is able to bring its hind limbs forewards to sweep the earth backwards. When enough soil has collected behind it, it moves backwards in a series of jerks, partly using its bottom as a bulldozer and partly hugging the soil between its forelegs and body. If you stand by an exit hole when a badger is digging you may be showered with earth and stones as it emerges backwards and gives a few last vigorous kicks before returning for another load.

As well as a home improver, the badger is also a tidy housekeeper and will spend a lot of time transporting grass, straw, moss or bracken to and from its sleeping chamber. Setts are handed down like family houses, from generation to generation, and the badger uses the same sett year after year. So regular airing of the bedding is vital as a safeguard against parasites (the scourge of all animals living a settled existence) and to prevent damp, cold conditions—especially harmful to young cubs.

Locating the sett A mild day in early spring is a good time to start looking for a badger community, although it is very unlikely that you will see a badger itself in broad daylight. Woods, copses and hedgerows are the most usual locations for setts, especially if these are

Above: Badgers usually have a black and white face and a grey body, although their fur is often stained yellow or reddish by the local soil.

Left: A sow bringing back bedding straw. As many as 30 bundles may be collected on a dry night to furnish the underground chambers used for sleeping and breeding.

on slopes bordering pastures. Here the badger can make its home where there is adequate cover and plenty of food in the vicinity.

Alders are often associated with badger setts, so look for patches of these trees. Elders will also grow near setts because badgers eat the berries and pass the seeds unharmed through their guts before depositing them in the droppings near their sett. Here the seeds will germinate and eventually become bushes or trees.

A well-established sett is unmistakeable. It will normally have anything from three to 10 entrances and a few have been found with more than 50. These entrances and exits are at least 25cm (10in) wide, much larger than rabbit holes. Outside each entrance is a large pile of earth which includes dried plant material such as hay or straw. This is old bedding which has been discarded. You will usually see a latrine close to an entrance, too. Near a main entrance you may see a tree, often an elder, with mud marks and scratches on it up to a height of about one metre. If you watch at dusk you may see a badger approach such a tree, raise itself on its hind legs, reach up with its forepaws and slowly drag these down the bark. Zoologists still don't know if the badger is merely stretching its limbs or perhaps marking a territory with its own particular scent.

Well-worn paths lead from the sett in

BADGER (*Meles meles*)
Also called brock
Size of adult heaviest in autumn, lightest in spring Male 11.6kg (25½lb). Female 10.1kg (23⅓lb). Average length of male 90cm (3ft) including tail. Female slightly smaller
Colour grey, rarely pale reddish, albino or blackish
Breeding season young usually born mid-Jan to mid-March
Gestation period 7-8 weeks of 'true gestation' preceded by a variable period of delayed implantation (2-10 months)
Number of young 1-5, average about 3. During first 8 weeks may reduce to 2
Lifespan Average 2-3 years, max about 15 in the wild
Food diet very variable, but earthworms by far the most important. Also insects (esp. beetles), small mammals, carrion, cereals, fruit
Predators adults seldom killed by predator, cubs occasionally killed by dogs and foxes. Many killed by gamekeepers and farmers
Distribution widespread. More in wild, wet areas of south and west, fewer in flat, heavily farmed areas, and above 500m (1640ft)

The badger's sett

In most setts badgers use only one chamber for breeding. Here the cubs will stay bedded down in a mass of hay or bracken. The sow will suckle them there but may sleep in a nearby chamber. Others in the group will often cuddle up in another chamber.

Badgers will enlarge some of the tunnels every few metres to form passing places. Tunnels can go as deep as 4m (13ft), but most are less than 1m (3ft) underground and often follow the contours of the surface. This allows better circulation of air. Ventilation holes sometimes connect a tunnel with the outside, but whether by design or accident is not known.

Above: The entrance to a sett; if you see one, check around for others. The entrance looks rather like a fox hole, but badgers scratch the earth away to a large heap nearby, leaving a furrowed track from the hole.

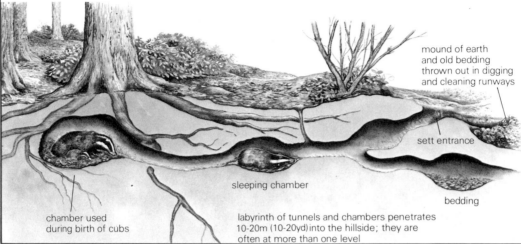

mound of earth and old bedding thrown out in digging and cleaning runways

sett entrance

bedding

sleeping chamber

chamber used during birth of cubs

labyrinth of tunnels and chambers penetrates 10-20m (10-20yd) into the hillside; they are often at more than one level

A motorway underpass built for badgers

A tunnel purpose-built for badgers, to prevent them from being run over by busy traffic, was constructed in 1976 under the M5 motorway near Wellington, Somerset, where it intersected a badger path leading from the sett to feeding grounds.

Although specially designed to save badgers' lives and to prevent accidents, this safe, underground route did not seem to be able to lure the badgers—despite the use of bait to attract them, and such ingenious methods as a man with badger's scent on his coat crawling through the tunnel.

Only when the rearing of cubs made them seek larger food supplies did the badgers 'officially open' the site in 1979 and claim the territory with the placing of latrines at either end.

various directions, joining one entrance to another and also leading off to different parts of the badgers' territory. It is interesting to map this system of paths, which alters little from year to year. Although visible to us these paths are really scent trails, since all the badgers using them mark them periodically with their own scent. Unfortunately some of these paths, which have been used by badgers for generations, are now crossed by roads and many badgers are run over by passing traffic.

Signs of foraging Look out for signs near the sett where the badgers have been foraging. You may see dead leaves disturbed where badgers have been rooting or shallow pits dug when they have been seeking out some beetle or earthworm. The corms (underground stems) of lords-and-ladies are favourites at this time of year; badgers bite off the poisonous yellow shoots and eat the succulent underground corms.

But what goes on in the depths of a sett? A large, well-established sett in the Cotswolds which was given a thorough survey had 12 exit holes and a maze of tunnels and chambers totalling 310m (1000ft). From the length and diameter of the tunnels it was estimated that over the years the badgers had excavated 25 tonnes of soil.

Birth of the cubs If you notice a spurt of digging activity in late December or in January and, if the weather is dry, some fresh grass or bracken dropped near an entrance,

you can be fairly certain that the birth of cubs is imminent and the breeding chamber is likely to be quite near that hole.

Bedding is also of great importance for the survival of the cubs as a chamber full of hay, straw and bracken will act as an insulator, helping the cubs conserve their body heat. For the first few weeks after birth they lie in this cosy nest and are suckled when the sow (female) returns from foraging trips.

The gathering of bedding is an interesting manoeuvre. The badger collects up bundles of dry vegetation, scraping the pieces together with its claws and biting off tough stalks with its teeth. Hugging each bundle in turn to its chest and using its chin and forelegs to keep it in place, it shuffles backwards towards the sett, eventually disappearing down the tunnel tail first.

Usually cubs are born during the first fortnight in February in the south and west, rather later as you go north. They are covered in grey silky hairs and already the dark facial stripes are visible. They are about 12cm (5in) long and weigh about 100g (3½oz). Their eyes are closed for about five weeks, but before long they are ready to explore the tunnels.

Mating period The first three months of the year are a busy and exciting time for the badger community. Soon after the birth of the cubs, most sows become ready to mate again and yearling females may come 'on heat' for the first time at this season. So mating can be a conspicuous feature to watch out for at this time of year.

The dominant boar (male) usually copies a part of the sett well away from where the sow has her cubs; and she will drive him off if he attempts to approach her litter. The boar's behaviour at this time is largely concerned with mating, territorial defence and feeding. On some evenings he will emerge early and visit the various sett entrances, sniffing and making a deep whinnying purr. If a sow emerges and is on heat he will mate with her. Mating can last half an hour and may be repeated over several nights.

At other times the boar may quickly leave the sett and follow one of the main tracks to the limit of territory owned by his social group. Here he will scent-mark the boundary with droppings, using latrines strategically placed to warn off intruders. He may also patrol the perimeter of the territory and if necessary fight with any trespassing badger.

Meanwhile the sow makes short foraging excursions nearer to home to find food for herself and to build herself up for suckling the cubs. On wet nights, earthworms will be the main source of food, but many other creatures will be taken including the occasional dead bird and any early litter of young rabbits she smells and digs out.

The cubs are weaned in summer and start to venture above ground to feed and play—so summer is a good time to watch badgers.

Watching badgers

Find the tell-tale signs of a badger sett, such as piles of discarded bedding straw and latrines, and you will soon discover badgers. To check if the sett is occupied, place a thorny bramble firmly inside the entrance and look next day to see if any black and white hairs are snagged on to the thorns. You may also notice hairs caught on barbed wire fences in the area (below left) badger footprints in the earth (below) or claw marks on nearby trees (left).

Watch for badgers from a well-concealed spot downwind from the sett or they will catch your scent; the best time is sunrise or at dusk. You may tempt them out with meat scraps or a bone near the hole. If badgers accept your offering, they may come back for more.

Above: Two well-grown cubs. The number in a litter varies from one to five, but two or three is most usual. Cubs are nearly always born in early February.

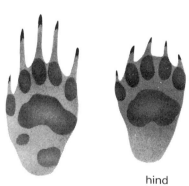

hind

fore

Above: On each foot the badger has five toes with strong claws. The claws on the forefeet are longer than those on the hind, which are often worn down by constant digging. Badgers tread heavily, but even so only four of the five toe pads may show up clearly in a track.

THE GREY SQUIRREL

The talents of the grey squirrel, one of the most acrobatic of British mammals, are best displayed in its natural habitat – our broad-leaved woodlands.

It is hardly surprising that the grey squirrel makes its home in wooded areas since its main source of food especially in autumn is the nuts, foliage and fruits that trees produce. Unfortunately the damage the squirrel can do to the bark of trees, which it gnaws for the sweet sappy tissue underneath, has led to its persecution by man. When driven from the woods, the grey squirrel will adapt to open country, as long as sufficient shelter is provided by hedges, bushes and individual trees.

Since its numerous introductions between 1877 and 1929 into the British Isles from North America, the grey squirrel has colonized most areas. However, in parts of north Norfolk, the Lake District, Northumberland and north Durham the red squirrel is the dominant species.

Versatile dweller Outside its natural woodland habitat, the grey squirrel has been known to cross water, marshland and bogs – even to swim rivers. It has adapted well to different environments including urban areas. You will often find it in town parks and gardens, in fact wherever there are hedges, bushes or trees in which it can make a home.

The squirrel has become so familiar with these populated surroundings that it sometimes appears almost tame, and takes food from the hand if approached carefully. People living in towns are also well aware of the raids made on bird tables. In an effort to prevent this, some people hang nets of nuts from plastic clothes lines. This does not however deter the squirrel, which finds its way along the slippery line and, turning upside down like a blue tit, hangs by its hind feet to get at the nuts.

Squirrel signs Even if you know where to look for grey squirrels, you may not always see them immediately since they have a marvellous ability to camouflage themselves. An obvious place to look for them is up in the tree-tops where they build their nest (drey). Even if the squirrels are too quick to catch sight of, you may see their tracks between the base of trees. About 3cm (1¼in) wide, these tracks show the four distinct claws of the forefeet and five of the hind feet; usually they are widely spaced with no signs of tail-dragging.

Another sign to look for is the stripped bark on the trunk of hardwood trees. You may also find split shells or husks of nuts and fruit, cut tree shoots and buds, strips of bud scales or toothmarks on fungi. And listen for the characteristic scolding cry of 'chuk-chuk-chuk', which you may hear before you see the squirrel.

Coat colouring The grey squirrel's summer coat is short, sleek and brownish-grey on the top of the body with a chestnut streak along the flanks and feet and often on the outer edges of the limbs. The tail hairs are thin with an indistinct white fringe. The winter coat is thicker and silver-grey on the top of the body, with yellowish-brown fur on the head and along the flanks; the legs and feet are grey, while the underneath of the body is white. The large, conspicuous bushy tail has dark grey fur with a white fringe. There is little difference in colouring between the males and females, but the young – before their first moult – usually have a greyer summer coat than the adults.

In certain areas you will notice some distinct variations in colouring. In southeast England you may even see white squirrels, particularly in Kent, Surrey and Sussex. These are albino greys and have reddish eyes – like all albinos. Some grey squirrels in this area have red-brown backs and can be confused with reds. In Bedfordshire, Cambridgeshire, Hertfordshire and Buckinghamshire you can find black (or melanic) squirrels. These are the descendants of about a dozen black squirrels introduced into the Woburn Estate in Bedfordshire shortly after the arrival of the first greys.

Incessant nibbler The grey squirrel gnaws at almost anything that grows on trees, including the tree itself – or more precisely the sappy tissue found under tree bark, especially of beech. It will occasionally take birds' eggs and even young birds and insects. In other habitats it will also eat farm crops such as swedes, wheat, barley and oat shoots, and the grain from these cereals at the 'milk' stage, as well as when ripe.

All rodents have teeth which grow continually and must be worn down before they become dangerous and possibly pierce the palate. With the squirrel these are the incisors, which are trimmed by continual gnawing on nuts and seeds.

Eating habits The squirrel gnaws its food on the spot or carries it to a safe eating place – either somewhere high in the trees or on a fence post or tree stump, where it can keep an eye on its surroundings. The squirrel's eyes are large and set in the side of the head to give wide-angle vision. It also has an acute sense of smell, but its hearing is unexceptional.

In the late summer and autumn the grey squirrel methodically sets about establishing caches to store its winter food. It will later remember the rough location of the cache and then smell out the exact position. Sometimes

Above: The squirrel's forefeet are ideally suited for clutching food while the animal nibbles away, as shown by the grey squirrel gnawing at a hazelnut. The longer hind feet help it to balance and get a firm grip on the branch.

Opposite page: The squirrel nibbles hazelnuts at one end until it can insert its lower incisors and split the shell; other nuts and mast with softer shells present no problems. It will also gnaw off pine cone scales and eat the seeds. Fruits, such as apples, pears, plums, cherries and strawberries, also supplement its diet. The grey squirrel will eat soil, too, for its mineral content and to provide roughage. It takes its normal water requirement from food and from the dew. In hot weather, however, it may drink from lakes, ponds or puddles.

it forgets where the food is hidden and here you will often see stored nuts sprouting.

Agile traveller The squirrel is extraordinarily graceful and agile and can run up and down tree trunks, no matter how smooth the bark, with the greatest of ease. It will balance on the flimsiest twig and leap from branch to branch and tree to tree with complete confidence using its tail as a rudder.

On the ground the squirrel progresses in a series of short leaps or runs on an erratic course with its tail held out straight behind. It can reach speeds of up to 20 miles per hour. It pauses frequently to reconnoitre and sniffs the air, sitting upright on its hind feet with its tail flat along the ground and its ears erect. Surprisingly, the squirrel is an adept swimmer; it keeps its head and tail above the water, with the tail held up in its characteristic curve like a bushy sail.

Cycle of activity The squirrel is active during the day, beginning before sunrise and ending well before sunset. It does not like extremes of temperature and in such cases will retreat to the cover of its drey. It cannot, however, spend more than two or three days without food and often comes out of the drey to forage even in adverse weather.

Until recently it was mistakenly thought both grey and red squirrels hibernated during the winter or slept for long periods. Although you are unlikely to see squirrels in cold weather, they are about since their presence is given away, for example, by tracks in the snow.

Apart from games played by the young and the play which forms part of the courtship ritual, male squirrels spend a great deal of time in high-spirited chases through the tree tops, tail-biting and screaming. Whether this is play or aggression is not known. Apart from the 'chuk-chuk-chuk' call, listen also for a barking note, variations of purring

Above: Stripped bark is one tell-tale sign that the grey squirrel is about—and this habit has made the animal a pest in the eyes of farmers and foresters. These two are making a meal out of a sycamore tree.

Right: Storing nuts in the ground is a vital business if the grey squirrel is to survive the cold winter months. Normally it will smell out its cache when the food is needed, although nuts left undiscovered may later sprout.

Tree-top families

Once she is pregnant, the female squirrel drives out the male and prepares the drey for her young by giving it a soft lining of grass, dry leaves, moss and any other available soft materials.

In the drey the female produces her young twice a year, six weeks after mating; this means litters appear in early-to-mid spring and mid-to-late summer. The young—usually three per litter—are born naked, blind and deaf; each weighs about 15g (½oz). They rely entirely on their mother's milk for seven weeks. After that the mother introduces them to solid food, but continues to suckle them for another three weeks or so. By this stage the young start to learn the tightrope tricks that mean survival in the tree-tops, while also foraging and feeding themselves.

noises and a vibrating sound (like the song of a grasshopper) made by males chasing females.

Courtship The grey squirrel has two mating seasons, the first occurring in May and the second in December. Courtship rituals involve display and chasing; a number of males sometimes pursue a female just before mating time, simultaneously engaging in running contests to see who gets the prize.

Preparing the drey The squirrel's nest (drey) is rounded (about the size of a football), close-knit and made of leaves, twigs, bark, grass and pliant stems of ivy. Found mostly in hardwoods, it is often built away from the main trunk of the tree. Each drey is isolated and from a distance is easily mistaken for a crow's nest, although the latter is an untidier affair.

After mating the female becomes the dominant of the sexes, driving out the male from the nest tree and constructing the drey in which she will give birth. As an alternative she may enlarge a previous one, or sometimes make her den in the hole of a tree trunk, possibly taking over a woodpecker's old nest.

The female squirrel is a model mother and weans her blind and furless infants with great care, licking and cleaning each one individually. By the time the young squirrels are ten weeks old they are scrabbling about outside the drey and within another three weeks they are out on their own. They either wander away or are turned out by the mother, who must soon prepare for her next litter. Young female squirrels are capable of breeding six or seven months after birth and usually do so by the time they are a year old. Grey squirrels have been known to live as long as eight years, but this is an exceptional age. Most die in their first couple of years and only a very small number live beyond six years.

Resisting attack The grey squirrel avoids most of its predators by living in trees, but it is still vulnerable to owls, hawks, wild and domestic cats, dogs and occasionally stoats. Birds and squirrels co-exist quite happily for the most part, although occasionally birds will mob a squirrel.

The greatest enemy is undoubtedly man. Squirrels cause extensive damage to valuable hardwoods and, since the 1920s, strenuous efforts have been made to curb the population. Dreys have been destroyed and squirrels shot, trapped, poisoned and set upon by dogs. In 1937 the Government prohibited the importation and release or the keeping of grey squirrels in captivity–except under licence. All these measures were to no avail and the problem has yet to be solved.

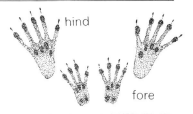

hind

fore

GREY SQUIRREL (*Sciurus carolinensis*)
Size of adult 25-30cm (10-12in) over head and body; 20-22cm (8-9in) along tail. Weighs about 500g (17oz), females slightly less
Breeding season Jan-July
Gestation period 42-45 days
No of young average 3, range 1-7
Lifespan known to live 8-9 years, but less than 1% reach more than 6 years
Food bark of oak, beech; acorns, nuts, fungi
Predators birds of prey; wild cat; casual hunters–stoat, pine marten, fox; control by man; traffic
Distribution Throughout England and Wales where there are trees; lowland Scotland and central counties of Ireland.

WOOD MICE: SILENT FORAGERS

The wood mouse is one of our commonest wild animals, yet it rarely attracts our attention as it scuttles noiselessly through the undergrowth in search of seeds and insects.

The wood mouse can easily be distinguished from the house mouse by its larger ears and eyes. Its warm brown coat cannot generally be confused with the dull greyish coat of the house mouse, although unusual colour variants and the grey fur of the young of both species may make identification more difficult. The wood mouse does not have the distinctive odour associated with the house mouse.

Wood mice have soft, smooth fur which is sandy or orange brown on the head and back, yellowish on the flanks and white on the belly. There is usually a small streak of yellow pigmentation in the otherwise white fur of the chest. The tail is almost as long as the body and has a sparse covering of black hairs. The tops of the feet are covered by short, white hairs and each toe–four on the forefeet and five on the hind–ends in a sharp, curved claw.

Mainland British and Irish mice do not vary much in size but forms 50-100% larger occur on Rhum, St Kilda, Fair Isle and several other islands. Mice probably reached these islands with the assistance of the Vikings and other settlers who brought livestock with them. The wood mice of mainland Britain, on the other hand, may have originated from southern stock which survived the last advance of the ice sheet. These groups of mice reinvaded the major part of England, Wales, Scotland and possibly Ireland as the ice

Above: Wood mice eat mainly tree seeds, but seeds from bushes and herbs are also taken. Other sources of food are fruits, seedlings, buds and fungi and, in late spring and summer, small snails, caterpillars and adult insects.

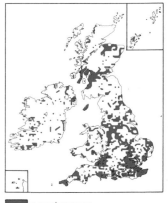

wood mouse

yellow-necked mouse

186

retreated 10,000 years ago.

Mixed habitats The wood mouse is undoubtedly the most widespread of our small mammals. Although more numerous in some habitats than others, it occurs in most places from coastal sand dunes to mountain tops and from mixed deciduous woodland to the increasingly prevalent forests of conifers. It is also found in towns and cities, lurking in suburban gardens, unkept graveyards and railway embankments. Researchers who examined mice caught near a railway station in Manchester found that they lived on a diet of biscuit crumbs, presumably from packets discarded by passengers.

Hedgerows, stone walls and ditches are frequent haunts in farmland, and wood mice also enter disused outbuildings and farmhouses. They avoid open pasture or grassland, where the field vole is present. Highest densities occur in mixed woodland. Here, the mice use extensive runway systems which follow tree roots, fallen branches, banks, rocks or any other feature close to the ground. Wood mice prefer areas with some low vegetation. Brambles are particularly favoured.

Woodland gatherers Wood mice are primarily seed-eaters (granivores), relying to a great extent on the seeds of trees such as oak, beech, ash, lime, hawthorn and sycamore. Every year they eat a high proportion of the annual seed crop and it seems likely that only small quantities of seeds therefore survive to germinate the following spring. The mice are efficient seed gatherers and when there is a plentiful supply on the ground, they carry them back to the nest for storage.

The seeds of bushes and herbs are also eaten, as well as fruits, seedlings, buds and sometimes fungi. Small invertebrates, particularly small snails and insects, may be eaten throughout the year, but are particularly important sources of food in late spring and summer. This is the time of year when seeds are least available and larval and adult insects are abundant. Moth caterpillars, which fall from the upper canopy of trees to pupate in the soil, are a common food in summer.

In Britain a number of predators eat wood mice but only two, the tawny owl and the weasel, kill large numbers. A third, the domestic cat, may have a major effect on mice living close to human habitation.

Fluctuating populations The density of population fluctuates markedly, following an annual cycle. Numbers are greatest in autumn and remain high throughout the winter, during which survival is determined by the size of the autumn seed crop. When seed production is very great, winter breeding may occur but generally breeding is restricted to spring, summer and early autumn.

Numbers do not increase with the first appearance of young in spring. In most years,

WOOD MOUSE *(Apodemus sylvaticus)*. Also known as field mouse and long-tailed field mouse.
Size varies according to season and locality. On mainland Britain in spring: male 25g (¾oz), female 20g (⅔oz) (unless in an advanced stage of pregnancy).
Colour sandy or orange brown on head and back, yellow on flanks, white on belly. Young: greyish brown.
Breeding season March/April to October/November.
Gestation 25-26 days.
No of young 2-9, average 5.
Lifespan average 2-3 months, may survive 18-20 months in wild, 2 years or more in captivity.
Food mostly seeds, but eats a wide range of plant and animal food.
Predators cat, weasel, tawny owl, long-eared owl.
Distribution widespread in Britain and Ireland and on many of the surrounding islands.

The yellow-necked mouse

The yellow-necked mouse is similar in appearance to the wood mouse, but it is larger, weighing up to 45g (1½oz), and has a distinctive collar of yellow fur (see illustration on following page). The two species behave differently when handled. While the wood mouse is relatively passive, the yellow-neck struggles and squeals.

The yellow-neck is restricted to the south-east, south and west of England and the eastern parts of Wales, where it is found mainly in mature, deciduous woodland areas. Although it is not aggressive towards the wood mouse, it is avoided by this smaller, less dominant animal and, within a shared area of woodland, the two species may rarely meet. Little is known about the diet of the yellow-neck, but it is probably similar to that of the wood mouse.

The annual population cycle of the yellow-neck differs slightly from that of the wood mouse. Numbers increase from the start of the breeding season in spring. At this time, the mice may move into a variety of habitats from the restricted woodland areas in which they have spent the winter. The population continues to increase throughout the autumn, but survival in winter is poor and by early spring the yellow-neck is scarce throughout its range of habitats.

Left: A sweet chestnut has to be eaten on the spot, but smaller tree seeds may be stored in the nest.

Below: Young wood mice are born naked and blind. They grow their first, greyish-brown coat after about six days, their eyes open after 16 days and they are weaned at around 18 days old. Survival of young and adults is poor during the first half of the breeding season. Adult males are aggressive to one another and to the young, who are driven from the nest soon after weaning. Adult females may be weakened by constant pregnancies and feeding of young.

survival of both young and adults is poor during the first half of the breeding season and the population declines rapidly before reaching a stable, low level in early summer. Survival of young mice improves as the last of the winter generation die off, and numbers increase during the late summer and autumn to reach a peak in the first half of winter. Juveniles which are born early in the season and which survive may breed in their first summer. Females may conceive at only seven or eight weeks, when they weigh 12g (less than $\frac{1}{2}$oz).

Timid explorers Wood mice have weak eyesight, but their hearing and sense of smell are both acute. It is therefore not surprising that they are largely nocturnal animals (although in captivity they become increasingly active in daylight.) The burrow systems which they excavate for themselves may have one or two nest chambers in which they spend most of the day and to which they return many times during the night. Wood mice do not hibernate but during cold weather their movements may appear slow and lethargic as they enter a temporary torpor, or they may huddle in groups to retain warmth.

In familiar areas, mice run or scurry along quickly. In exploration, they move slowly and deliberately as they are nervous and timid. They are good climbers and use low branches – where running is silent and does not attract the attention of predators–as freely as the runways at ground level.

Social behaviour The structure of wood mouse society is still not well understood but in the breeding season it is likely that dominant males patrol large areas which include subordinate males, females and young. Mice may sleep and forage for food in family groups. In captivity, fights are rarely seen as dominant relationships are quickly established. Subsequently most social contact is amicable and contrasts markedly with the more aggressive lifestyle of the house mouse.

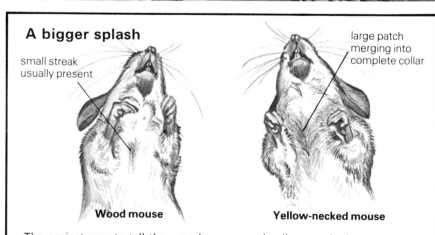

A bigger splash

small streak usually present

large patch merging into complete collar

Wood mouse

Yellow-necked mouse

The easiest way to tell the wood mouse and yellow-necked mouse apart is by looking at the chest. On the wood mouse (above, left), there is a small, yellow streak or, occasionally, no mark at all. On the yellow-neck (above, right), the golden fur extends over the chest and around the neck, forming a collar. In Britain, the collar is always complete; elsewhere in Europe it may be no more than a large patch. The colour of the chest spot or collar is similar in both species, although the main body fur is a brighter shade of brown in the yellow-neck. The chest markings are present, though less obvious, in the greyish fur of the young of both species.

Woodlands to visit

1 Killarney Woods Oak
2 Derryclare Wood Nature Reserve Oak wood beside Lough Inagh. Good for lichens. Access by permit only.
3 Glen of the Downs Nature Reserve nr Greystones. Mainly oak.
4 Minnowburn Beeches nr Belfast.
5 Banagher Glen NNR Mixed woods in river valleys Altnaheglish and Owenrigh. Interesting flora.
6 Inverpolly NNR Birch woods.
7 Torrachilty NW of Inverness. Includes oak and birch woods and Lael Forest Garden with a collection of broadleaved trees.
8 Craigellachie NNR Birch wood.
9 Ariundle NNR W of Fort William. Oak, birch, rowan. nt
10 Pass of Killiecrankie, N of Perth. Wooded gorge. nt
11 Old Forest of Drum W of Aberdeen in grounds of Drum Castle. Mainly oak.
12 Dollar Glen E of Stirling. Mixed wood in steep ravine.
13 Inchcailloch Wooded island, mainly oak. Part of NNR. nt
14 Galloway Forest Park Includes two old woods, and Kirroughtree Forest Gardens with over 60 species of trees.
15 Great Wood, Brandelhow, and Ashness Woods Three ancient oak-woods around Derwent Water.
16 Eaves Wood nr Silverdale. Mixed wood on limestone.

17 Malham Tarn Woods in Yorkshire Dales National Park. Mixed woods on limestone. Interesting flora.
18 Derbyshire Dales Woods NNR in Peak District National Park. Oak, ash on limestone.
19 Coedydd Maentwrog NNR nr Ffestiniog. Oak. nt
20 Coed Lletywalter W of Dolgellau. Woodland with rich variety of habitats.
21 Bishopston Valley SW of Swansea. Steep limestone slopes with whitebeam, ash.
22 Dinas Woods nr Llandovery. Oakwoods in river gorge. Red kite.

23 Forest of Dean Large medieval royal forest in angle of Rivers Wye and Severn. Includes ancient oaks.
24 Wyre Forest NNR W of Birmingham. Ancient oakwood with interesting flora. Redstart, woodcock.
25 Cannock Chase N of Birmingham. Royal Forest. Oak, birch. Fallow deer.
26 Aversley Wood S of Peterborough. Mainly ash, oak, wild service tree.
27 Hatfield Forest SE of Bishop's Stortford. Ancient royal forest. Pollarded hornbeam. Fallow deer.
28 Epping Forest NE of London. A very large ancient forest. Chiefly beech. Other species include pollarded hornbeam. Hawfinch. Herd of dark brown fallow deer. Field Studies Centre.
29 Denge Wood SW of Canterbury. Includes chestnut coppice.
30 Burnham Beeches W of London. Famous for ancient pollarded beech. Oak, holly.
31 Windsor Forest W of London. Old oak, beech.
32 Box Hill nr Dorking. Beech, box and mixed woods on steep chalk slopes. Whitebeam.
33 Avon Gorge Woods NNR Bristol. Unusual plants present.
34 Savernake Forest nr Marlborough. Ancient oak and beech forest.
35 New Forest SW of Southampton. Ancient mixed woods with interesting flora. New Forest ponies, roe, fallow, sika and red deer. Insects include the rare forest cicada and purple emperor butterfly.

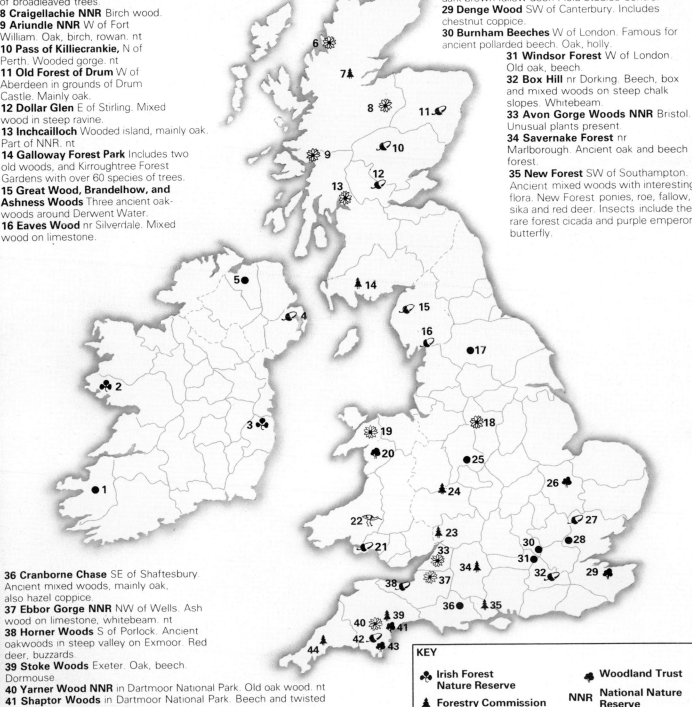

36 Cranborne Chase SE of Shaftesbury. Ancient mixed woods, mainly oak, also hazel coppice.
37 Ebbor Gorge NNR NW of Wells. Ash wood on limestone, whitebeam. nt
38 Horner Woods S of Porlock. Ancient oakwoods in steep valley on Exmoor. Red deer, buzzards.
39 Stoke Woods Exeter. Oak, beech. Dormouse.
40 Yarner Wood NNR in Dartmoor National Park. Old oak wood. nt
41 Shaptor Woods in Dartmoor National Park. Beech and twisted oak. Wood warbler, red deer.
42 Hembury Woods N of Buckfastleigh, by River Dart.
43 Avon Valley Woods N of Kingsbridge. 2m of mixed woodland along River Avon. Common dormouse.
44 Cardinham Woods E of Bodmin. Oak coppice, beech.

KEY

♣ Irish Forest Nature Reserve	🌲 Woodland Trust
🌲 Forestry Commission	NNR National Nature Reserve
🐦 Royal Society for the Protection of Birds	nt nature trail
🐚 National Trust	✻ Nature Conservancy Council

INDEX

The entries listed in **bold** type refer to main subjects. The page numbers in *italics* indicate illustrations. Medium type entries refer to the text.

INDEX

ACKNOWLEDGEMENTS

Photographers' credits: A-Z Collection 26(top right), 38: Heather Angel 8, 9, 12, 14(bottom), 18(bottom), 19(top right), 20, 21(bottom), 23, 26(bottom left), 29, 33, 40, 47(top, bottom), 49, 50(bottom), 51, 52, 53, 55, 56(top, bottom right), 57, 58, 59, 61(bottom), 64(top), 65, 66, 67(top, middle), 73(bottom left, right), 76, 78, 84, 85, 87, 90, 91, 92(bottom), 95, 105, 108(middle), 164(top), 165, 168(middle), 181(bottom right), 185: Aquila Photographics/SC Brown 142 (bottom); PT Castell 152(left); GF Date 150(top); NW Harwood 149(bottom left); EA Janes 75; DI McEwan 103; AT Moffett 139; R Siegal 60-1; A Wharton 114(bottom right); MC Wilkes 124(top), 131: Ian Beames 96-7, 114(top right, middle right), 115(top right, bottom right): bottom left): JB&S Bottomley 179(top); M Chinery 16, 102: JPA Clare 120: Bruce Coleman Ltd/M Boulton 162-3(top); E Breeze-Jones 174; J Burton 42, 104, 122, 132(bottom); B Coleman 156; E Crichton 18(top), 19(bottom left); 45; S Dalton 116, 134; L Lee Rue 169(top); H Reinhard 62, 153, 166, 170, 173 (top), 178, 181(top); P Wakefield 19(upper middle left); R Wilmshurst 136: D Corke 63(top): E Crichton 73(top): G Dickson 86: M Dohrn 44: Bob Gibbons Photography/ R Fletcher 15, 17(bottom right); Bob Gibbons 19(middle right, lower middle right, bottom right), 21(middle) 22 (bottom), 28(top), 31(top), 80(bottom), 94(bottom), 100 (bottom), 159; A Hammer 15, 17(bottom right); P Wilson 21(top): D Green 123, 133: M Grey 144: E&D Hosking 118: GE Hyde 54,80(top),113, 114(bottom left): EA Janes front cover, 115(bottom left), 132 (top), 151: M King & M Read/G Dore 69: S Lane 41:

R Littleton 146(top): J Mason 47(middle), 99(top), 114(top left), 146(bottom): RT Mills 31(bottom), 147(top), 164 (bottom): P Morris 64(bottom right), 169(bottom), 173 (bottom): NHPA/A Barnes 149(bottom), 157(top), 158: FV Blackburn 28(bottom), 30(bottom), 101; NA Callow 14 (middle), 108(top, bottom); GJ Cambridge 92(top); GJ Cambridge & J&M Bain 67; L Campbell 19(upper middle left), S Dalton 129, 137(bottom), 143; R Fotheringham 100(top); J Good 147(bottom), 167, 177, 177(bottom); EA Janes 19(top left), 24, 32, 48, 50(top), 71, 135, 140(top right); J Jeffery 130; T Jenkyn 82; WJC Murray 22(top, middle), 112(bottom right), 162(bottom), 175, 176; KG Preston-Mafham 109; K Williams 30(top): Nature Photographers Ltd/SC Bisserot 94(top); FV Blackburn 14 (top), 18(middle), 19(lower middle left), 99(bottom), 140 (top left); A Cleave 39; J Hyett 81; EA Janes 6-7, 35(top), 149(bottom); C&J Knights 128; O Newman 79; C Palmer 60; D Smith 124(bottom); P Sterry 100(middle); E Neal 179 (bottom), 180, 181(middle); J Norris-Wood 181(bottom left): Oxford Scientific Films 184(top); K Porter 111(top), 112 (top, bottom left); Premaphotos Wildlife/KG Preston-Mafham 17(top), 93,98,107; Press-tige Pictures/D Avon & T Tilford 163 (bottom), 172, 186; C Read 188(top); R Revels 56(bottom left), 144(far left, middle left), 115(top right, bottom right): John Robinson 10, 17(bottom left), 34,35(middle, bottom), 36, 37, 61(top), 111(bottom), 125, 140(bottom), 141, 142 (top), 145, 150(bottom), 154, 157(bottom), 168(top), 182, 187: Harry Smith Collection 26(top left): DA Sutton 25, 26 (bottom right): MWF Tweedie 106: UNHA/A Goodger 137 (top); I Malin 138: Wildlife Services/M Leach 88, 152(right),

184(bottom): G Wilkinson 63(bottom), 64(bottom right).
Artists' credits: G Allen/Linden Artists 161: N Arlott 119, 120, 121, 127, 129, 154, 155: R Bampton/The Garden Studio 43, 49(middle): R Barnett 92, 104, 140, 146: E Fleury 11: W Ford 32, 117, 124, 125, 131, 135, 136, 137, 139, 141, 145, 148, 158: W Giles 29: Hayward Art Group title page, 46(leaf close-ups), 49(top), 52, 58, 59, 62, 70, 71, 72, 74, 75, 76, 77, 78, 79(right), 83, 171, 173, 180, 181, 183, 185: K Jacob/ The Garden Studio 95: F Kayes/The Garden Studio 97: R Lewington/The Garden Studio 99, 102, 103, 106, 109, 111, 113, 115: D More/Linden Artists 27, 46(tree portraits), 49 (top), 52(top), 55, 56, 59(tree portraits), 61, 63, 66: K Oliver 151: D Ovenden 172, 176: P Pearce/ The Garden Studio 13: S Pond 39, 40(left), 148(line), 152, 165: J Redfern/The Garden Studio 69, 87, 89: G Riley 105: C Salmon 37, 40 (middle), 139(map), 144, 148(maps), 151(maps), 157: J Sellwood/The Garden Studio 167, 188: E Stewart 189.

Index compiled by Richard Raper of Indexing Specialists, Hove, East Sussex.

Typesetting PHOTOCOMP LTD, BIRMINGHAM; Printing & Binding PRINTER INDUSTRIA, GRÁFICA S.A. BARCELONA; Separations YORK HOUSE GRAPHICS, HANWELL; COLOURSCAN OVERSEAS CO PTE LTD, SINGAPORE; Paper KNP MILL, HOLLAND